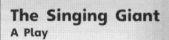

The Singing Giant
A Play

George the giant likes to sing.
But he's very LOUD! Join
Mum, Grandpa, the children
and the baby as they decide
what to do.

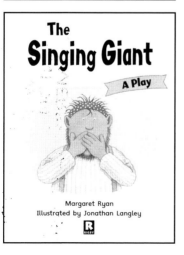

Walkthrough

..., a

... story
... them
... ory
... .

Hold up the story version and the
play version and look through
both, comparing them.

Walkthrough

This is the back cover – let's read
the blurb together.

What must it be like living near a
giant who sings a lot?

Walkthrough

What is George doing in
this picture?
Why has he got his hands over
his mouth?

What do we know about a play?
(*The characters talk and this tells us
the story. It can be acted out.*)

The story and the play were
written and illustrated
by the same people.

1

Walkthrough

This page shows us the characters.

Do you recognise some of them from the story?

After we have had a quick look through the book we are each going to read a part of the play. (Give each child a character.)

 Observe and Prompt

Word Recognition

- If the children have difficulty reading 'Narrator', model the blending of this word for them.

- Check the children can read the words 'George' and 'Giant'.

- Prompt the children to break the words 'morning' and 'evening' down into two syllables, before blending each word together.

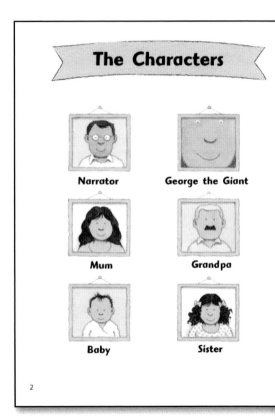

The Characters

Narrator

George the Giant

Mum

Grandpa

Baby

Sister

2

Walkthrough

What does 'Scene One' mean?

Do you know what a narrator does?
(*A narrator tells the story.*)

Scene One

Narrator: We are in George the
Giant's house.

George: I love to sing. I love to sing.
I sing in the morning,
I sing in the evening,
I sing in the bath.
Tra, la, la.

3

Observe and Prompt

Language Comprehension

- Check the children identify their character on the left, and the spoken words on the right.

- Check the children have grasped the difference between a story and a play.

- Tell the children that they should only read the character's words, not their name.

Walkthrough

This is Scene Two.

Who do you think will be speaking on this page?

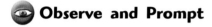 **Observe and Prompt**

Word Recognition

- Help the children with the 'ing' suffix at the end of 'singing' if they have difficulty with this word.
- If the children have difficulty reading 'television', model the blending of this word for them.
- Help the children with the 'ear' sound in 'hear' if they have difficulty with this word.

Scene Two

Narrator:	We are now in the house next door.
George:	*I LOVE TO SING. I LOVE TO SING.*
Mum:	Stop that singing. I can't sleep at night.
Grandpa:	Stop that singing. I can't sleep in the morning.
Sister:	Stop that singing. I can't hear the television.

4

5

Language Comprehension

- Check that the children are following the text, and know when it is their turn to speak.

- Check the children are reading with expression.

- What do all the people want George to do?

Walkthrough

Who can we see in this picture?

Where are the family going? Why?

What do you think they will say to George?

 Observe and Prompt

Word Recognition

- Check the children are using their decoding skills to tackle the more difficult words on these pages, such as 'noise' and 'house'.

- Check the children can read the sight words on these pages with confidence.

George:	*I LOVE TO SING.* *HOW I LOVE TO SING.* *TRA LA LA LA LA.*
Mum:	George must stop singing.
Sister:	Yes, we have to stop him making so much noise.
Grandpa:	Let's go and see him.

6

Walkthrough

What scene is this?

Why does George think they have come?
Is he right?

> **Scene Three**

Narrator: We are now at George's house again.

George: Hello, everyone. Nice to see you. Have you come to hear me sing?

Everyone: No, we have not!

7

👁 Observe and Prompt

Language Comprehension

- Check that the children are reading 'in character'.
- Check that all the children speak together for 'Everyone'.
- What do the children think the people will say to George?

Walkthrough

How does George feel now? How do you know?

 Observe and Prompt

Word Recognition

- If the children have difficulty with the words 'Listen', 'Peace' and 'Sigh', model the blending of these words for them.

- Check the children are using their decoding skills to tackle the more difficult words on these pages, such as 'because' and 'quiet'.

Mum: We have come to tell you to stop singing.

Grandpa: Yes, I can't sleep because of all the noise.

Sister: And I can't hear the television because of all the noise.

Everyone: You must stop singing, George.

George: But I love to sing. Ohhhh. Sniffle, sniffle.

8

Walkthrough

What scene is this?

What do you think happens now?

Scene Four

Narrator: We are now next door again.

Mum: Listen, it's very quiet.

Grandpa: Now I can sleep.

Sister: Now I can hear the television.

Everyone: Peace and quiet at last. *Sigh.*

Baby: *WAAAAA!*
WAAAAA!
WAAAAA!

9

Observe and Prompt

Language Comprehension

- Ask the children what 'Everyone' says. Do they like the peace and quiet?
- Ask the children why it is not quiet for long.
- Observe the children taking turns, without prompting, to say their lines.

Walkthrough

What is happening in this scene? Why is everyone so tired?

Why do you think the baby won't stop crying?

What could the people do to make the baby stop?

 Observe and Prompt

Word Recognition

- If the children have difficulty reading 'night', model the reading of this word for them.
- Help the children with the 'aw' sound in 'Yawn' if they have trouble with this word.

> **Scene Five**

Narrator:	It is now the next morning.
Baby:	*WAAA! WAAA! WAAA!*

Mum:	I didn't sleep a wink all night. Yawn.
Grandpa:	I didn't sleep at all. Yawn.
Sister:	I couldn't hear the television and I couldn't sleep! Yawn.

10

11

👁 Observe and Prompt

Language Comprehension

- Tell the children that 'Yawn' is a stage direction. Check that the children act out the word and don't say it.

- Check the children are reading with expression.

- Ask the children what the people might do to stop the baby crying.

Walkthrough

How do the people feel about the baby crying?

Look at the picture. What do the bubbles mean?
(*they are thinking*)

What do they think they could do? Do you think
anything will work?

 Observe and Prompt

Word Recognition

- If the children have
  difficulty reading 'maybe',
  prompt them to break
  the word down into two
  syllables, before blending
  the whole word together.

- Check the children can
  read the 'ing' suffix at the
  end of 'crying'.

Baby:	*WAAA! WAAA! WAAA!*

Mum:	Maybe if we rock the baby, the baby will stop crying.
Grandpa:	Maybe if we take the baby for a walk, the baby will stop crying.
Sister:	Maybe if we play with the baby, the baby will stop crying.
Baby:	*WAAAAAAAAAAAAAAAAAAAA!*
Everyone:	PLEASE STOP CRYING!

12

If this was your baby, how would you make him/her stop crying?

13

Observe and Prompt

Language Comprehension

- Check the children are reading with appropriate expression.
- Ask the children who might be able to help get the babies to sleep.

What do you think they decide to do?

What do you think George will say to them? Do you think he will be pleased to see them?

 Observe and Prompt

Word Recognition

- Check the children are using their decoding skills to tackle the words on these pages.
- If the children have difficulty reading 'gurgle', model the blending of this word for them.
- Prompt the children to break the word 'FANTASTIC' down into three syllables, before blending the whole word together.

Sister: The baby didn't cry when George was singing.

Mum: Oh! You're right! When George sang, the baby slept.

Grandpa: We must go to see George again.

14

14

Walkthrough

Do you think this is the final scene? Why?

Scene Six

Narrator: We are at George's house again.

George: Hello, I'm not singing now.

Everyone: Please start singing again, George. The baby loves your singing. We're sorry we asked you to stop.

Baby: Gurgle, gurgle. Sing song.

George: You really mean it? You want me to sing again? FANTASTIC! I'll sing my favourite song.

15

Language Comprehension

- Check that the children continue to take turns reading their parts appropriately and also follow other parts as they are read.

- Check the children are reading with appropriate expression, taking note of punctuation.

- Do the children think George's singing will stop the baby crying?

Walkthrough

How has George got the baby to sleep? How do you think George feels?

How do the people feel?

Do you think George will be allowed to carry on singing now?

George: *SLEEP LITTLE BABY,*
         DON'T YOU CRY . . .

Baby: *Zzzz Zzzz Zzzz . . .*

Everyone: Bravo, George! Bravo!

16

 Observe and Prompt

Word Recognition

- Check the children are using their decoding skills to read 'Bravo'.

 Observe and Prompt

Language Comprehension

- Ask the children what 'Zzzz' means.

- Check the children all join in at the end and read with appropriate expression.

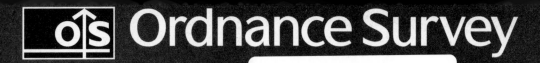

STREET ATLAS
Bristol and Avon

Contents

III *Key to map symbols*

IV *Key to map pages*

VI *Administrative boundaries*

1 *Street maps*

140 *Index explanation and abbreviations*

141 *Index of towns, villages and rural localities*

142 *Index of street names*

PHILIP'S

First edition published 1995
Reprinted 1998, 1999 by

Ordnance Survey®   and   George Philip Ltd, a division of
Romsey Road   Octopus Publishing Group Ltd
Maybush   2-4 Heron Quays
Southampton   London
SO16 4GU   E14 4JP

ISBN 0-540-06140-9 (Hardback)
ISBN 0-540-06141-7 (Softback)

To the best of the Publishers' knowledge, the information in this atlas was correct at
the time of going to press. No responsibility can be accepted for any errors or their
consequences.

The representation in this atlas of a road, track or path is no evidence of the
existence of a right of way.

Printed and bound in Great Britain by Bath Press, Bath

Key to map symbols

⊛	British Rail station
⊖	Underground station
🚂	Private railway station
⊷	Bus or coach station
Ⓗ	Heliport
♦	Police station (may not be open 24 hours)
✚	Hospital with casualty facilities (may not be open 24 hours)
☐	Post office
+	Place of worship
◼	Important building
P	Parking
174	Adjoining page indicator
⨯	No adjoining page
═══	Motorway
═══	Dual carriageway
───	Main or through road
A27	Road numbers (Department of Transport)
─┬─	Gate or obstruction to traffic (restrictions may not apply at all times or to all vehicles)
-----	Path, bridleway, byway open to all traffic, road used as public path, dismantled railway etc.
═══	Track

The representation in this atlas of a road, track or path is no evidence of the existence of a right of way

Amb Sta	Ambulance station	LC	Level crossing
Amb Dpo	Ambulance depot	Liby	Library
Coll	College	Mus	Museum
FB	Footbridge	Acad	Academy
F Sta	Fire station	Sch	School
Hospl	Hospital	TH	Town Hall or Town House

0		¼		½		¾		1 mile
0	250 m		500 m		750 m		1 Kilometre	

The scale of the maps is 3½ inches to 1 mile (1:18103)

The small numbers around the edges of the maps identify the 1 kilometre National Grid lines

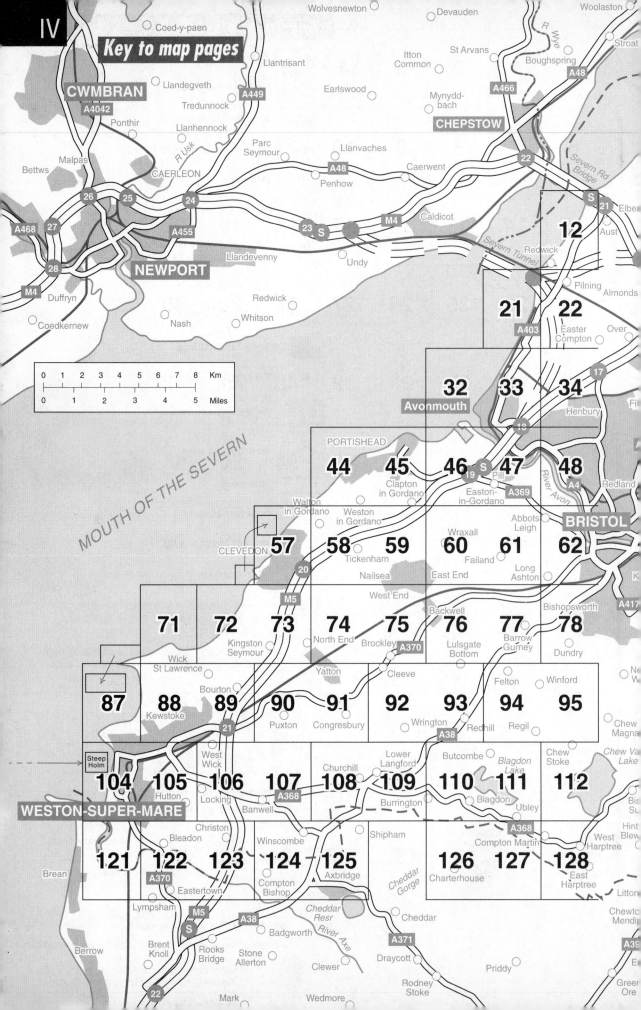

Key to map pages

IV

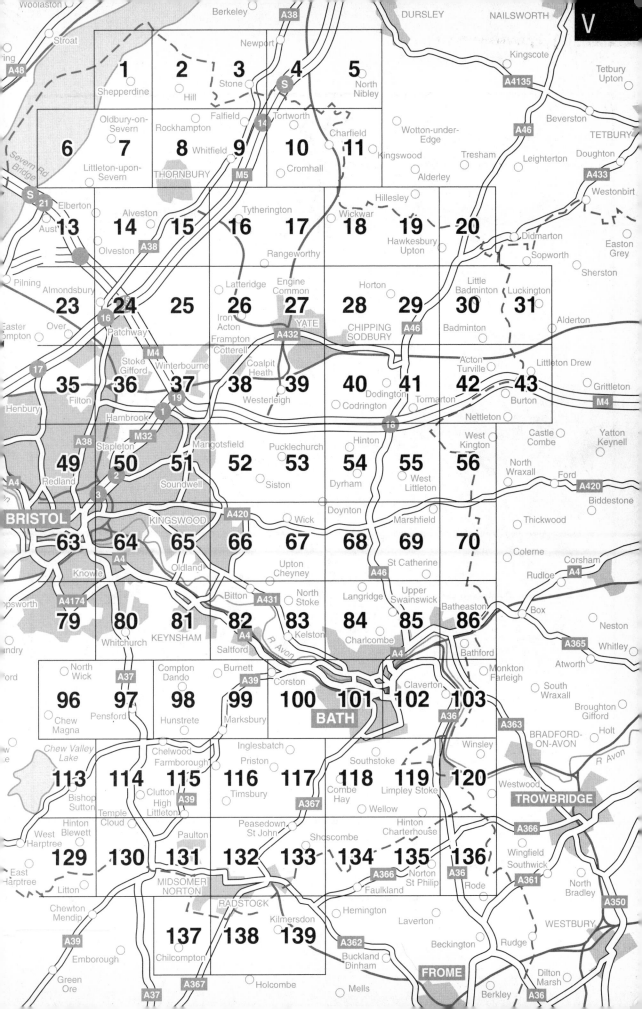

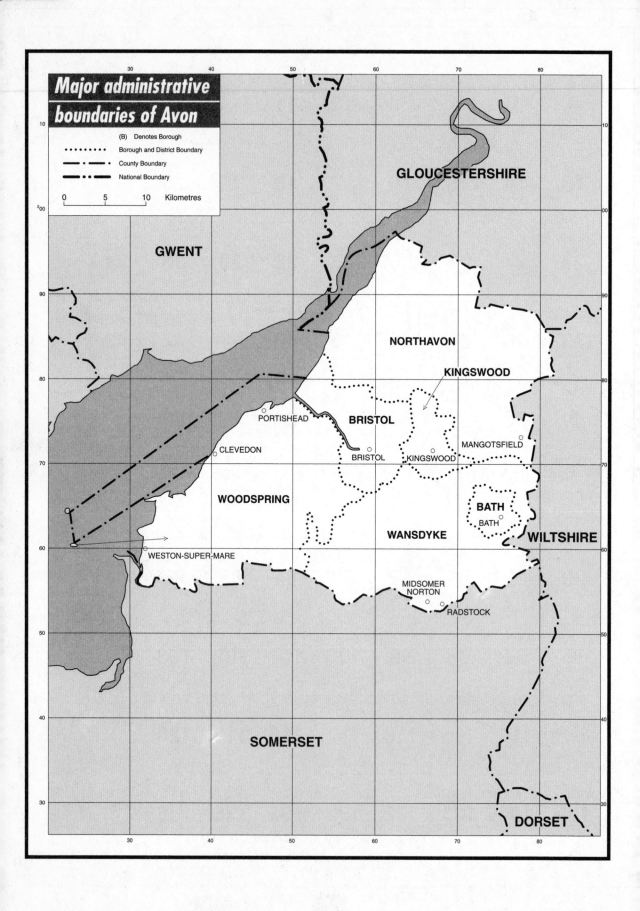

Major administrative boundaries of Avon

(B)   Denotes Borough

••••••••   Borough and District Boundary

—·—·—·—   County Boundary

—··—··—   National Boundary

0   5   10   Kilometres

GLOUCESTERSHIRE

GWENT

NORTHAVON

KINGSWOOD

PORTISHEAD

BRISTOL

CLEVEDON

MANGOTSFIELD

BRISTOL   KINGSWOOD

WOODSPRING

BATH

BATH

WANSDYKE

WILTSHIRE

WESTON-SUPER-MARE

MIDSOMER
NORTON

RADSTOCK

SOMERSET

DORSET

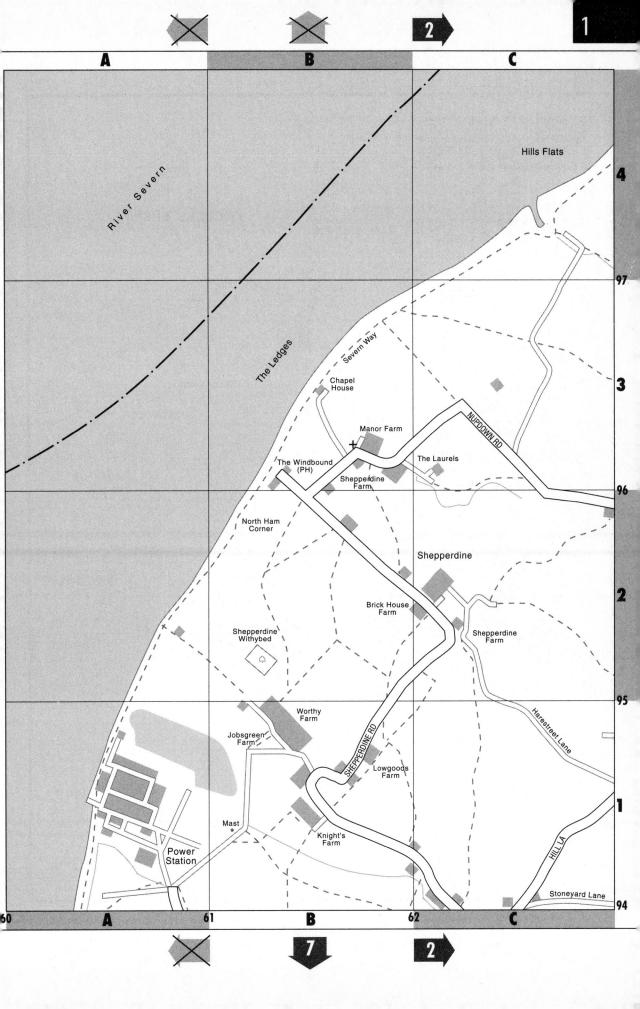

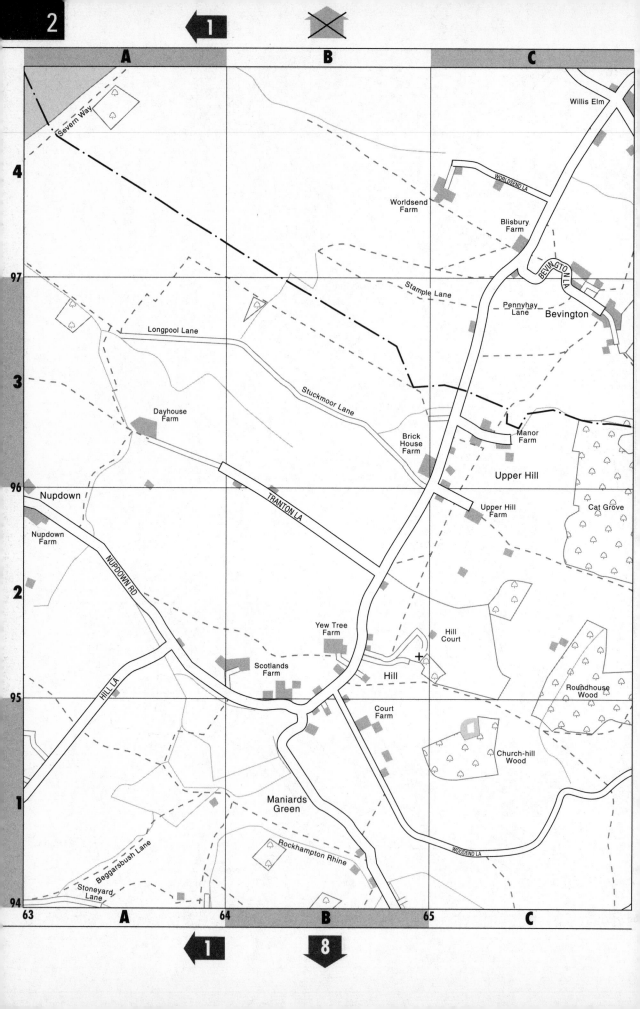

Willis Elm

WORLDSEND LA

Worldsend
Farm

Blisbury
Farm

BEVINGTON LA

Stample Lane

Pennyhay
Lane

Bevington

Severn Way

Longpool Lane

Stuckmoor Lane

Dayhouse
Farm

Brick
House
Farm

Manor
Farm

Upper Hill

Nupdown

Cat Grove

TRANTON LA

Upper Hill
Farm

Nupdown
Farm

NUPDOWN RD

Yew Tree
Farm

Hill
Court

Roundhouse
Wood

Scotlands
Farm

HILL LA

Hill

Court
Farm

Church-hill
Wood

Maniards
Green

Beggarsbush Lane

Rockhampton Rhine

WOODEND LA

Stoneyard
Lane

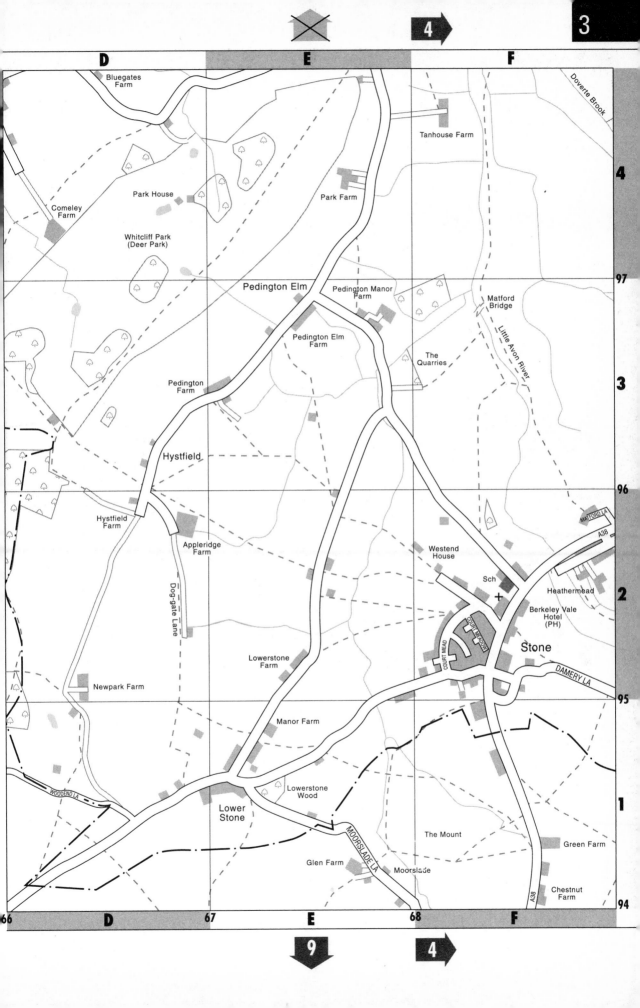

Bluegates Farm

Comeley Farm

Park House

Whitcliff Park (Deer Park)

Park Farm

Tanhouse Farm

Doverte Brook

Pedington Elm

Pedington Manor Farm

Matford Bridge

Pedington Elm Farm

The Quarries

Little Avon River

Pedington Farm

Hystfield

Hystfield Farm

Appleridge Farm

Dog-gate Lane

Westend House

MATFORD LA

A38

Sch

Heathermead

Berkeley Vale Hotel (PH)

Stone

COURT MEADOW

COURT MEAD

DAMERY LA

Newpark Farm

Lowerstone Farm

Manor Farm

WOODEND LA

Lower Stone

Lowerstone Wood

MOORSLADE LA

The Mount

Green Farm

Glen Farm

Moorslade

A38

Chestnut Farm

A   B   C

4

Newport

Greenways

Goldwick Farm

CROSSWAYS
Baynhamcourt Farm

Hotel

Hogsdown Farm

CHURCH VIEW

A38

CHAPEL HILL

Doverte Brook

97

Oakleaze Farm

Lower Wick

M5

Swanley Farm

HAYCROFT LA

3

Manor Farm

Swanley

SWANLEY LA

Lowerwick Farm

Woodfordgreen Farm

Middle Wick

Middlewick Farm

Whitehall Farm

96

A38

Pickwick Inn (PH)

Woodford

Wick Bridge

Michaelwood Farm

Harold's Brake

2

Woodford Farm

MULE ST

Michael Wood Service Area

Sweetbrier Brake

Middle Mill Farm

DAMERY LA

Furzeground Wood

95

Little Avon River

DAMERY LA

Michaelwood Lodge Farm

Michael Wood

1

Crockley's Farm

Damery

Damery Bridge

Iron Mill Grove

M5

Daniel's Wood

94

69   A   70   B   71   C

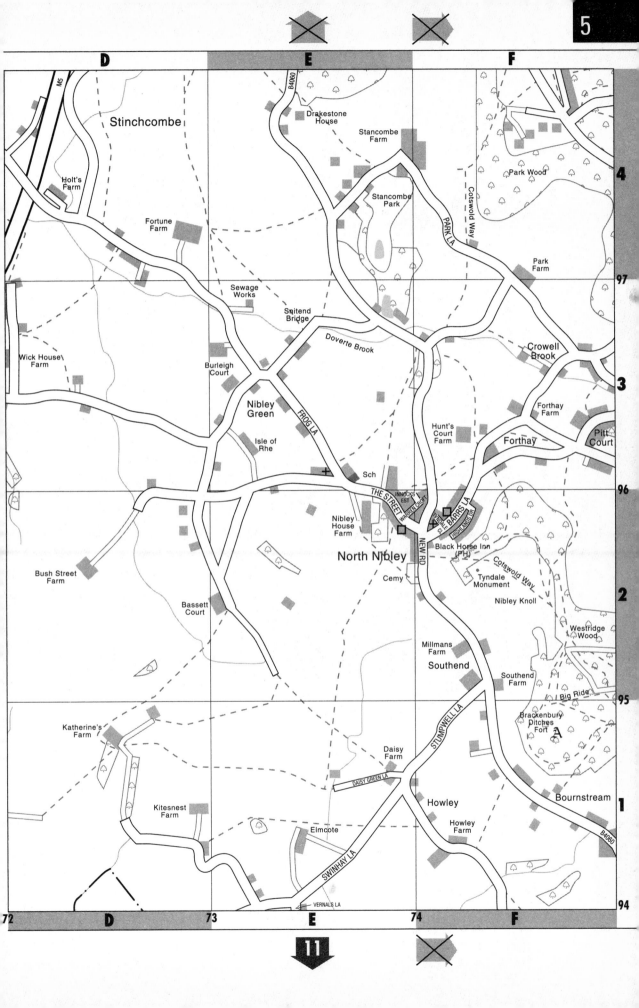

D   E   F

Stinchcombe

Drakestone
House

Stancombe
Farm

Park Wood

Holt's
Farm

Stancombe
Park

Cotswold Way

4

Fortune
Farm

PARK LA

Park
Farm

97

Sewage
Works

Snitend
Bridge

Doverte Brook

Crowell
Brook

Wick House
Farm

FROG LA

Burleigh
Court

Nibley
Green

Forthay
Farm

3

Hunt's
Court
Farm

Forthay

Pitt
Court

Isle of
Rhe

Sch

96

THE STREET

INNOCKS
EST

WARREN CROFT

BARRS LA

HIGHLANDS DR

Nibley
House
Farm

NEW RD

Black Horse Inn
(PH)

North Nibley

Bush Street
Farm

Cemy

Tyndale
Monument

Cotswold Way

Nibley Knoll

Bassett
Court

Westridge
Wood

2

Millmans
Farm

Southend

Southend
Farm

Big Ride

95

Katherine's
Farm

Brackenbury
Ditches
Fort

STUMPWELL LA

Daisy
Farm

Kitesnest
Farm

DAISY GREEN LA

Howley

Bournstream

1

Elmcote

Howley
Farm

B4060

SWINHAY LA

VERNALS LA

94

72   D   73   E   74   F

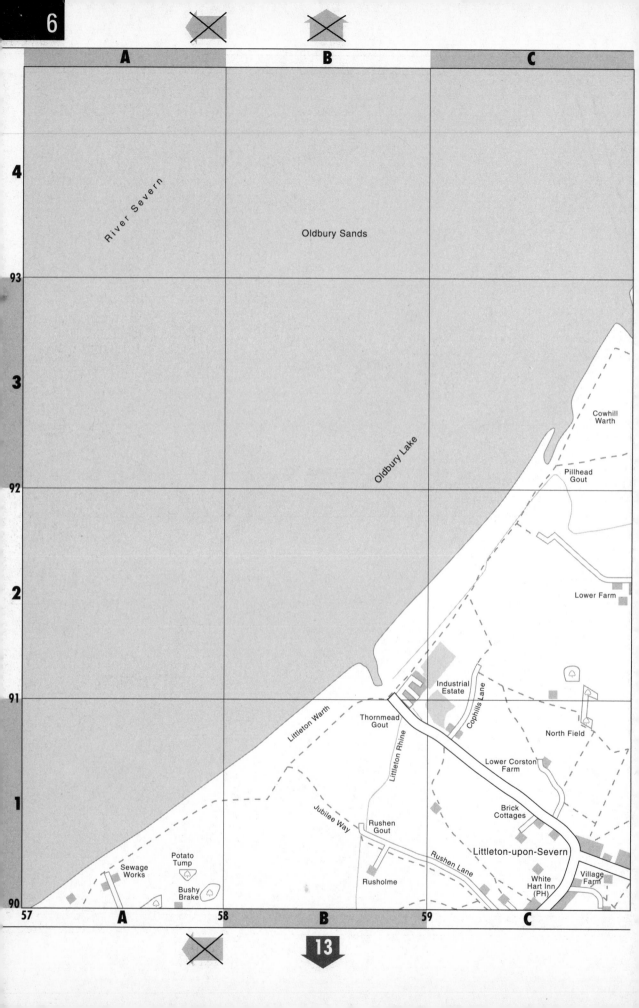

A   B   C

4

River Severn

Oldbury Sands

93

3

Cowhill
Warth

Oldbury Lake

Pillhead
Gout

92

Lower Farm

2

91

Littleton Warth

Industrial
Estate

Cophills Lane

North Field

Thornmead
Gout

Littleton Rhine

Lower Corston
Farm

1

Jubilee Way

Brick
Cottages

Rushen
Gout

Littleton-upon-Severn

Sewage
Works

Potato
Tump

Rushen Lane

White
Hart Inn
(PH)

Village
Farm

Rusholme

Bushy
Brake

90

57   A   58   B   59   C

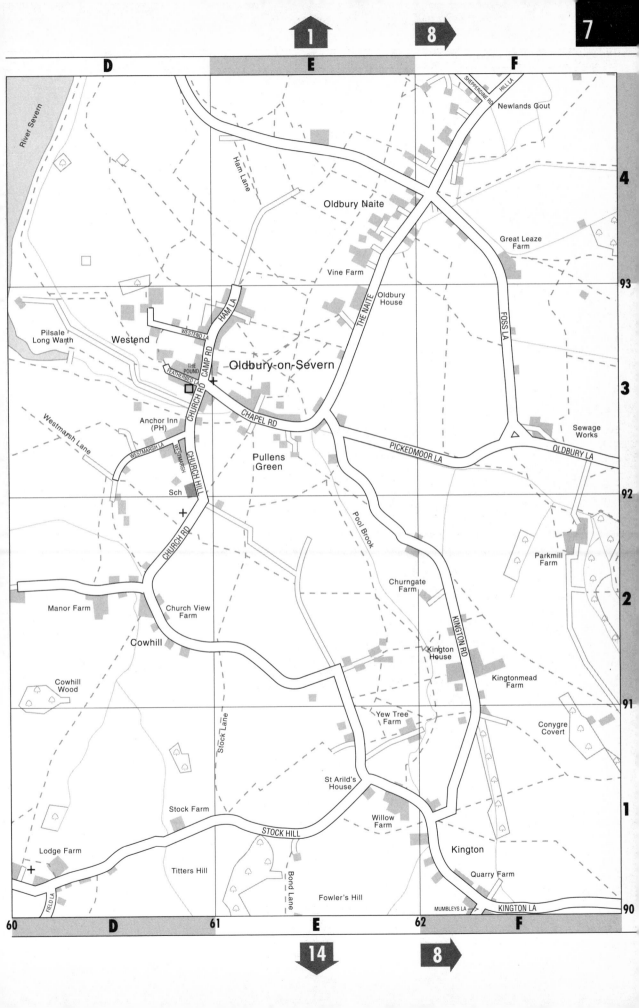

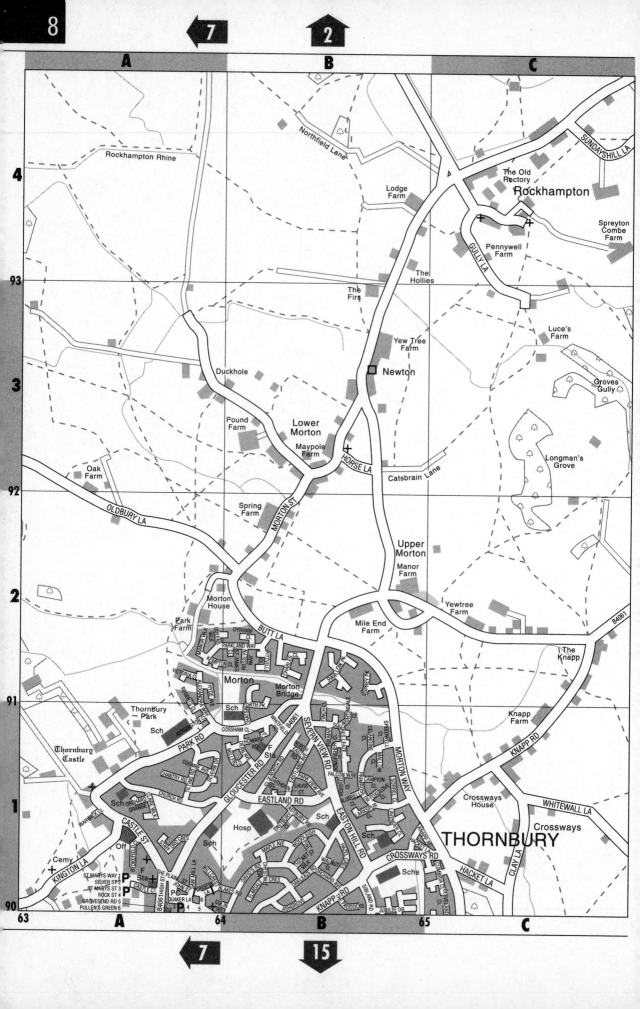

A · B · C

4

Rockhampton Rhine

The Old Rectory

Rockhampton

SUNDAYSHILL LA

Lodge Farm

Pennywell Farm

Spreyton Combe Farm

93

The Hollies

The Firs

Luce's Farm

Yew Tree Farm

Duckhole

Newton

Groves Gully

3

Pound Farm

Lower Morton

Longman's Grove

Maypole Farm

Oak Farm

HORSE LA

Catsbrain Lane

92

OLDBURY LA

MORTON ST

Spring Farm

Upper Morton

Manor Farm

2

Morton House

Park Farm

BUTT LA

Yewtree Farm

Mile End Farm

B4061

The Knapp

MANOR PK WALK · DYRHAM CL · PARKLAND WAY · ST JAMES CL · KEMPTON CL · WM

CHARLES CL

OSPREY PK

Victoria CL · ALEXANDRA WAY · HYDE AVE · NORTH PK · ST JAMES · TILL

SNA LOWE

NIGHTINGALE

91

Thornbury Park

Morton

Morton Bridge

Sch

FINCH CL

SPEEDWELL CL · CELANDINE CL · MALLOW CL

Knapp Farm

Sch

KENSINGTON CL

COSSHAM CL

WHITEFIELD B4061

SEVERN VIEW RD

WYM

PRIMROSE CL

KNAPP RD

PARK RD

HOWARD CL

F Sta

DAVIS CL

PARK VIEW AVE

FALCON WAY

CAMPION CL

Crossways House

WHITEWALL LA

Thornbury Castle

CHANTRY RD

COOMBE AVE · KENNEDY WAY · PENN LEA RD

HAWTHORN CL

CRES

LARKSPUR CL

MORTON WAY

SORREL CL

Crossways

1

CHURCH RD

GLOUCESTER RD

EASTLAND RD

EASTBURY RD

Sch

EASTON HILL RD

Sch

CROSSWAYS RD

THORNBURY

WARWICK CL

Sch ORCHARD GRANGE

CLARE WLK

Hosp

MAPLE AVE

WOOD HIGH CL

WALNUT CL

HACKET LA

CLAY LA

Cemy

CASTLE ST

STOKEFIELD CL

Sch

HILLCREST CL

DAVID'S RD

OAK LEAZE · ORCHARD RD

Schs

KINGTON LA

Off

B4061 HIGH ST · SAW MILL LA · THE PLAIN · JOHN ST

CRISPIN LA

BLAKES RD

KNAPP RD

SIBLAND RD

CUMBERLAND · CLEVELAND

90

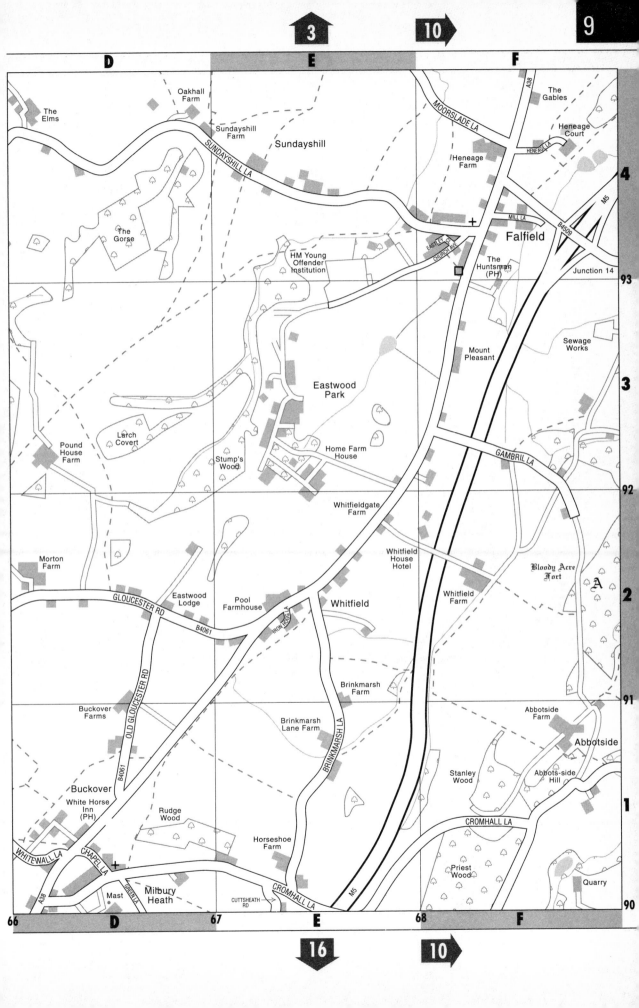

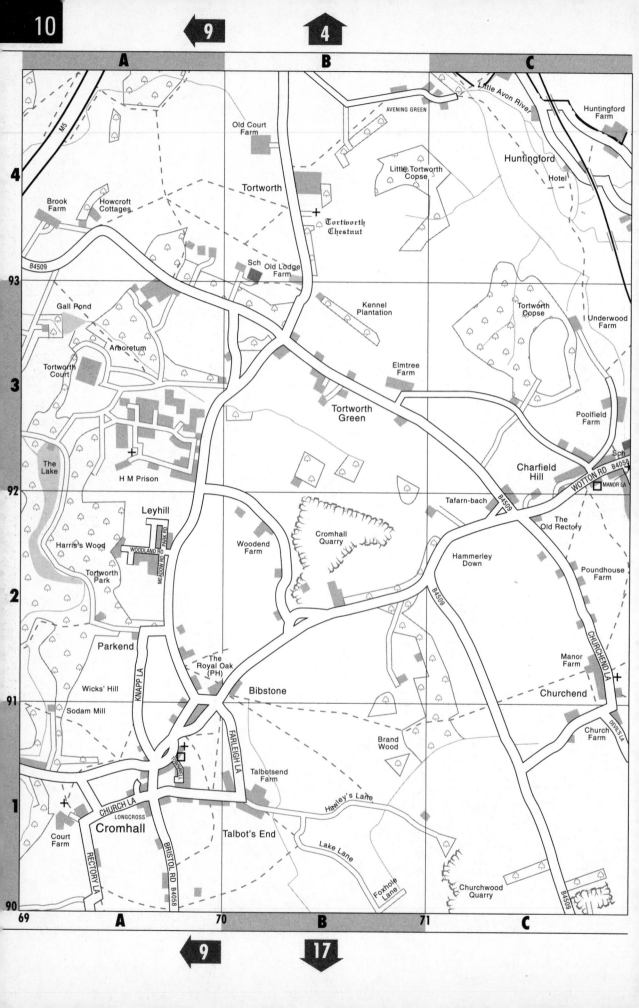

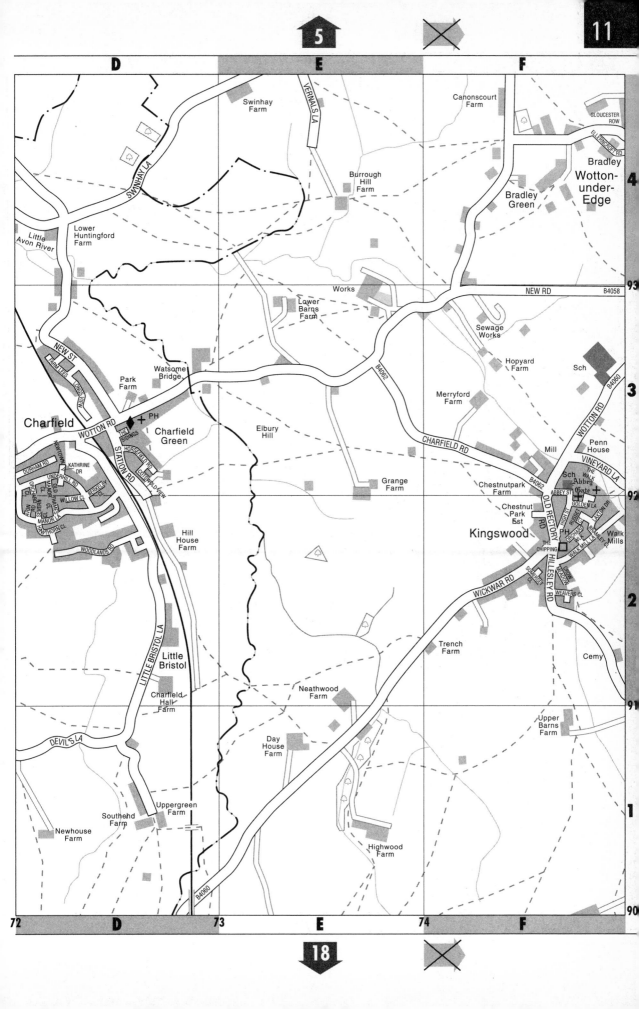

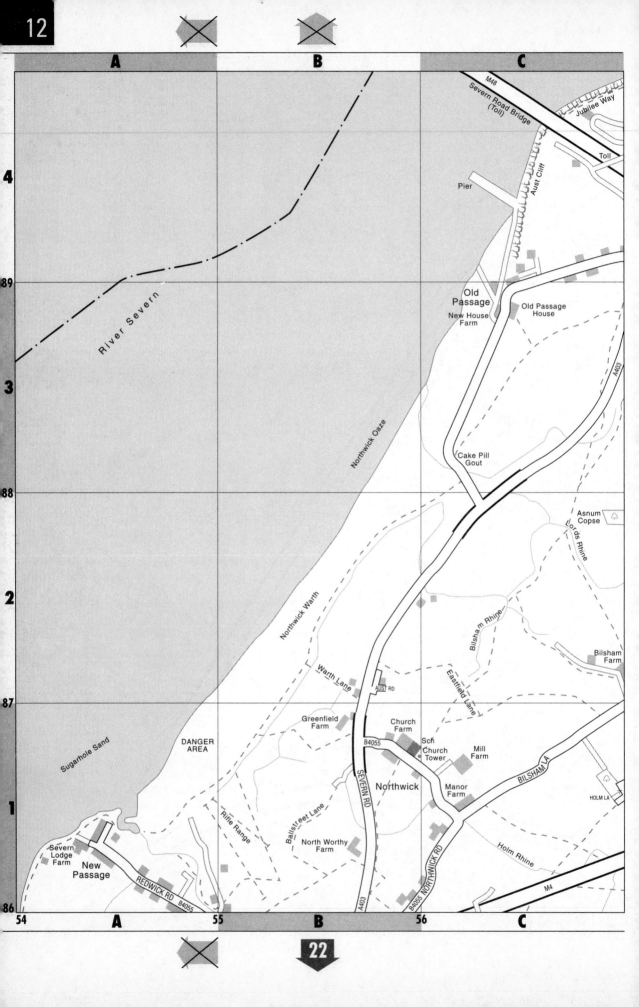

A   B   C

4

89

3

88

2

87

1

86

54   A   55   B   56   C

M48
Severn Road Bridge (Toll)
Jubilee Way
Toll
Aust Cliff
Pier

Old Passage
Old Passage House
New House Farm

River Severn

A403

Cake Pill Gout

Northwick Oaze

Asnum Copse

Lords Rhine

Bilsham Rhine

Bilsham Farm

Northwick Warth

Warth Lane
AUST RD

Eastfield Lane

Sugarhole Sand

DANGER AREA

Greenfield Farm

Church Farm

Scn
Church Tower

Mill Farm

BILSHAM LA

HOLM LA

B4055

SEVERN RD

Northwick

Manor Farm

Rifle Range

Ballstreet Lane

North Worthy Farm

Severn Lodge Farm

New Passage

REDWICK RD

B4055

A403

B4055 NORTHWICK RD

Holm Rhine

M4

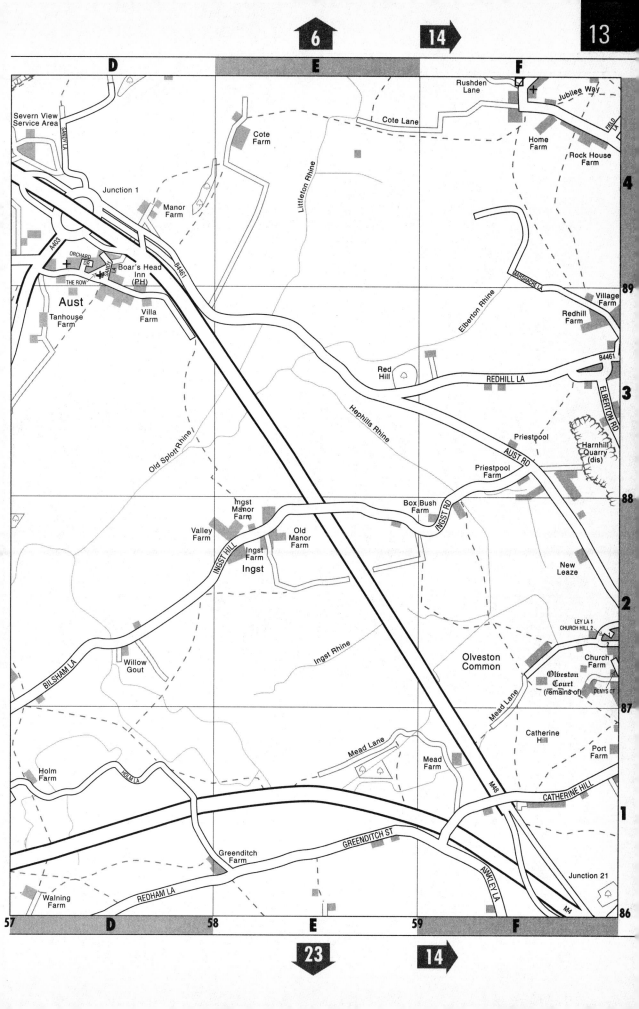

6
14

D   E   F

Rushden Lane

Jubilee Way

FIELD LA

Cote Lane

Severn View Service Area

Cote Farm

Home Farm

Rock House Farm

SANDY LA

4

Junction 1

Manor Farm

Littleton Rhine

B4461

ORCHARD DR

Boar's Head Inn (PH)

THE ROW

SANDY LA

Elberton Rhine

MARSHACRE LA

Village Farm

89

Aust

Redhill Farm

A403

Villa Farm

Tanhouse Farm

Red Hill

REDHILL LA

B4461

ELBERTON RD

3

Hephills Rhine

Priestpool

Harnhill Quarry (dis)

Old Splott Rhine

AUST RD

Priestpool Farm

88

Ingst Manor Farm

Box Bush Farm

INGST RD

Valley Farm

Old Manor Farm

Ingst Farm

New Leaze

INGST HILL

Ingst

2

Ingst Rhine

LEY LA 1
CHURCH HILL 2

BILSHAM LA

Willow Gout

Olveston Common

Church Farm

Olveston Court (remains of)

DENYS CT

Mead Lane

87

Catherine Hill

Port Farm

Mead Lane

Holm Farm

Mead Farm

M48

HOLM LA

CATHERINE HILL

1

ANKLEY LA

Junction 21

GREENDITCH ST

Greenditch Farm

M4

Walning Farm

REDHAM LA

86

23
14

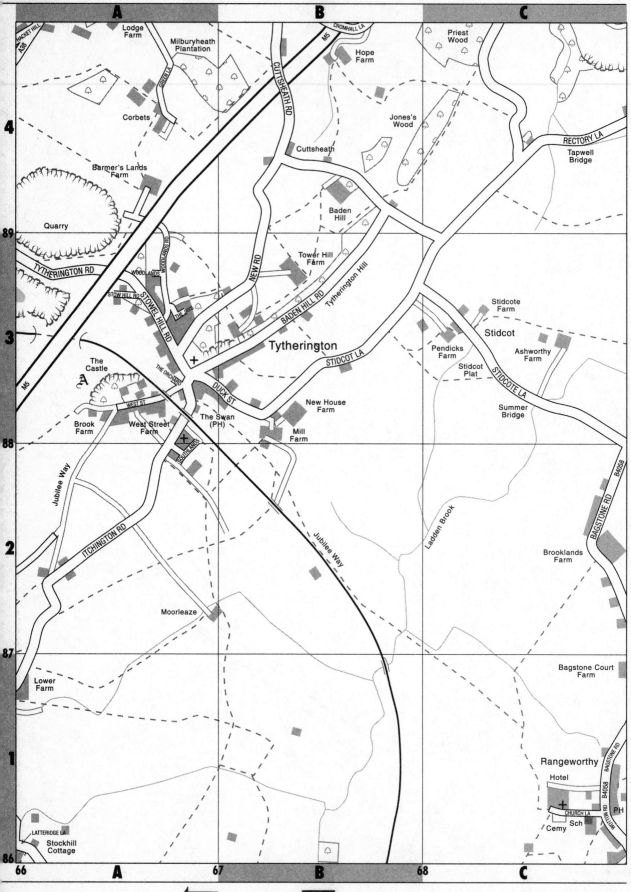

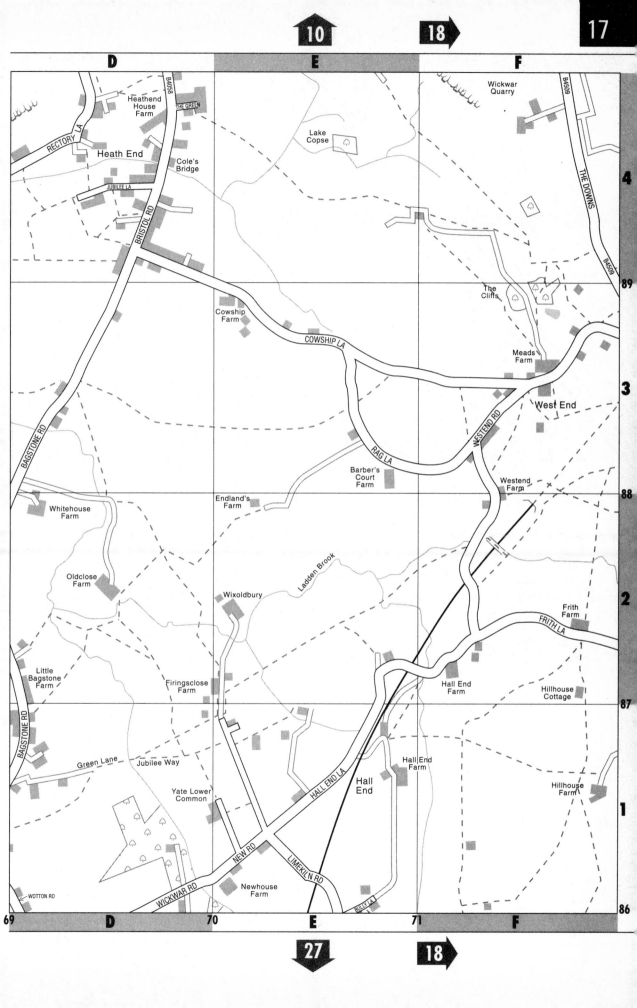

Wickwar Quarry

B4058

THE GREEN

Heathend House Farm

RECTORY LA

Heath End

Cole's Bridge

JUBILEE LA

BRISTOL RD

Lake Copse

THE DOWNS

B4509

The Cliffs

Cowship Farm

COWSHIP LA

Meads Farm

West End

WESTEND RD

BAGSTONE RD

RAG LA

Barber's Court Farm

Westend Farm

Endland's Farm

Whitehouse Farm

Oldclose Farm

Ladden Brook

Wixoldbury

Frith Farm

FRITH LA

Little Bagstone Farm

Firingsclose Farm

Hall End Farm

Hillhouse Cottage

BAGSTONE RD

Green Lane   Jubilee Way

Yate Lower Common

HALL END LA

Hall End Farm

Hillhouse Farm

Hall End

NEW RD

LIMEKILN RD

Newhouse Farm

WOTTON RD

WICKWAR RD

BULLY LA

A **B** **C**

Bunsall
Bridge

B4060

Haroldfield
Farm

Cherryrock
Farm

Southwood
Farm

4

Cherryrock
Brake

Mounteney's
Farm

Station
House

STATION RD

Kites
Farm

Chase House
Farm

MOUNTENEY'S LA

Trading
Est

89

CHURCH LA

CHASE LA

Chaselane
Farm

IInglestone
Farm

B4509

Saltmoors/Ditch

THE DOWNS

WESTEND
RD

B4509

TURNPIKE GATE

PH

AVON CRES

NORTH ST

COTS/OLD VIEW

South Moon
Ridings

3

Trading
Est

TH

HIGH ST

BACK LA

HONEYBORNE WAY

Wickwar

Sturt
Farm

The Walk

Little Stanley
Wood

Sturt
Bridge

88

ALDER LA

CANTERS LA

POPLAR LA

South
Farm

Lower Woods
Lodge

Little Avon River

Harwood
Farm

Wetmoor
Nature Reserve

Poplar
Farm

HORWOOD LA

SODBURY RD

Lower Wetmoor
Wood

2

Bishop's Hill
Wood

Upper
Wetmoor

Littley
Wood

Hill View
Farm

FRITH LA

Bishop's Hill Brook

PINCOTS LA

Pulling's
Trench

87

Pincots
Farm

Burnt
Wood

Sturgeon
Wood

Bedford's
Wood

WICKWAR RD

1

Bays
Wood

Stonybridge
Wood

Shortwood
Farm

Little Shortwood
Farm

Haskin's
Farm

WOOD LA

Birdsbush
Farm

B4060

86

72 **A** **73** **B** **74** **C**

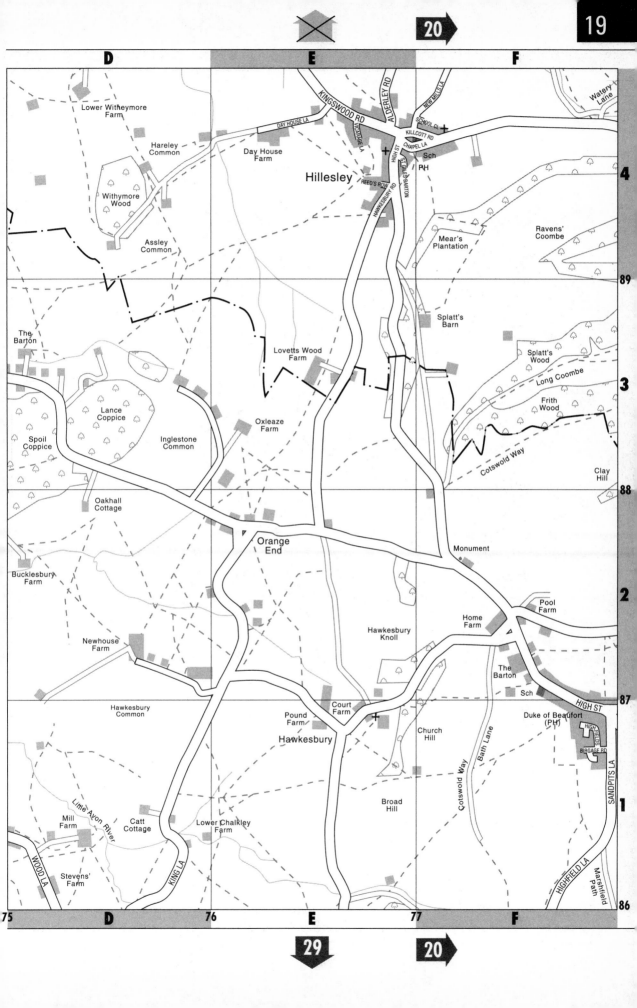

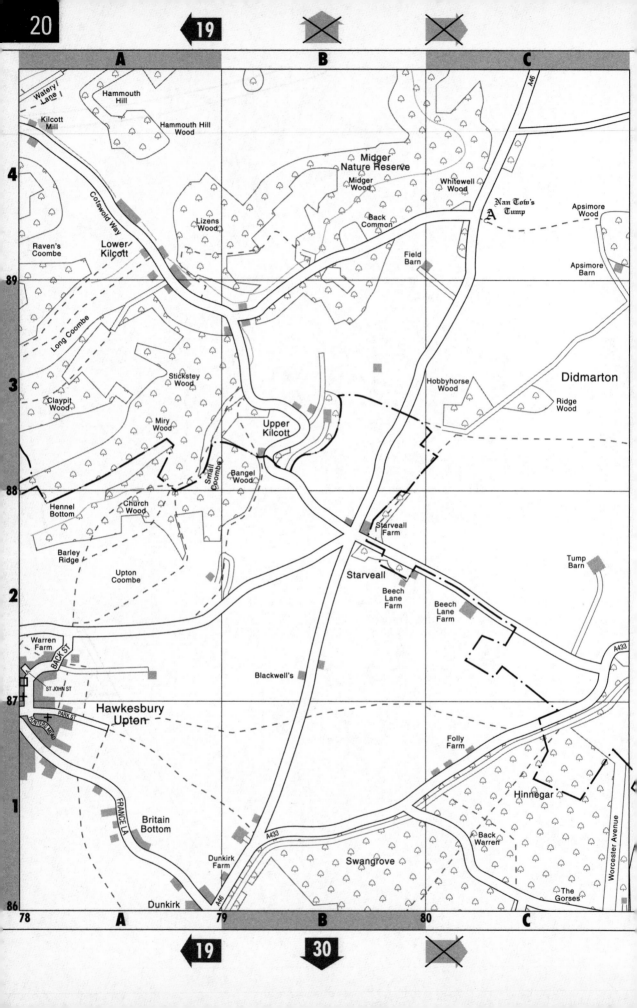

English Lake

Salmon Pool

English Stones

The Binn Wall

M4

BEACH RD

BEACH AVE

P

New Pill Gout

Works

Chittening Warth

Red Rhine

SEVERN RD

A403

Works

Tanks

Crook's Marsh

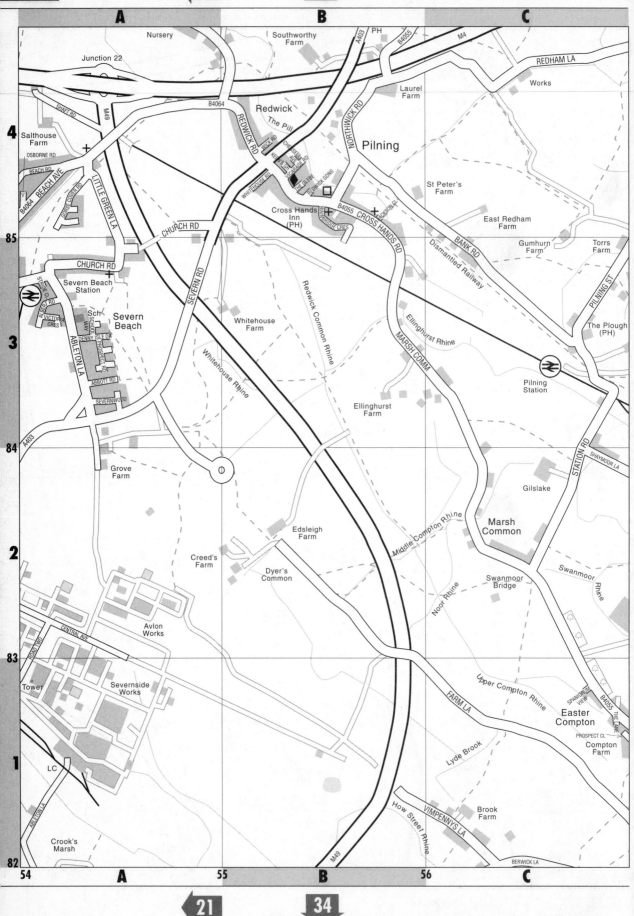

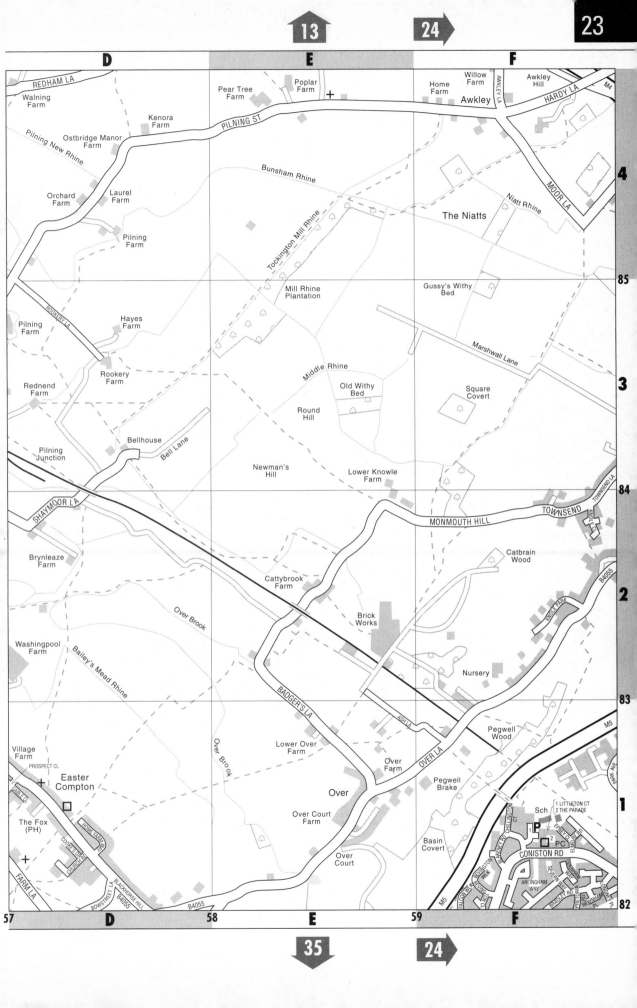

D E F

REDHAM LA
Walning Farm
Kenora Farm
Pear Tree Farm
Poplar Farm
Home Farm
Willow Farm
Awkley Hill
HARDY LA
Awkley
M4
PILNING ST
Ostbridge Manor Farm
Pilning New Rhine
AWKLEY LA
MOOR LA
Bunsham Rhine
4
Orchard Farm
Laurel Farm
Niatt Rhine
Pilning Farm
Tockington Mill Rhine
The Niatts
85
Mill Rhine Plantation
Gussy's Withy Bed
ROOKERY LA
Pilning Farm
Hayes Farm
Marshwall Lane
Middle Rhine
Rookery Farm
Old Withy Bed
Square Covert
3
Rednend Farm
Round Hill
Bellhouse
Bell Lane
Pilning Junction
Newman's Hill
Lower Knowle Farm
84
SHAYMOOR LA
MONMOUTH HILL
TOWNSEND
TOWNSEND LA
KNOLE LA
Brynleaze Farm
Catbrain Wood
KNOLE PARK
B4055
Cattybrook Farm
2
Over Brook
Brick Works
Washingpool Farm
Bailey's Mead Rhine
Nursery
BADGER'S LA
ASH LA
83
Over Brook
OVER LA
Pegwell Wood
M5
Lower Over Farm
Over Farm
Pegwell Brake
Village Farm
PROSPECT CL
1 LITTLETON CT
2 THE PARADE
Sch
Easter Compton
Over
Pegwell Brake
P
The Fox (PH)
HOME FARM LA
COOKE'S
CHURCHPATH
Over Court Farm
Basin Covert
PC
CONISTON RD
ARLINGHAM WAY
FARM LA
BLACKHORSE HILL
BOWSTRET LA
B4055
Over Court
B4055
M5

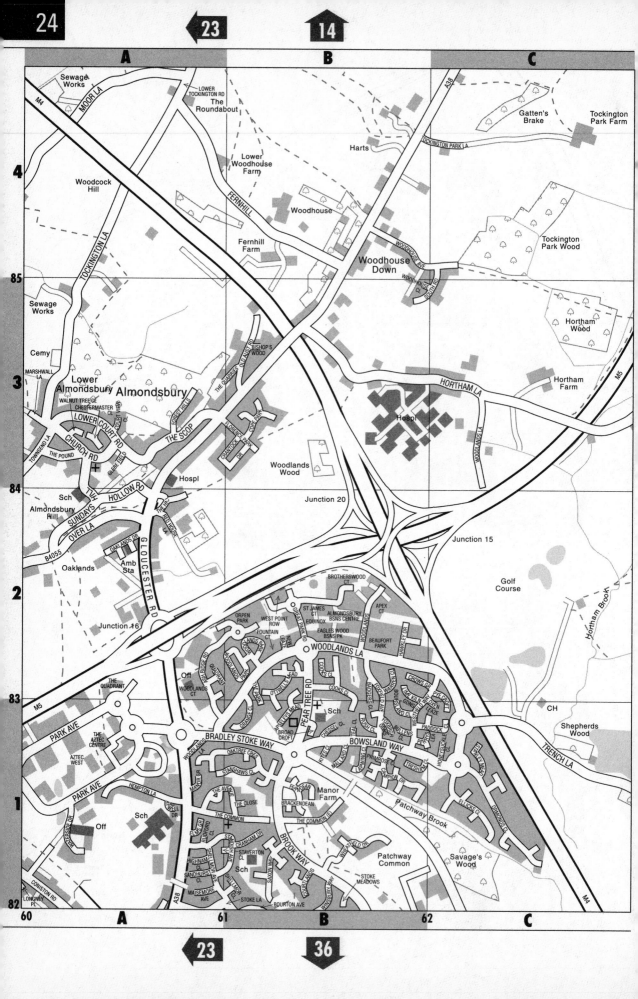

A
B
C

Sewage Works

MOOR LA

LOWER TOCKINGTON RD

The Roundabout

Lower Woodhouse Farm

Harts

A38

Gatten's Brake

Tockington Park Farm

TOCKINGTON PARK LA

4

Woodcock Hill

FERNHILL

Woodhouse

TOCKINGTON LA

Fernhill Farm

Woodhouse Down

WOODHOUSE AVE

Tockington Park Wood

85

Sewage Works

Cemy

BISHOP'S WOOD

WOODHOUSE CL

WOODHOUSE SOUTH RD

Hortham Wood

M5

MARSHWALL LA

Lower Almondsbury Almondsbury

WALNUT TREE CE CHESTERMASTER CL

THE QUARRIES

OLD AUST RD

HORTHAM LA

Hortham Farm

Hortham

3

LOWER COURT RD

FOREST HILLS

THE SCOP

FLORENCE PARK

ROPE PARK

Hosp

WOODLANDS LA

TOWNSEND LA

CHURCH RD

THE POUND

GLEBE FIELD

CRANTOCK DRIVE

Woodlands Wood

Hosp

84

Sch

TVH

HOLLOW RD

THE HILLS

Junction 20

Junction 15

Almondsbury Hill

SUNDAYS

OVER LA

OAKLANDS DR

Golf Course

Hortham Brook

B4055

Oaklands

Amb Sta

GLOUCESTER RD

BROTHERSWOOD CT

2

Junction 16

ORPEN PARK

WEST POINT ROW

FOUNTAIN CT

ST JAMES CT EQUINOX

ALMONDSBURY BSNS CENTRE

EAGLES WOOD BSNS PK

APEX CT

Beaufort Park

M5

THE QUADRANT

ASH RIDGE RD

QUADRANT

WOODLANDS PARK

GREAT PARK RD

WOODLANDS LA

HAWKLEY DR

CROWS GR

PYE CROFT

83

Park Ave

THE AZTEC CENTRE

AZTEC WEST

Off WOODLANDS CT

THE PARK

GRANGE CT

OLDWELLS

COOKS CL

COOKS CL

BADGERS CL

TANFIELD AVE

BOURG CL

THE KILNS

OVEN

REAZE

WESTLEY CL

PADDOCK

CH

Shepherds Wood

Park Ave

WOODLANDS LA

OAKTREE CRES

PEAR TREE RD

BROAD CROFT

ORPELL'S MEAD

Sch

CHESSEL CL

TEAL CL

MALLARD CL

RUSH CL

BULLENS

HOMESTEAD

HOME FIELD CL

EMLEY MEAD

TRENCH LA

Bradley Stoke Way

MANOR DR

STANSHAWS CL

KITES CL

Bowsland Way

SPINNEY

PRIMROSE

TRESHAM

CAMPION DR

ELLICKS CL

ORMONDS CL

1

HEMPTON LA

STILWELL DR

THE AVENUE

THE CLOSE

BRACKENDEAN

Manor Farm

Patchway Brook

Savage's Wood

Off

Sch

ELLSFORD

RUFFORD

STANSHAW AV

THE COMMON

CRAINHAM DR

STAVERTON CL

Sch

SAXON WAY

BROOK WAY

THE COMMON

COURTLANDS

WHITEFIELD AV

Patchway Common

STOKE MEADOWS

82

CONISTON RD

LONGNEY PL

WATERSIDE DR

HIGHNAM CL

SANDHURST CL

MAISEMORE AVE

SHELLMOR CL

SHELLMOR AV

STOKE LA

BOURTON AVE

KINSBURY WAY

A38

M4

60
A
61
B
62
C

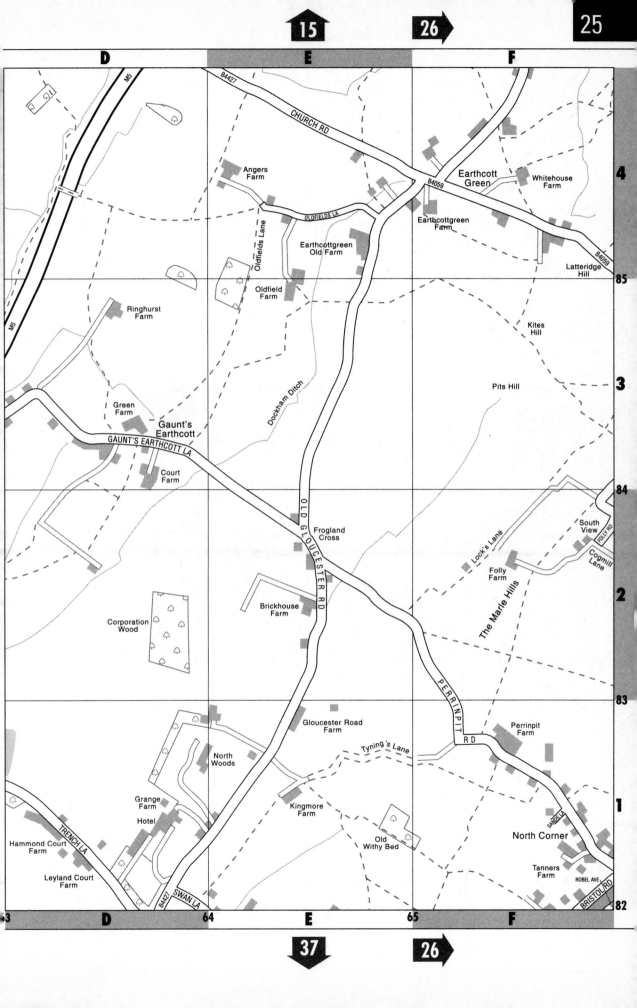

D E F

4

85

3

84

2

83

1

82

M5

B4427

CHURCH RD

Angers Farm

OLDFIELDS LA

Oldfields Lane

Earthcottgreen Old Farm

Oldfield Farm

B4059

Earthcott Green

Earthcottgreen Farm

Whitehouse Farm

Latteridge Hill

B4059

Kites Hill

Pits Hill

Ringhurst Farm

Dockham Ditch

Green Farm

Gaunt's Earthcott

GAUNT'S EARTHCOTT LA

Court Farm

OLD GLOUCESTER RD

Frogland Cross

South View

FOLLY RD

Lock's Lane

Cogmill Lane

Folly Farm

The Marle Hills

Corporation Wood

Brickhouse Farm

PERRINPIT RD

Perrinpit Farm

Gloucester Road Farm

North Woods

Tyning's Lane

Kingmore Farm

Old Withy Bed

SANDS LA

North Corner

Tanners Farm

ROBEL AVE

BRISTOL RD

TRENCH LA

Grange Farm

Hotel

Hammond Court Farm

Leyland Court Farm

B4427

SWAN LA

D 64 E 65 F

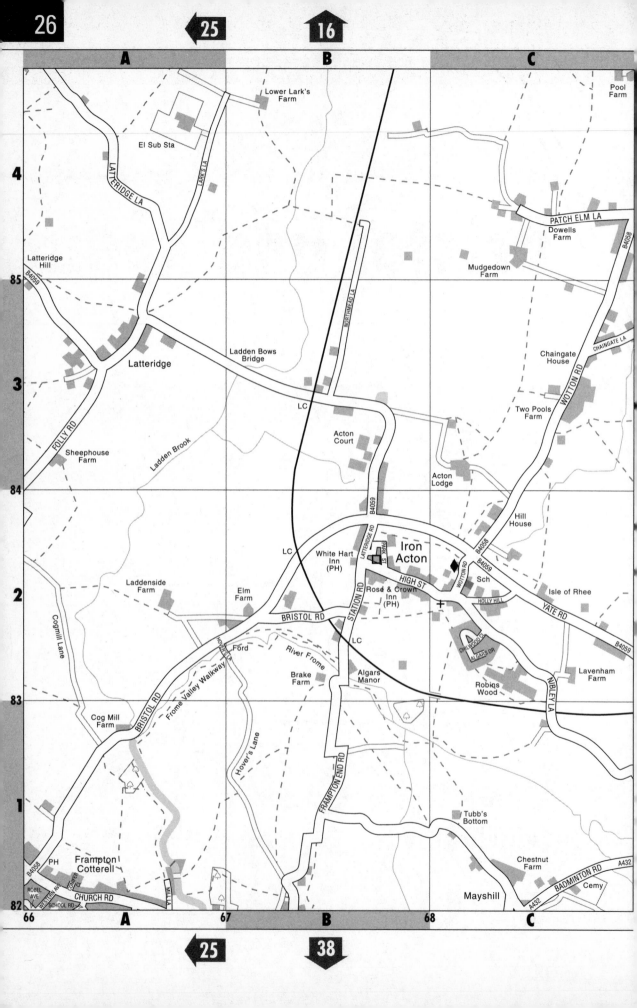

A   B   C

4

Pool Farm

Lower Lark's Farm

El Sub Sta

LATTERIDGE LA

LARK'S LA

PATCH ELM LA

B4058

Dowells Farm

Mudgedown Farm

85

B4059

Latteridge Hill

NORTHMEAD LA

Chaingate House

CHAINGATE LA

Ladden Bows Bridge

WOTTON RD

3

Latteridge

LC

Two Pools Farm

FOLLY RD

Sheephouse Farm

Ladden Brook

Acton Court

Acton Lodge

84

Hill House

B4059

Iron Acton

LATTERIDGE RD

PARK ST

White Hart Inn (PH)

Sch

B4058

B4059

2

Laddenside Farm

Elm Farm

HIGH ST

Rose & Crown Inn (PH)

WOTTON RD

Isle of Rhee

HOLLY HILL

YATE RD

Cogmill Lane

BRISTOL RD

STATION RD

LC

CHILWOOD CL

ALGARS DR

B4059

Lavenham Farm

Ford

River Frome

Brake Farm

Algars Manor

Robins Wood

NIBLEY LA

83

Cog Mill Farm

BRISTOL RD

Frome Valley Walkway

HOVER'S LA

Hover's Lane

FRAMPTON END RD

1

Tubb's Bottom

Chestnut Farm

A432

BADMINTON RD

Frampton Cotterell

PH

B4058

CONIFER CL

WESTERN AVE

ROBEL AVE

MILL LA

CHURCH RD

SCHOOL RD

Mayshill

Cemy

A432

82

66   A   67   B   68   C

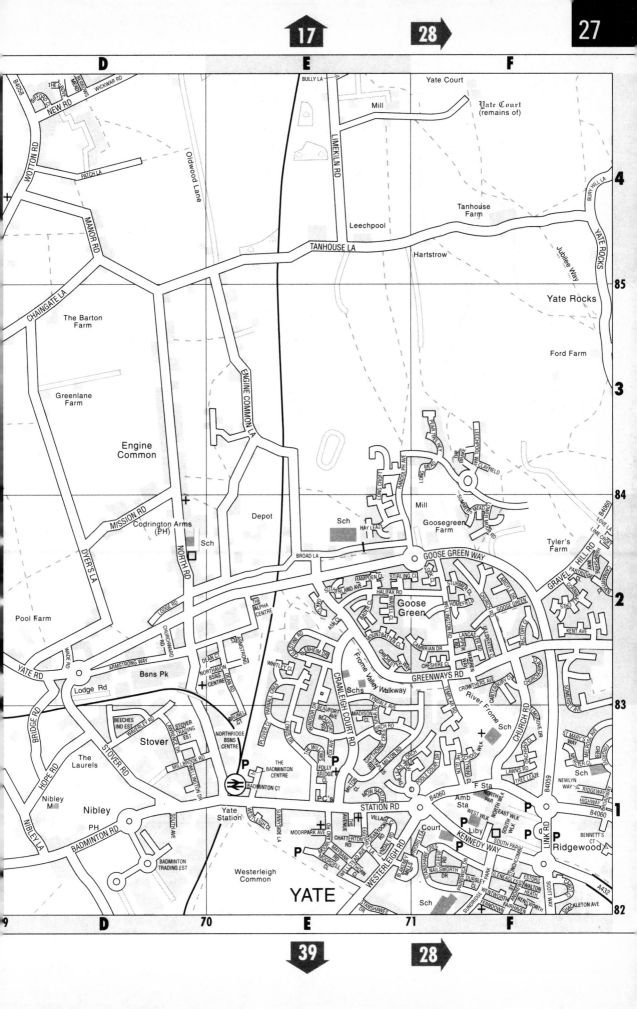

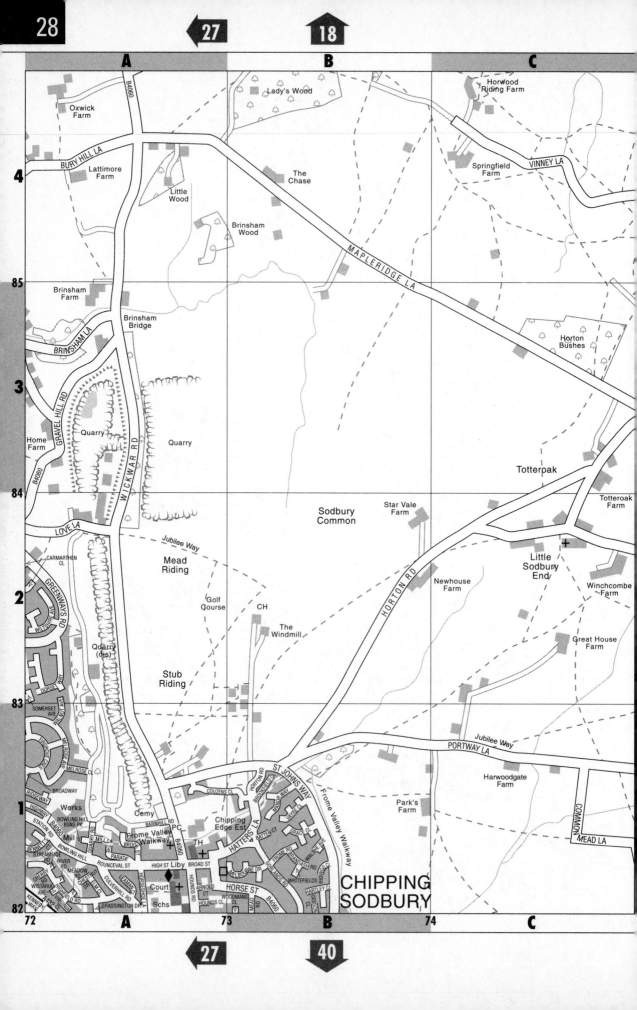

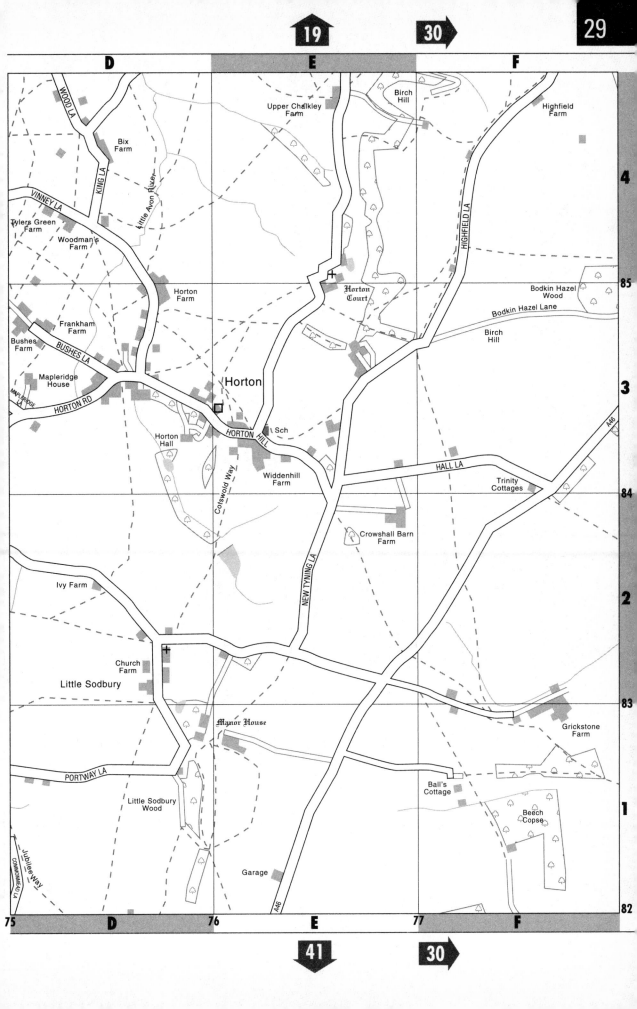

WOOD LA
KING LA
Bix Farm
Upper Chalkley Farm
Birch Hill
Highfield Farm
VINNEY LA
Little Avon River
Tylers Green Farm
Woodman's Farm
Horton Farm
Horton Court
Bodkin Hazel Wood
HIGHFIELD LA
Bodkin Hazel Lane
Birch Hill
Frankham Farm
Bushes Farm
BUSHES LA
Mapleridge House
MAPLERIDGE LA
HORTON RD
Horton
Horton Hall
HORTON HILL
Sch
Widdenhill Farm
Cotswold Way
A46
HALL LA
Trinity Cottages
Crowshall Barn Farm
NEW TYNING LA
Ivy Farm
Church Farm
Little Sodbury
Manor House
Grickstone Farm
PORTWAY LA
Little Sodbury Wood
Ball's Cottage
Beech Copse
Jubilee Way
COMMONMEAD LA
Garage
A46

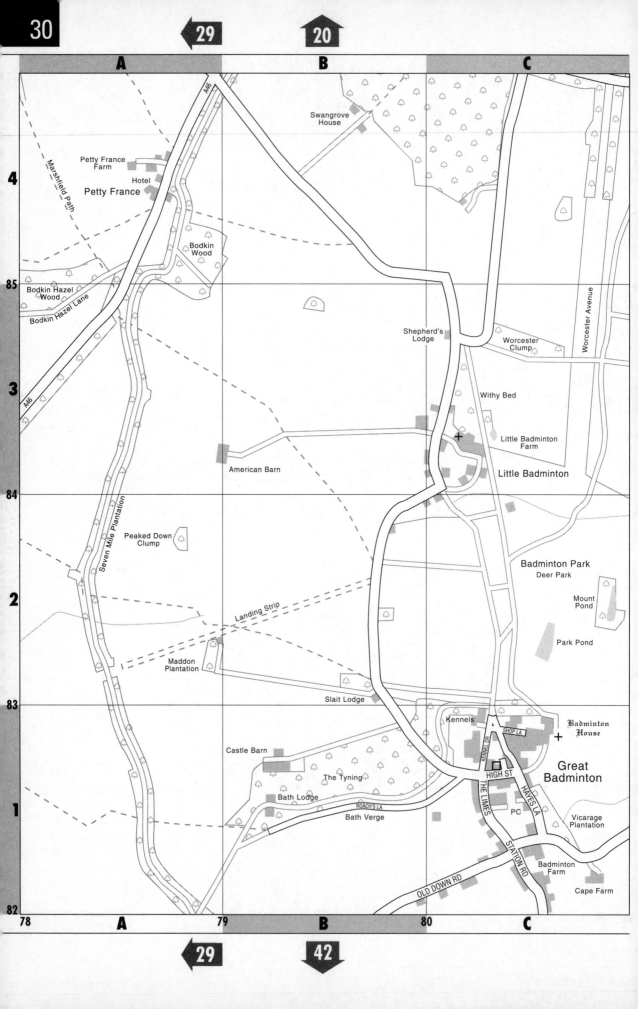

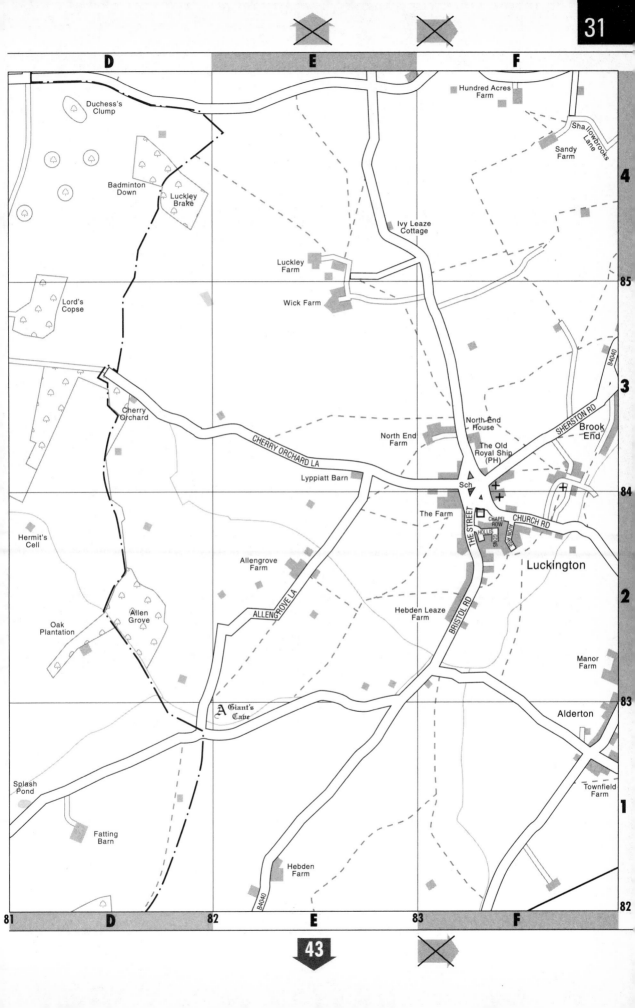

D · E · F

Hundred Acres Farm

Shallowbrooks Lane

Duchess's Clump

Sandy Farm

4

Badminton Down

Luckley Brake

Ivy Leaze Cottage

85

Luckley Farm

Lord's Copse

Wick Farm

B4040

3

Cherry Orchard

North End House

SHERSTON RD

Brook End

CHERRY ORCHARD LA

North End Farm

The Old Royal Ship (PH)

Lyppiatt Barn

Sch

+ +

+

84

The Farm

CHURCH RD

Hermit's Cell

CHAPEL ROW

THE STREET

HOLLIS

Luckington

Allengrove Farm

ALLENGROVE LA

Oak Plantation

Allen Grove

Hebden Leaze Farm

BRISTOL RD

2

Manor Farm

83

Giant's Cave

Alderton

Splash Pond

Townfield Farm

1

Fatting Barn

Hebden Farm

B4040

82

81 · D · 82 · E · 83 · F

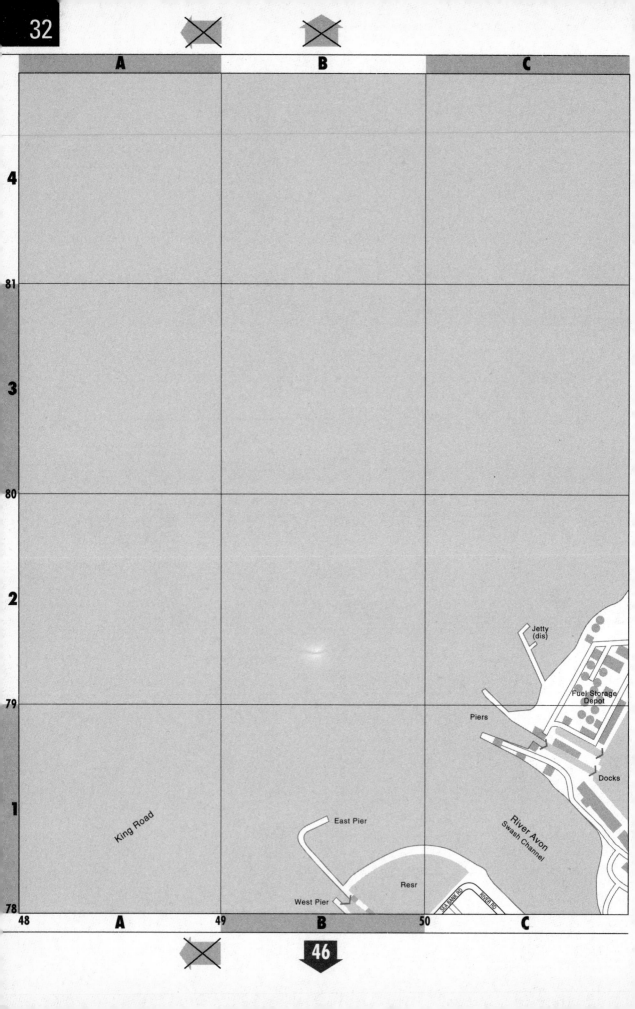

4

81

3

80

2

Jetty
(dis)

Fuel Storage
Depot

79

Piers

Docks

1

King Road

East Pier

River Avon
Swash Channel

Resr

West Pier

SEA BANK RD

RIVER RD

78

D
E
F

4
81
3
80
2
79
1
78

Works

Docks
Industrial Estate

SEVERN RD
A403
ABLETON LA
WASHINGPOOL LA
CHITTENING RD

BANK RD
WORTH RD
GREENSPLOTT RD

SMOKE LA
LC's

Fuel
Depot

West House
Farm

Hallen Marsh
Junction

Rockingham
Farm

Works

Madam
Farm

Moorend
Farm

Kites
Farm

LAWRENCE WESTON RD

MOORHOUSE LA

LC

DEAN RD
TROONCHURCH RD

BURCOTT RD
HUMBER WAY

Resr

Fuel
Depot

LC

STORES RD
SPAR RD

LC

ST ANDREW'S RD
SEVERN RD

WORKSHOP RD
ACID RD

ZINC RD
RETORT RD
ST RD

LC's

BOUNDARY RD

Katherine
Farm

Poplar
Farm

P
St Andrews Road
Station

Sewage Works

Mere Bank Rhine

KINGS WESTON LA

M49

Royal Edward Dock

Avonmouth
Docks

Royal Edward Dock

St Georges
Industrial Estate

Works

79
Junction 18a

M5

JUBILEE WAY
ST ANDREWS
TRADING EST

HASLEMERE
IND EST

THIRD WAY

New Rhine
ELLAS LA

Avonmouth

Shirehampton
Rhine

FIFTH WAY

King Road
P AVE

F Sta

WILLMENT WAY

AVONMOUTH WAY
LEDEN WAY
SECOND WAY

FOURTH WAY

Campbell
Farm

Swing-bridge

P

NAPIER RD
KINGS WESTON ST
BUCKINGHAM TERR
A403
LC
GLOUCESTER RD

QUEENS RD
KING ST
SKIPPON

A4
St BRENDAN'S WAY
COLLINS ST
SMYTHS
CL
ATLANTIC RD

FIRST WAY

GREEN LA
NAPIER RD
AVONMOUTH RD A4

Avonmouth
Station

AVONBRIDGE
TRADING EST

Junction 18

M5

CAMPBELL FARM DR
LONG
CROSS

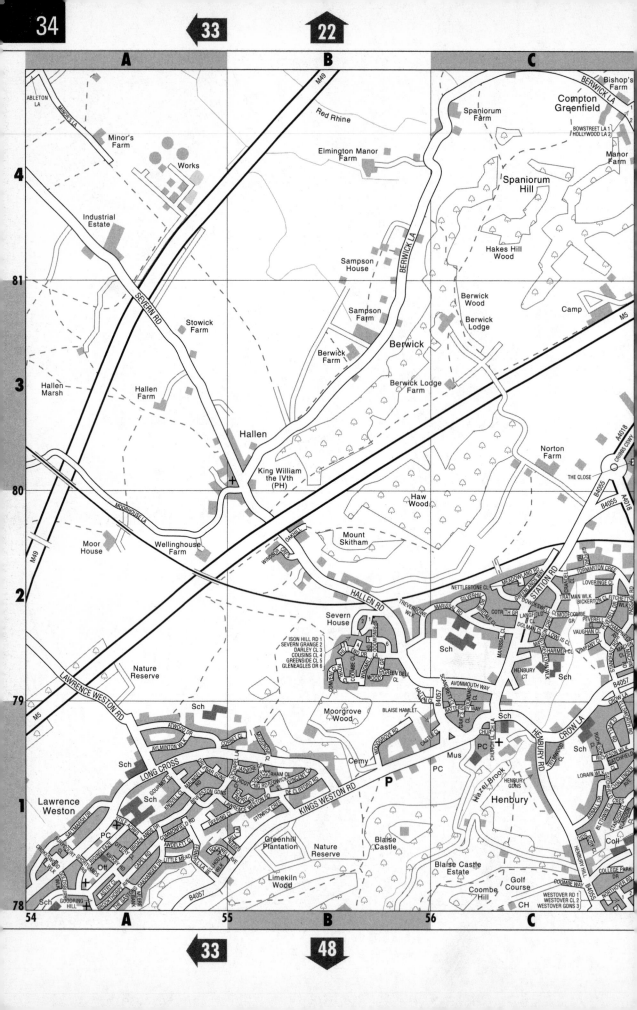

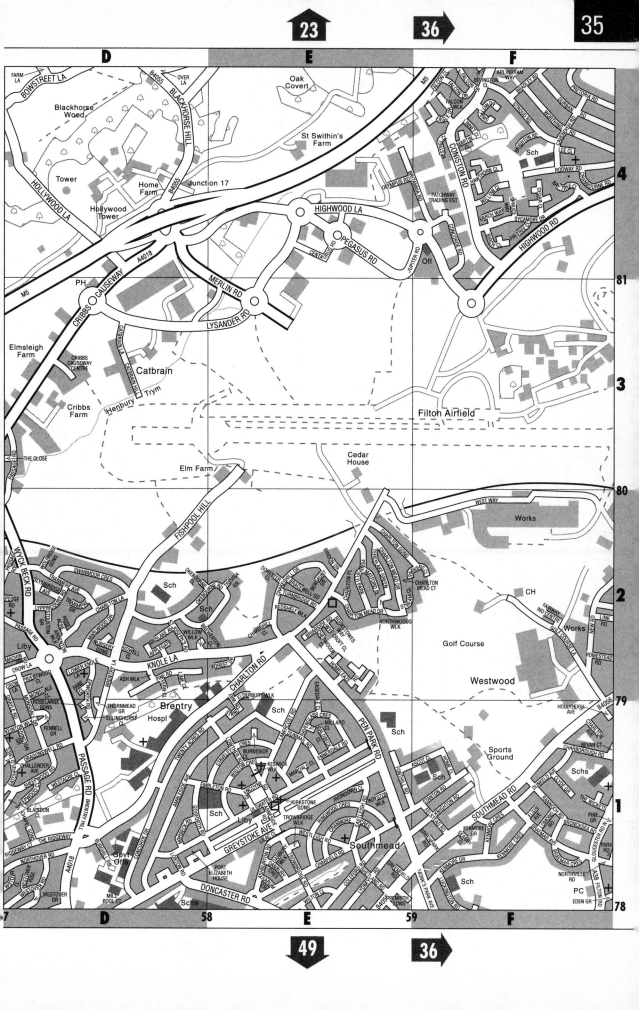

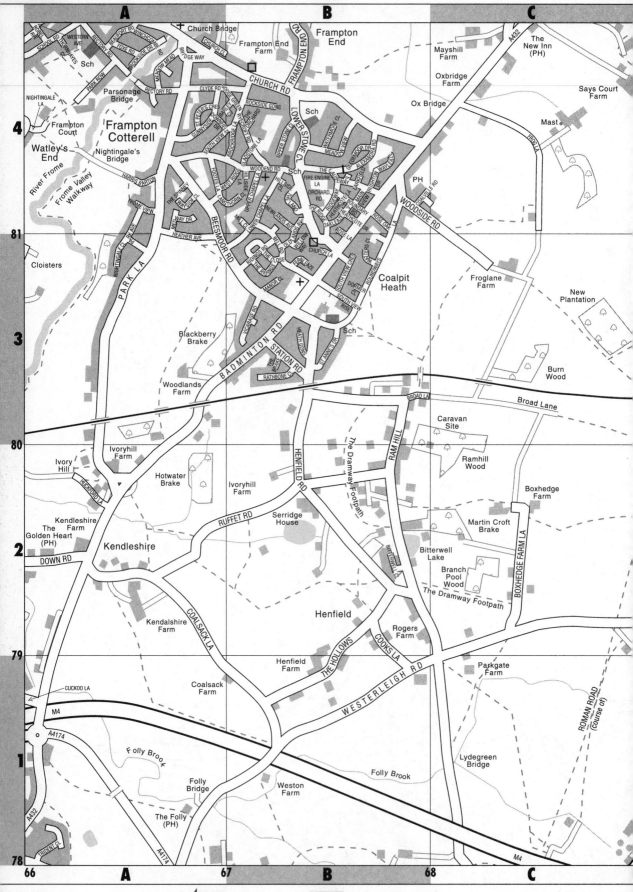

39 28

A B C

Kennedy Way
A432
MALLARD CL
VIRGINIA CL
DELLA
DOWN EAZE
CULVERHILL RD
HOUNDS RD
WOODMANS RD
KINGROVE CRES
WOODMANS
BURGAGE
MEAD RD
WOODMANS VALE
TWO STONES
GORLANDS
CRES
GORLANDS WAY
TOWER CL
ST WICKHAM
HORSE ST
FINCH RD
GRASSINGTON DR
GAUNTS RD
HERON HAYES
SMARTS GREEN
ST JOHNS WAY
STATION CL
BLANCHERS CRES
COTSWOLD RD
Blanchards Farm
BADMINTON RD
Colts Green
Colt's Green
River Frome
Frome Valley Walkway
COMMONMEAD LA
A432

HERON WAY
KINGFISHER RD
LILLIPUT AVE
BULLENS
PLOVERS
ROBIN WAY
ROBIN WAY
Sch
Sch
P

BOWLING RD
DODINGTON RD
CLAYPIT HILL
KINGSHOLE LA

Smart's Green
Frome Bridge

4

Homestead Farm
Kingrove Farm

Kingrove Common
Lower Kingrove Farm
Fatting House Farm

81

MILL LA
Bungalow Farm

Mouswell Farm
Hamwood Farm

Branchley Farm
DODINGTON LA

3

Ham Wood
Dodington Manor

80

The Grove

Lydes Farm

2

The Link

B4465
Downs Farm
Lean Tom Plantation
Shepherds Close Farm

Codrington
Long Sands

79

WAPLEY RD
Codrington Arms (PH)
Barleyclose Cottages
Fat Jack Plantation
Sands Court

Ostlands Farm

1

Tyning Farm
Codrington Court

Quarry (dis)
River Boyd

Barley Close Farm
Springs Farm
B4465
M4

78

39 54

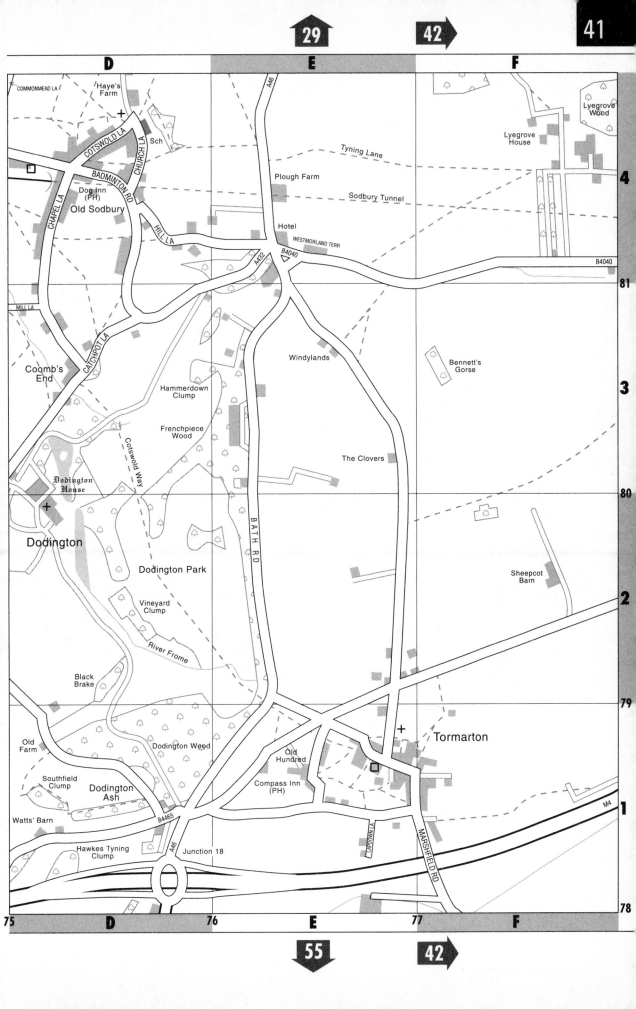

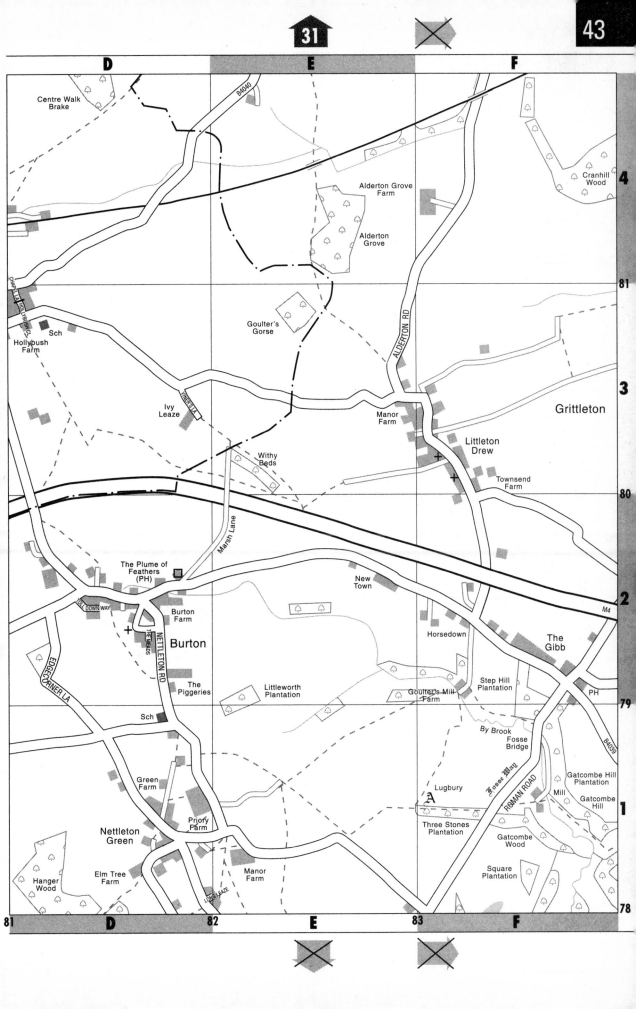

D **E** **F**

Centre Walk Brake

B4040

Cranhill Wood

4

Alderton Grove Farm

Alderton Grove

81

CHAPEL LA

HOLLYBUSH

Sch

Hollybush Farm

Goulter's Gorse

ALDERTON RD

Grittleton

3

Ivy Leaze

VINER'S LA

Manor Farm

Littleton Drew

Townsend Farm

Withy Beds

80

Marsh Lane

The Plume of Feathers (PH)

New Town

M4

2

TOLL DOWN WAY

Burton Farm

THE MEADS

NETTLETON RD

Burton

Horsedown

The Gibb

EDGECORNER LA

The Piggeries

Littleworth Plantation

Goulter's Mill Farm

Step Hill Plantation

PH

79

B4039

Sch

By Brook

Fosse Bridge

Green Farm

Fosse Way

Gatcombe Hill Plantation

Mill

Lugbury

ROMAN ROAD

Gatcombe Hill

Priory Farm

A

Three Stones Plantation

Gatcombe Wood

1

Nettleton Green

Hanger Wood

Elm Tree Farm

LONG LEAZE

Manor Farm

Square Plantation

78

81 **D** **82** **E** **83** **F**

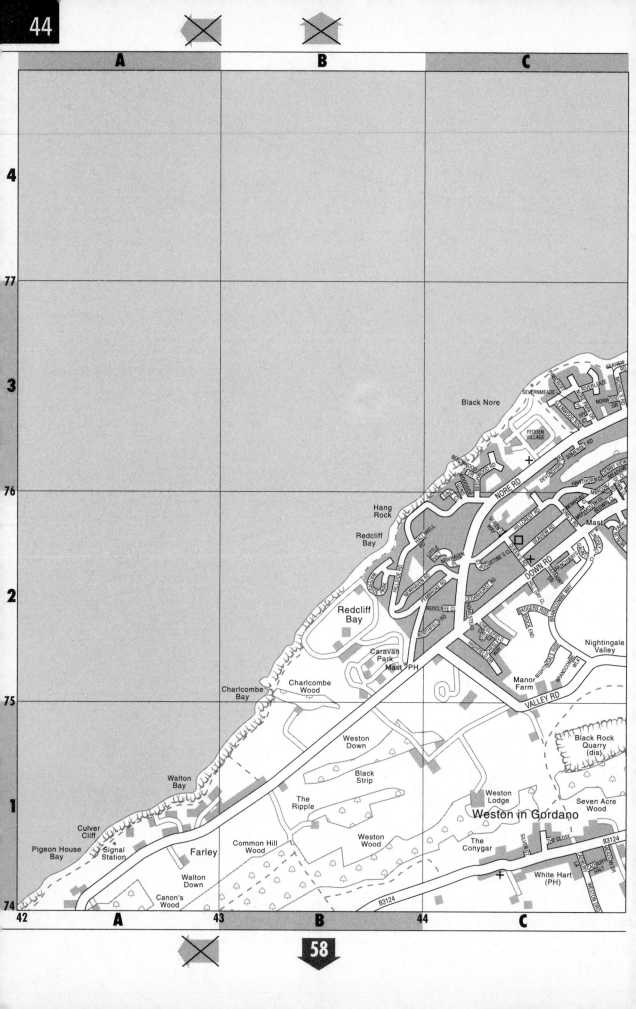

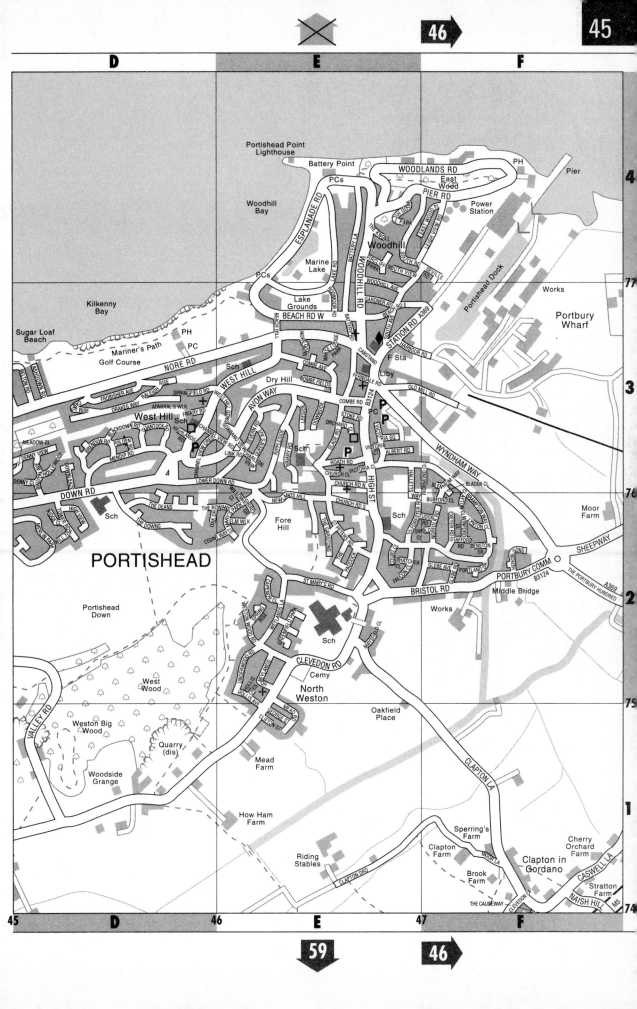

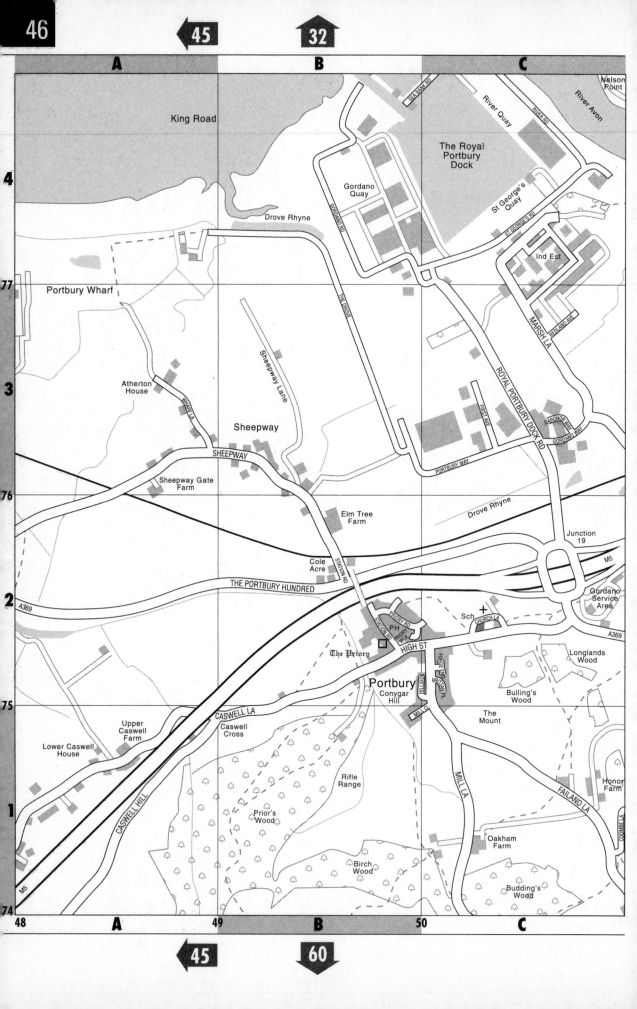

4

King Road

Nelson Point

River Avon

River Quay

River Rd

Sea Bank Rd

The Royal
Portbury
Dock

St George's Quay

St George's Rd

Ind Est

77

Portbury Wharf

Drove Rhyne

Gordano
Quay

Gordano Rd

The Drove

Marsh La

Bedland Ave

3

Atherton
House

Wharf La

Sheepway Lane

Sheepway

First Ave

Royal Portbury Dock Rd

Garonor Way

Gordano Way

SHEEPWAY

Sheepway Gate
Farm

Portbury Way

Elm Tree
Farm

76

Drove Rhyne

Junction
19

M5

Cole
Acre

Station Rd

THE PORTBURY HUNDRED

Gordano
Service
Area

2

A369

Priory Rd

Priory Way

Station Rd

PH

Sch

Church La

A369

The Priory

HIGH ST

Longlands
Wood

Portbury

Conygar
Hill

Hillside

Forge End

Britton Pl

Mill Cl

Bulling's
Wood

The
Mount

75

CASWELL LA

Caswell
Cross

Upper
Caswell
Farm

Lower Caswell
House

Rifle
Range

Mill La

Failand La

Honor
Farm

Coombe La

Caswell Hill

Prior's
Wood

Oakham
Farm

1

Birch
Wood

Budding's
Wood

M5

74

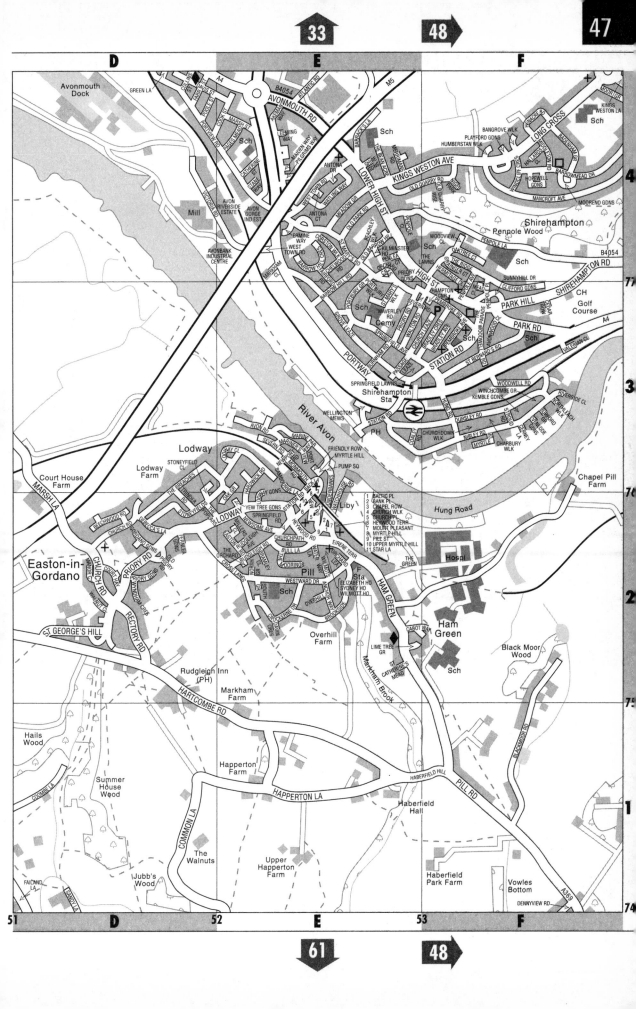

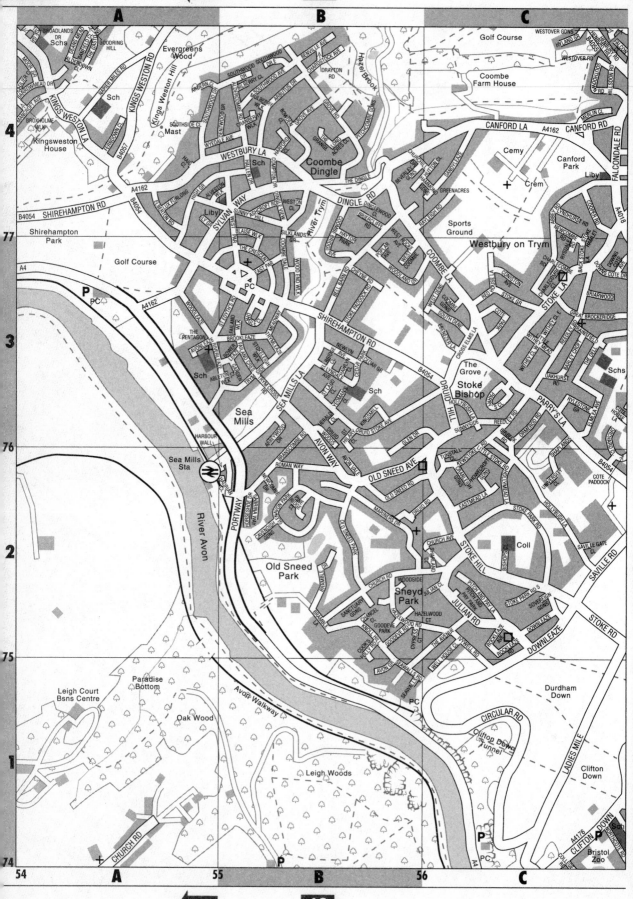

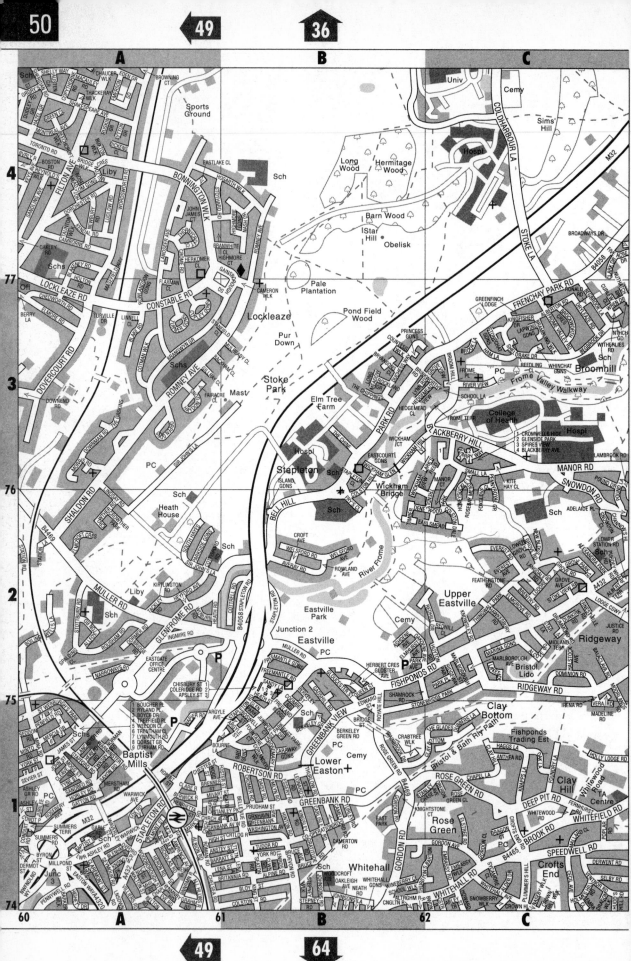

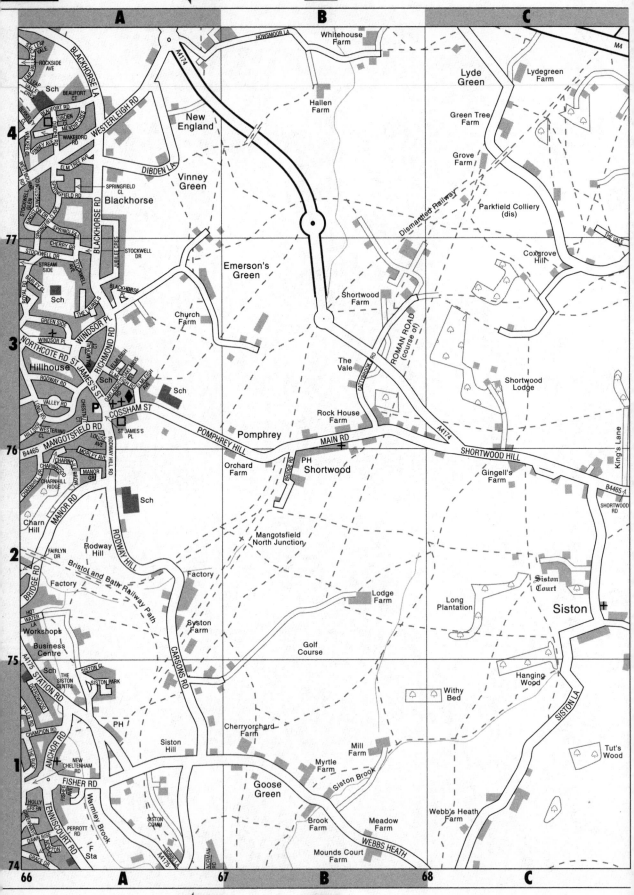

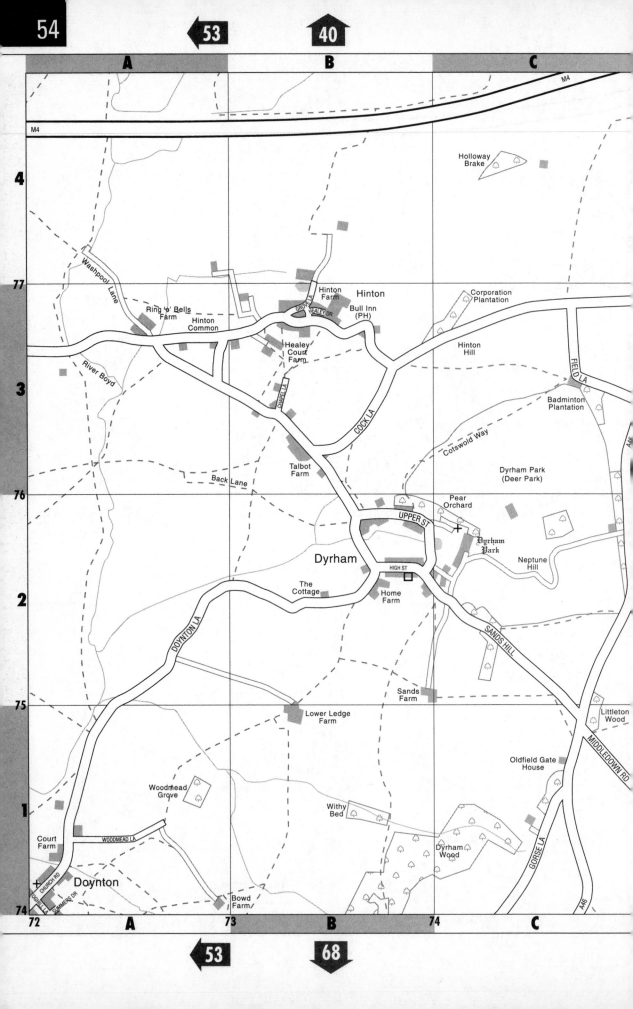

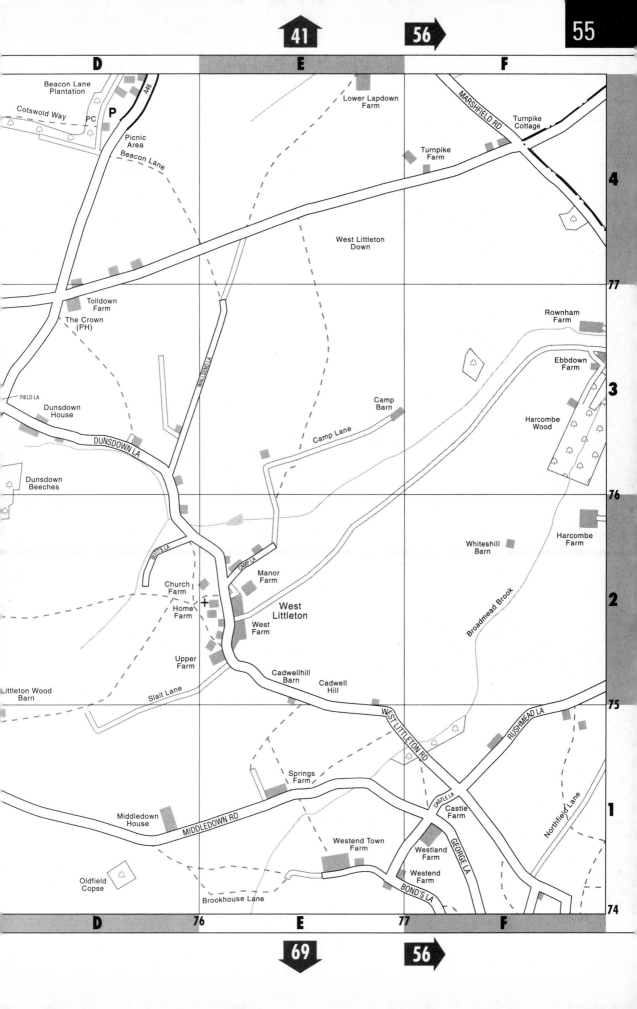

Beacon Lane
Plantation

Cotswold Way

PC   P

Picnic
Area

Beacon Lane

A46

Lower Lapdown
Farm

MARSHFIELD RD

Turnpike
Cottage

Turnpike
Farm

West Littleton
Down

4

77

Tolldown
Farm

The Crown
(PH)

Rownham
Farm

Ebbdown
Farm

FIELD LA

Dunsdown
House

WALLSEND LA

Camp
Barn

Camp Lane

Harcombe
Wood

3

DUNSDOWN LA

Dunsdown
Beeches

76

Harcombe
Farm

BUTT'S LA

Whiteshill
Barn

Church
Farm

CAMP LA

Manor
Farm

Home
Farm

West
Littleton

West
Farm

Broadmead Brook

2

Littleton Wood
Barn

Upper
Farm

Slait Lane

Cadwellhill
Barn

Cadwell
Hill

WEST LITTLETON RD

RUSHMEAD LA

75

Springs
Farm

CASTLE LA

Castle
Farm

Northfield Lane

Middledown
House

MIDDLEDOWN RD

Westend Town
Farm

Westland
Farm

GEORGE LA

1

Oldfield
Copse

Brookhouse Lane

Westend
Farm

BOND'S LA

74

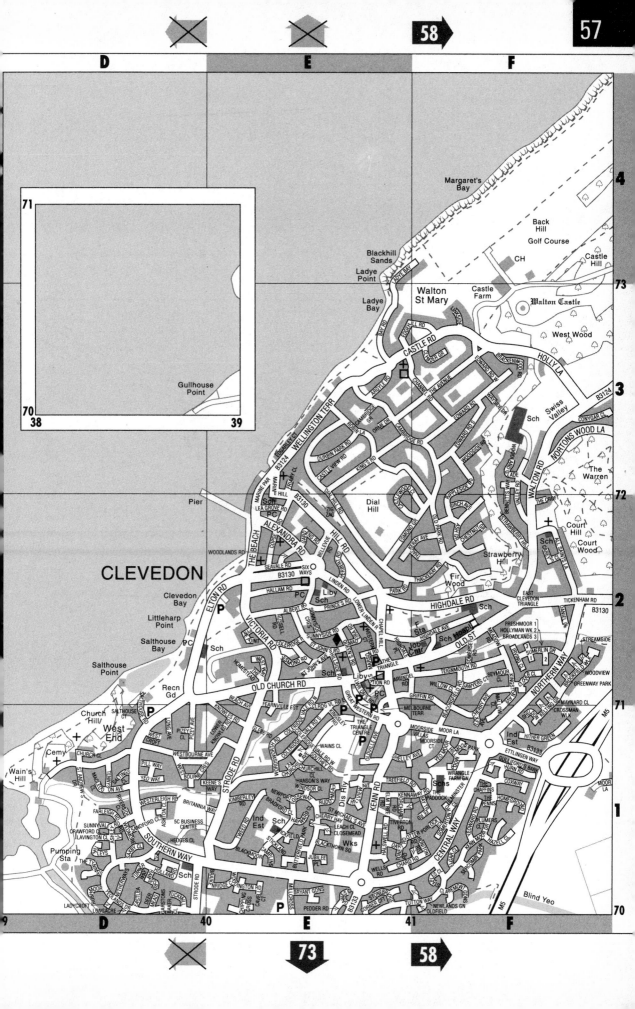

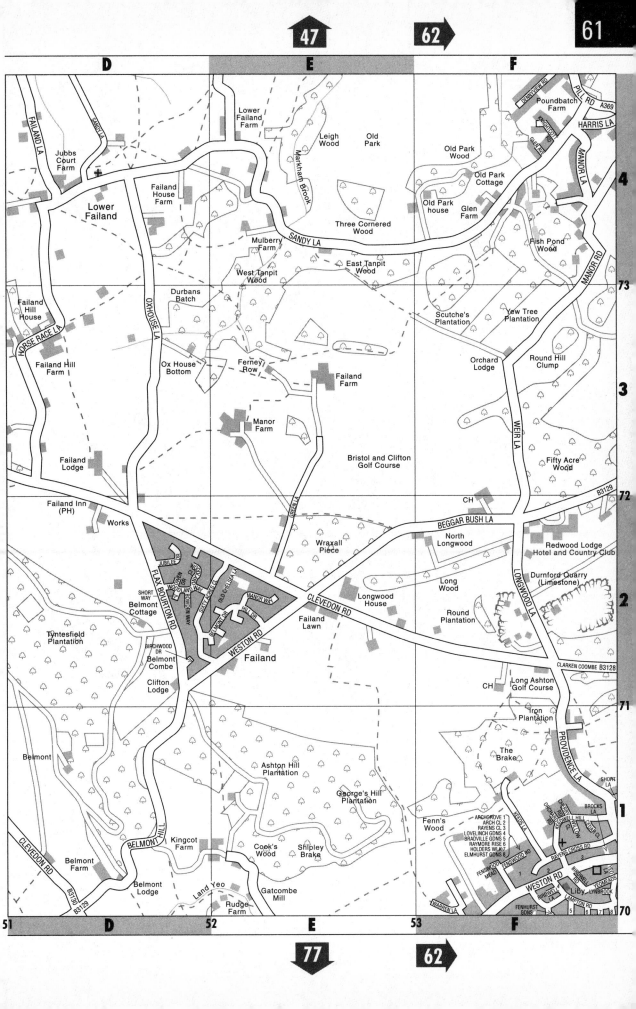

D
E
F

Failand La

Jubbs Court Farm

Lower Failand Farm

Leigh Wood

Old Park

Sandy La

Old Park Wood

Deanview Rd

Poundbatch Farm

Pill Rd

A369

Knighton Rd

Harris La

Glen Ave

Manor La

Lower Failand

Failand House Farm

Mulberry Farm

Markham Brook

Sandy La

Three Cornered Wood

Old Park Cottage

Old Park house

Glen Farm

Fish Pond Wood

Manor Rd

4

West Tanpit Wood

East Tanpit Wood

73

Failand Hill House

Durbans Batch

Scutche's Plantation

Yew Tree Plantation

Horse Race La

Oxhouse La

Ox House Bottom

Ferney Row

Failand Farm

Orchard Lodge

Round Hill Clump

Weir La

3

Failand Hill Farm

Manor Farm

Bristol and Clifton Golf Course

Fifty Acre Wood

Failand Lodge

B3129

72

Failand Inn (PH)

Works

Green La

CH

Beggar Bush La

Wraxall Piece

North Longwood

Redwood Lodge Hotel and Country Club

Flax Bourton Rd

Jubilee Dr

Woodland Way

Apollo Dr

Bowden Way

Short Way

Belmont Cottage

Old Chelsea La

Sixty Acres La

Belmont Dr

Manor Dr

Manor Way

Hill Dr

Clevedon Rd

Failand Lawn

Longwood House

Long Wood

Round Plantation

Durnford Quarry (Limestone)

Longwood La

2

Tyntesfield Plantation

Birchwood Dr

Belmont Combe

Weston Rd

Failand

Clarken Coombe B3128

Clifton Lodge

CH

Long Ashton Golf Course

71

Belmont

Iron Plantation

Providence La

The Brake

Short La

Ashton Hill Plantation

George's Hill Plantation

Fenn's Wood

Archgrove 1
Arch Cl 2
Rayens Cl 3
Lovelinch Gdns 4
Bradville Gdns 5
Raymore Rise 6
Holders Wlk 7
Elmhurst Gdns 8

Brocks La

Keedwell Hill

Willow Cl

1

Clevedon Rd

Belmont Hill

Kingcot Farm

Cook's Wood

Shipley Brake

Acers La

Fenswood Mead

Fenswood Rd

Rayens Cross Rd

Weston Rd

Liby

Lynbrook

Belmont Farm

B3130 B3129

Belmont Lodge

Land Yeo

Rudge Farm

Gatcombe Mill

Warren La

Fenhurst Gdns

Lampton Rd

Yeomeads

70

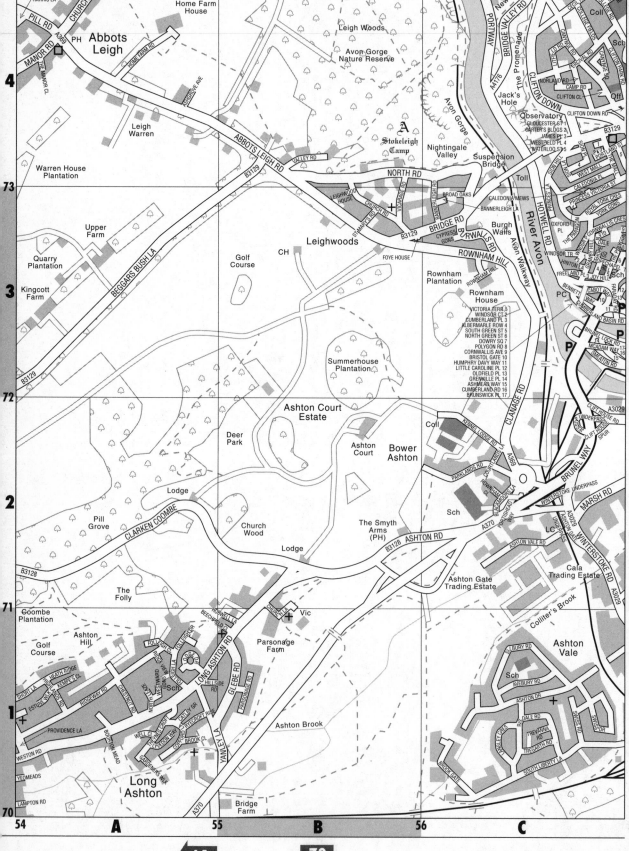

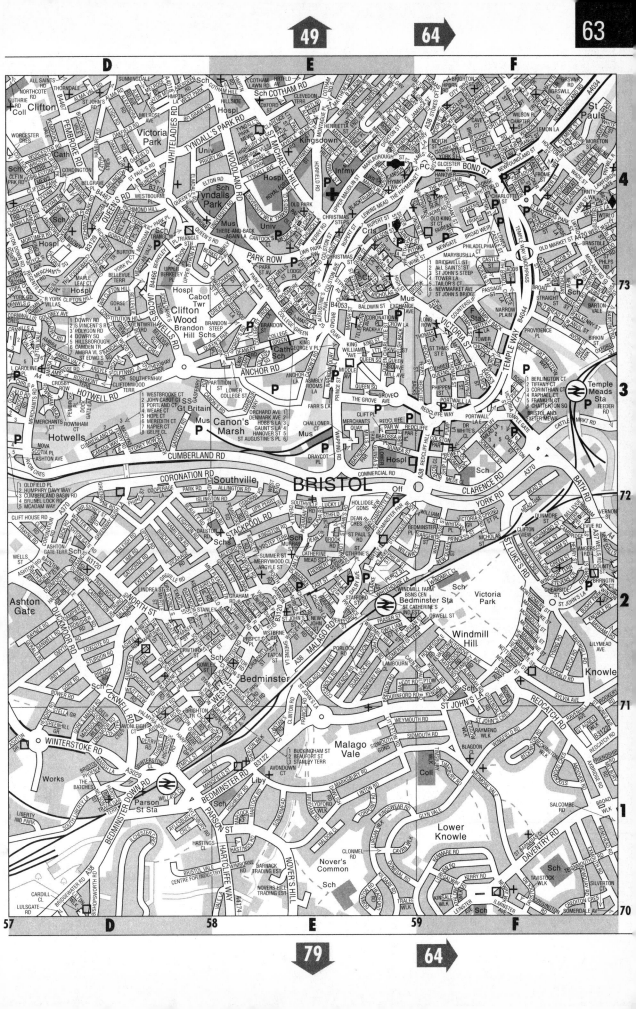

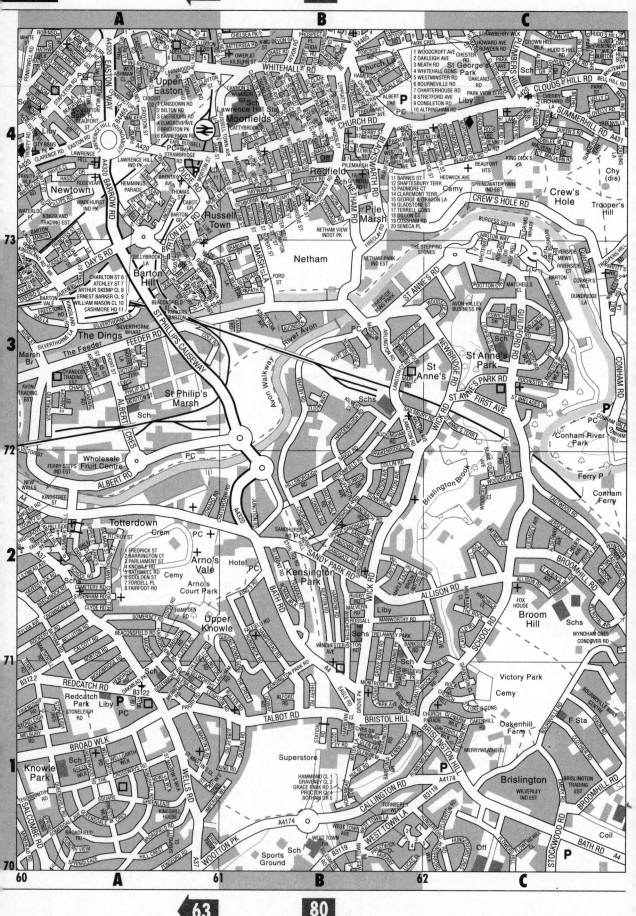

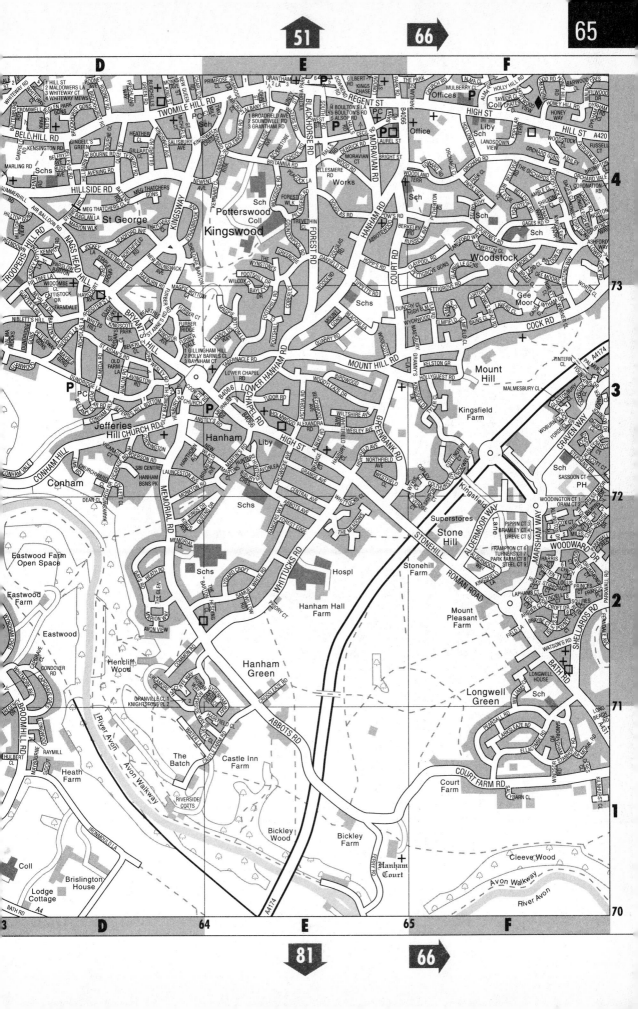

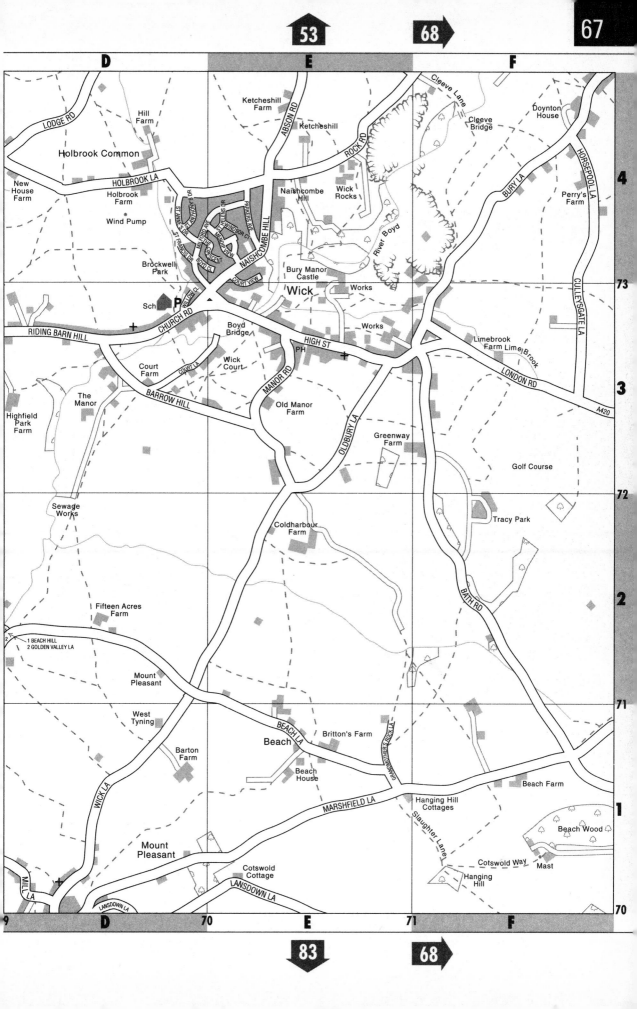

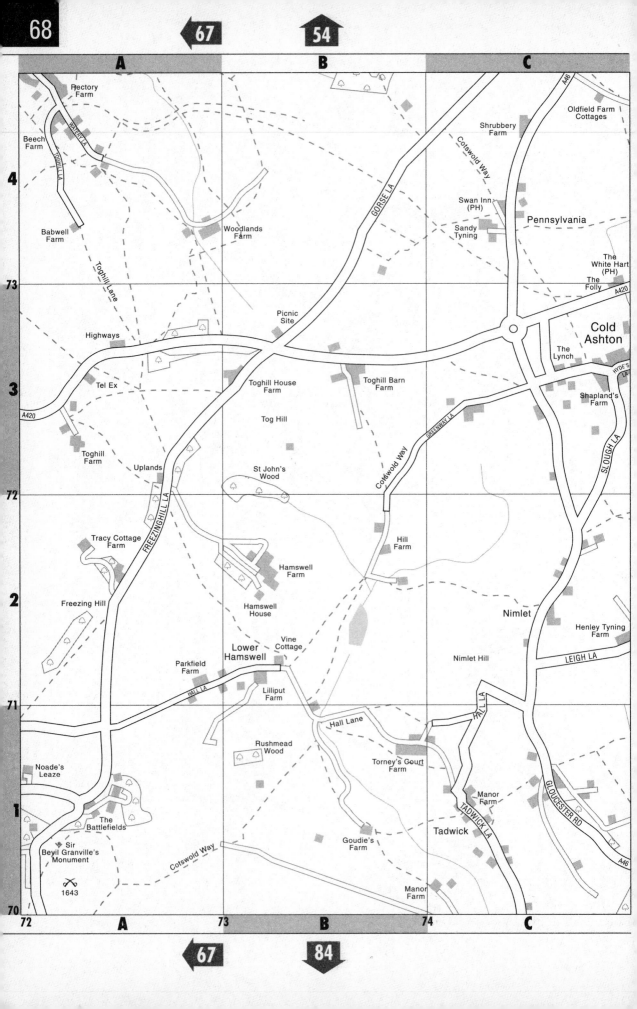

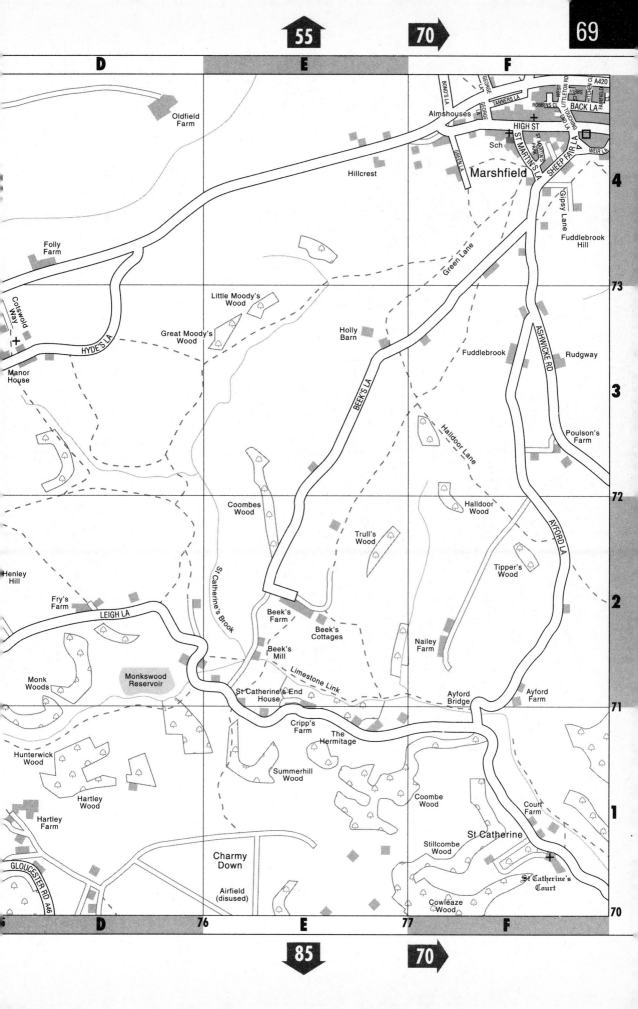

D E F

Oldfield
Farm

Almshouses

BOND'S LA
GEORGE LA
GEORGE

WEST
LITTLETON RD
HIBBS CL
FAIRFIELD

A420
BACK LA

TANNERS LA
ROBBINS CL

HIGH ST

Hillcrest

Sch

ST MARTIN'S LA

Marshfield

ST KATHERINE'S
PARK

WEIR LA

SHEEP FAIR LA

4

Gipsy Lane

Fuddlebrook
Hill

Folly
Farm

Cotswold Way

Green Lane

73

Little Moody's
Wood

Fuddlebrook

ASHWICKE RD

Rudgway

Great Moody's
Wood

Holly
Barn

HYDE'S LA

Manor
House

BEEK'S LA

Halldoor Lane

Fuddlebrook

Poulson's
Farm

3

Coombes
Wood

Halldoor
Wood

72

Henley
Hill

St Catherine's Brook

Trull's
Wood

AYFORD LA

Tipper's
Wood

2

Fry's
Farm

LEIGH LA

Beek's
Farm

Beek's
Cottages

Nailey
Farm

Monk
Woods

Monkswood
Reservoir

Beek's
Mill

Limestone Link

St Catherine's End
House

Ayford
Bridge

Ayford
Farm

71

Hunterwick
Wood

Cripp's
Farm

The Hermitage

Summerhill
Wood

Coombe
Wood

Court
Farm

1

Hartley
Wood

Hartley
Farm

St Catherine

Stillcombe
Wood

GLOUCESTER RD
A46

Charmy
Down

St Catherine's
Court

Airfield
(disused)

Cowleaze
Wood

70

D 76 E 77 F

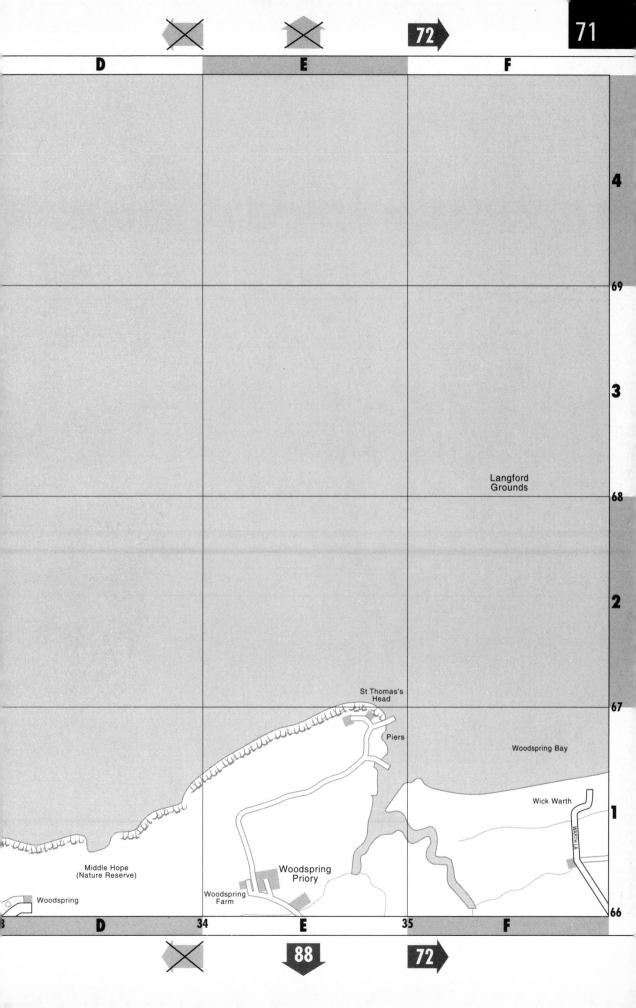

D

E

F

4

69

3

68

Langford
Grounds

2

67

St Thomas's
Head

Piers

Woodspring Bay

Wick Warth

1

Middle Hope
(Nature Reserve)

Woodspring

Woodspring
Farm

Woodspring
Priory

66

A   B   C

4

69

Dowlais Ditch

Kingston Pill

Hook's Ear

Sea Wall Farm

Treble House Farm

3

68

Channel View Farm

Broadstone Rhyne

MIDDLE LA

2

Broadstone Farm

BROADSTONE LA

Wharf Farm

67

Ham Farm

HAM LA

Ham Rhyne

Pool Farm

1

Sewage Works

Mendip View Farm

YEO BANK LA

Muddy Lane

Yeo Bank Farm

Tutshill

66

36   A   37   B   38   C

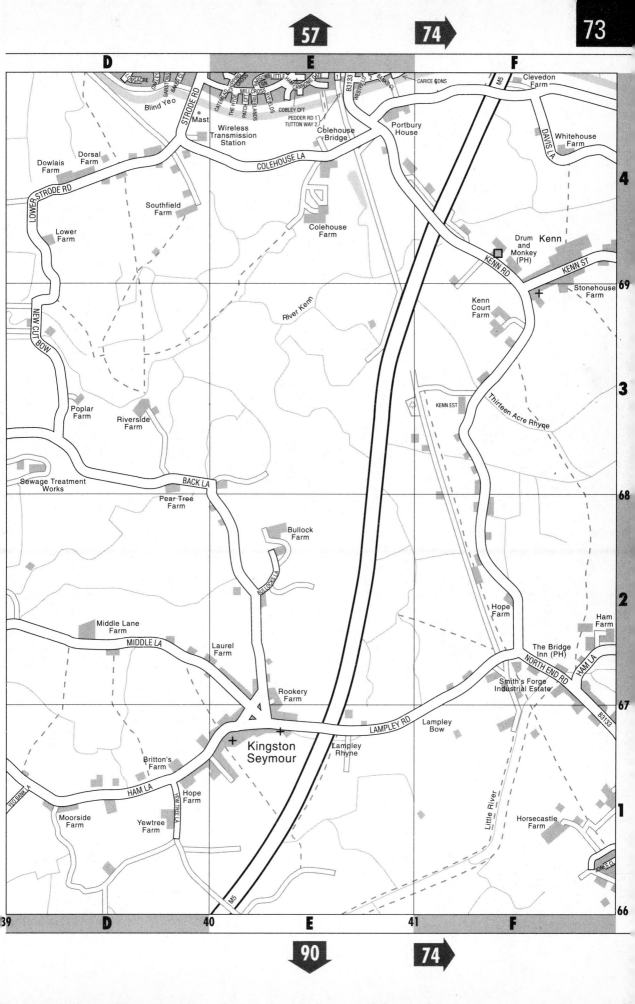

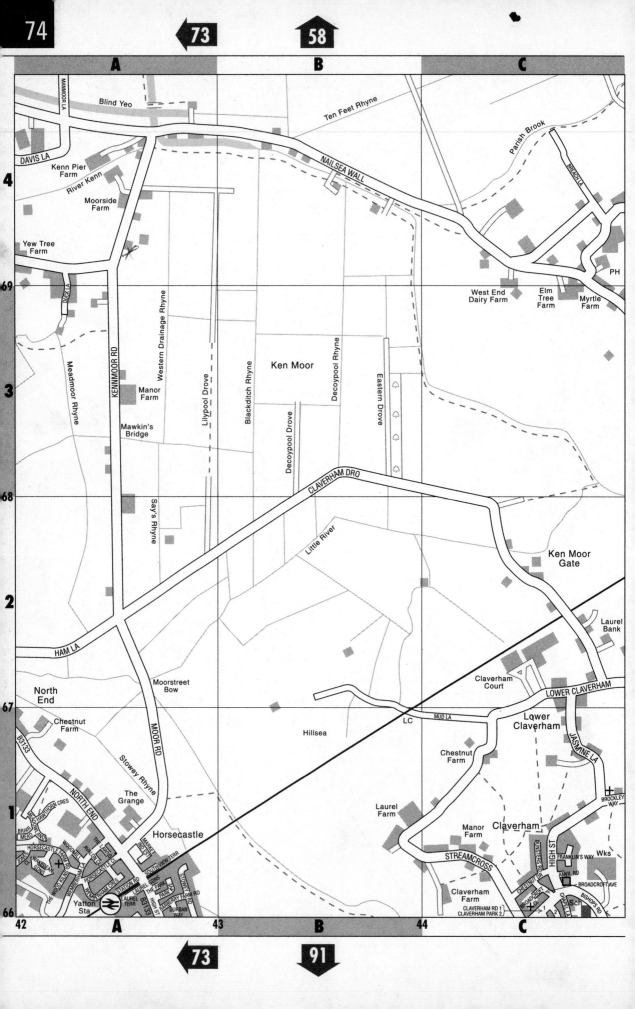

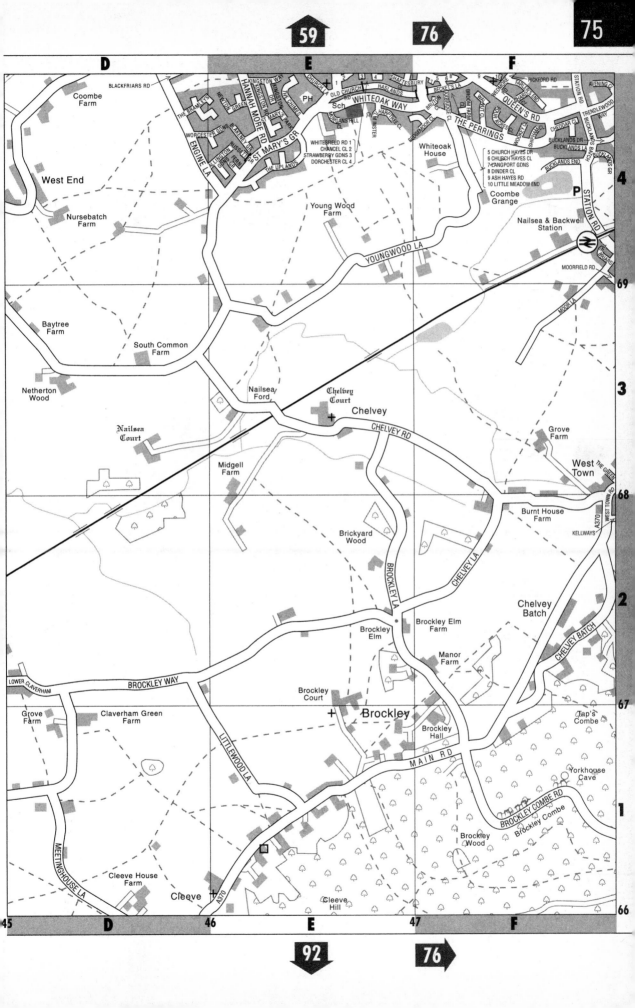

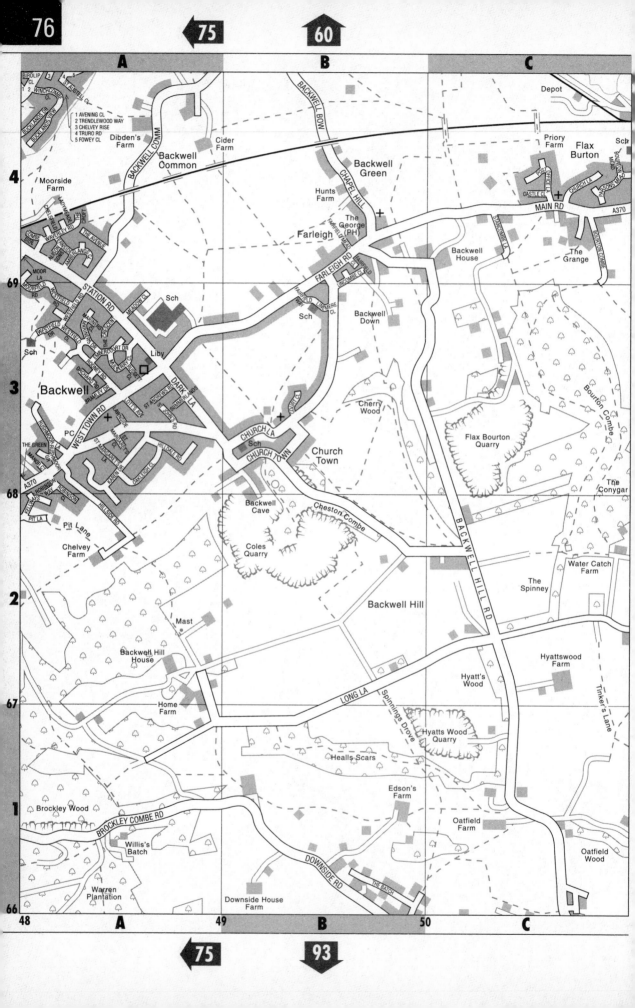

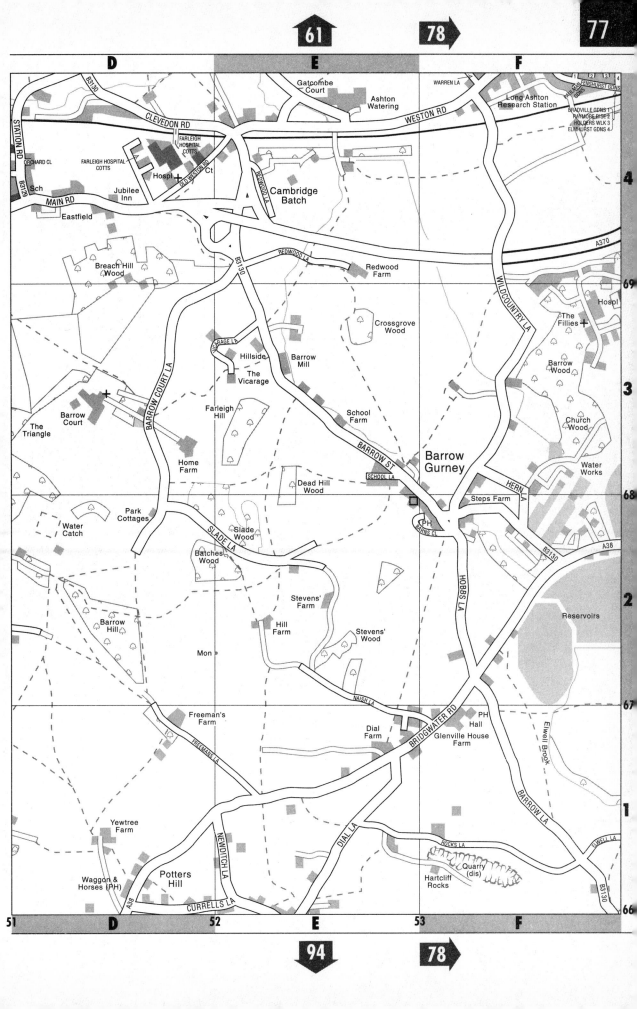

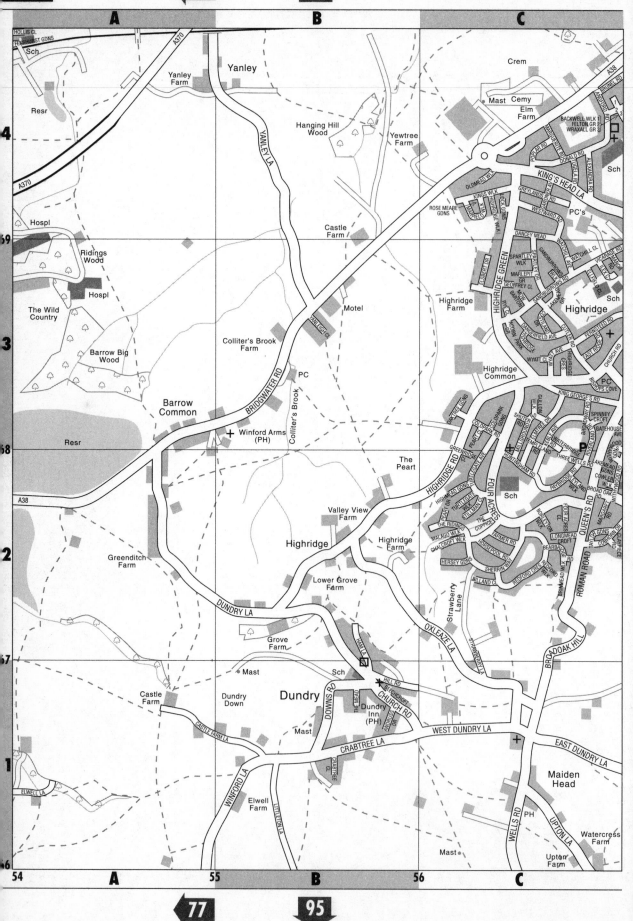

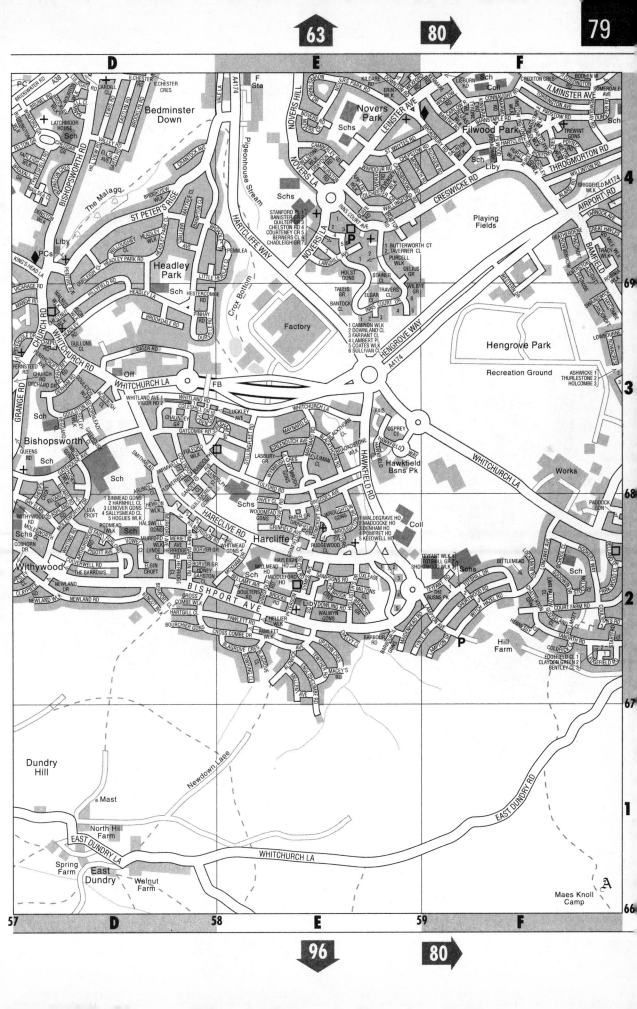

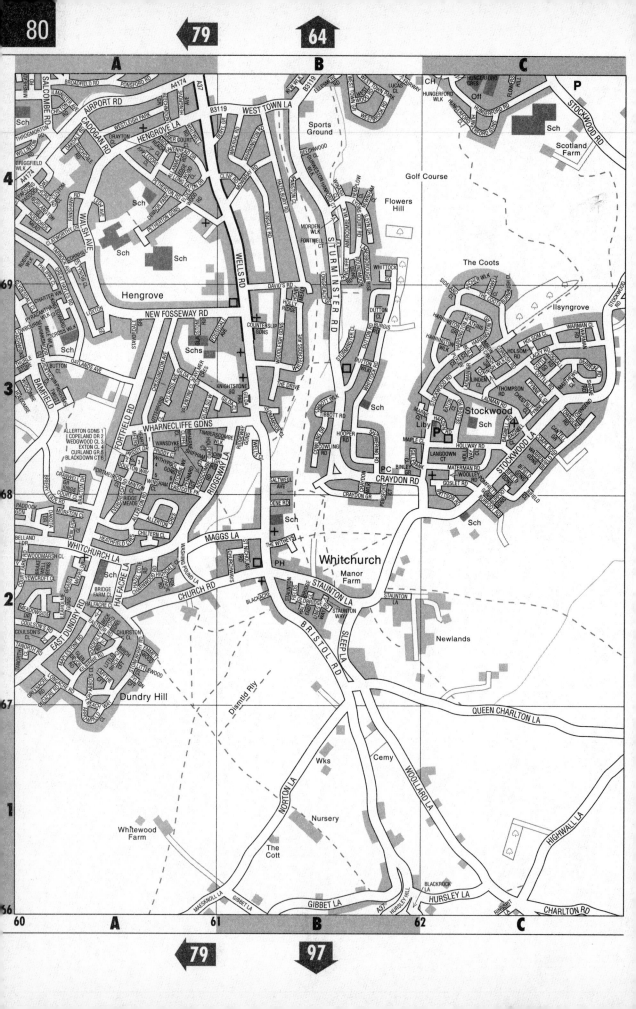

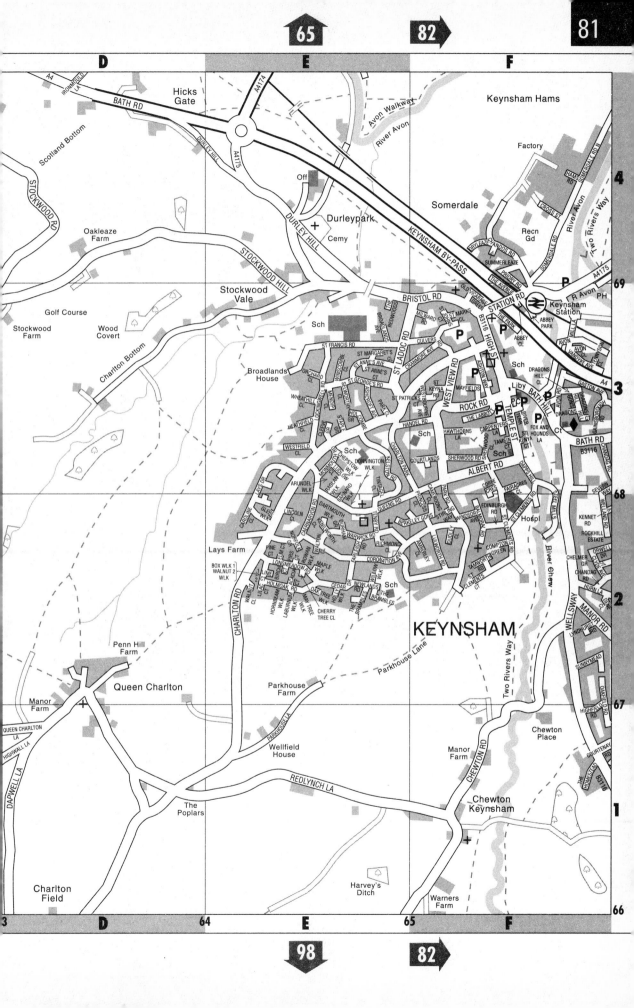

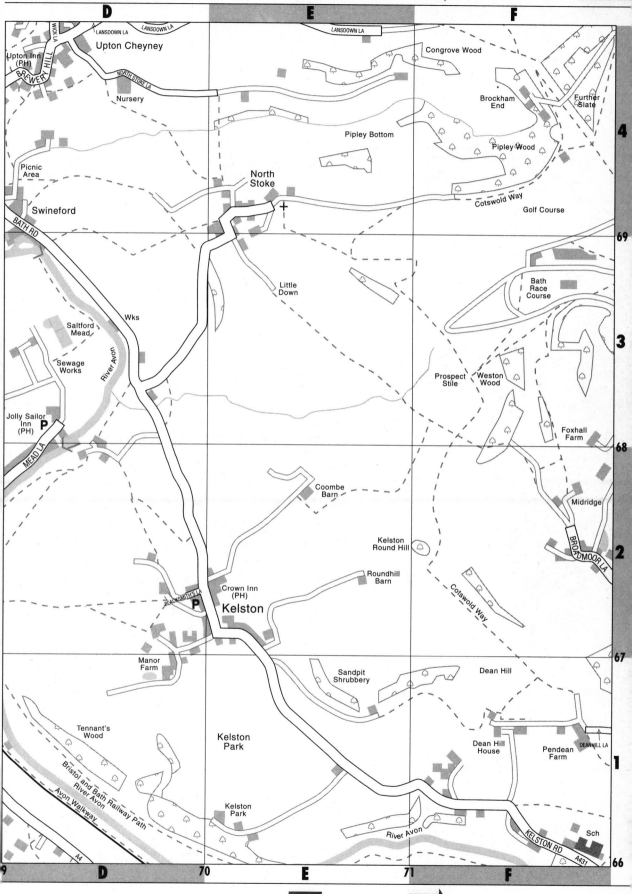

D LANSDOWN LA LANSDOWN LA
LANSDOWN LA
Upton Cheyney
Congrove Wood
Upton Inn
(PH)
BREWERY HILL
WICK LA
NORTH STOKE LA
Nursery
Brockham
End
Further
Slate
4
Pipley Bottom
Pipley Wood
Picnic
Area
North
Stoke
Swineford
Cotswold Way
Golf Course
BATH RD
69
Wks
Little
Down
Bath
Race
Course
Saltford
Mead
River Avon
3
Sewage
Works
Prospect
Stile
Weston
Wood
Jolly Sailor
Inn
(PH) P
Foxhall
Farm
MEAD LA
68
Coombe
Barn
Midridge
BROADMOOR LA
Kelston
Round Hill
2
Roundhill
Barn
Crown Inn
(PH)
Cotswold Way
BLACKSMITHS LA P Kelston
Manor
Farm
67
Sandpit
Shrubbery
Dean Hill
Tennant's
Wood
Kelston
Park
Dean Hill
House
Pendean
Farm
DEANHILL LA
1
Bristol and Bath Railway Path
River Avon
Avon Walkway
Kelston
Park
River Avon
KELSTON RD
Sch
A4
A431
66
9 D 70 E 71 F

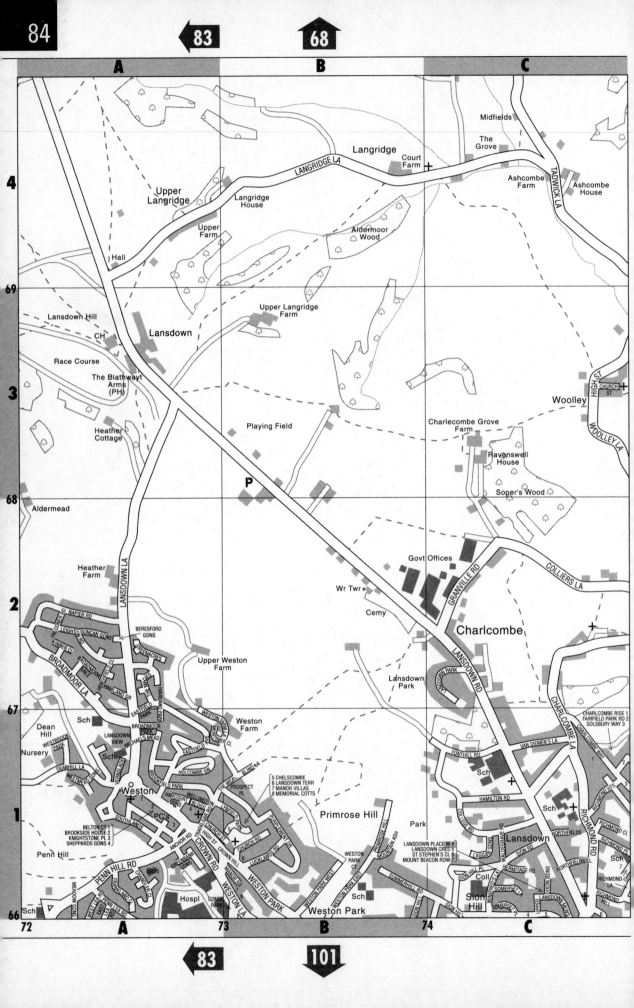

D E F

Charmy Down

Lyegrove Wood

Down Farm

Wingfield Farm

Holts Down

Holtsdown Lane

Stony Lane

4

A46

Bailey's Wood

Cherrywell Wood

HOLLIES LA

69

Charmydown Farm

Ramscombe Bottom

Ramscombe La

Short Wood

Chilcombe Bottom

TADWICK LA

Kennel La

BLACKSMITH LA

GLOUCESTER RD

Sch

Northend

EAGLE PARK

EAGLE RD

STEWAY LA

BROOKSIDE

3

Manor Farm

Prospect Gdns

Lower Northend

Stambrook Park

Crossleaze Farm

INNOX LA

Upper Swainswick

Rising Sun (PH)

Northend Inn

Northend Inn

Church La

Sch

Sch

68

Lam Brook

Little Solsbury Hill

Church Farm

WAIFIELD GDNS

WOOLLEY LA

COLLIERS LA

Common

Batheaston

Little Solsbury La

Solsbury Ct

Brow Hill

Potts Cl

A4

London Rd E

2

Twinfield Farm

SWAINSWICK LA

Bailbrook

High St

Vale View Terr

Avondale

Richens

Kyrle Gdns

PC

P

CHARLCOMBE LA

Bennetts Rd

Deadmill La

Valley View Rd

Ferndale Rd

Bailbrook La

Bailbrook La

Lower Swainswick

Tollbridge Rd

The Willows

Malls

67

Valley View

Ross Hill

Hill View Rd

Larkhall

Catsley Pl

Brooklyn Rd

Swainswick Gdns

Miller La

Oriel Gdns

Elm Gr

Coll

London Rd W

Roman Road

Bathampton Bridge (Toll)

Limestone Link

Bathampton Junction

Fairfield Park

Schs

Eldon Pl

Barford St

Larkhall Pl

Pitman Ct

Jesse Hughes Ct

Woodlands

Lambridge

Fosse Way

River Avon

Road under construction

Sch

MILL LA

TYNING RD

1

FAIRFIELD PARK RD

RAGLAND ST

RAGLAND LA

KINGSDOWN VIEW

Avondale

Worcester Bldgs

Salisbury Rd

P

Brookleaze Bldgs

P

PC

A46

1 UPPER LAMBRIDGE ST
2 LAMBRIDGE PL
3 LAMBRIDGE ST

George Inn (PH)

ARBUTUS

HIGH ST

Kennet Park

The Normans

Holcombe Vale

St Nicholas Cl

CLAREMONT RD

ST SAVIOUR'S RD

LONDON RD

Grosvenor

St Saviours Way

Avon Walkway

Kennet and Avon Canal

MEADOW LA

BATHAMPTON LA

DOWN LA

Holcombe La

Devonshire Rd

Holcombe Cl

66

D 76 E 77 F

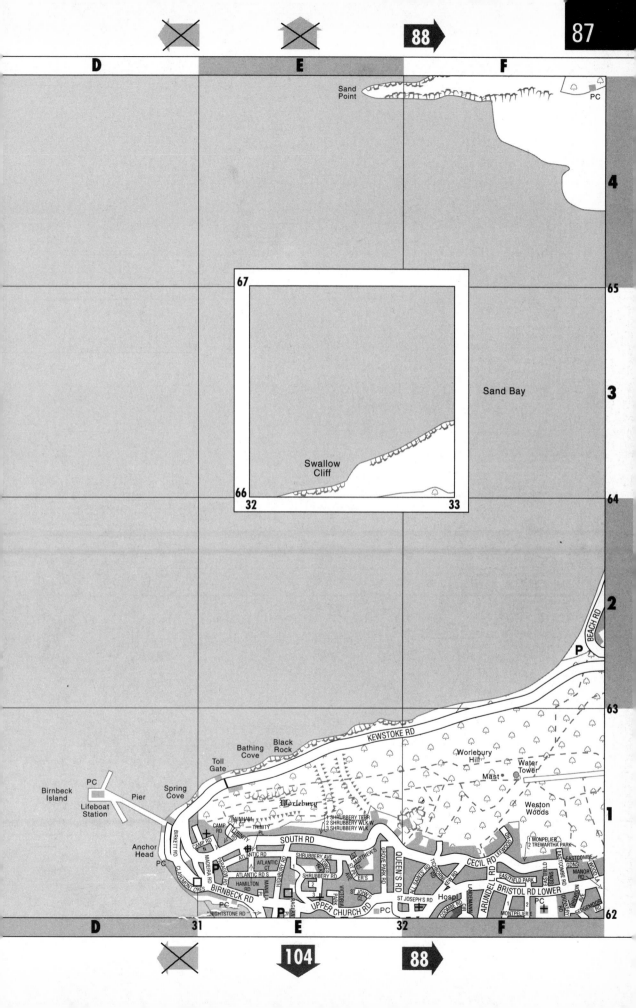

Sand
Point

PC

4

65

Sand Bay

3

67

Swallow
Cliff

66

64

32   33

2

BEACH RD

P

63

Bathing
Cove

Black
Rock

KEWSTOKE RD

Worlebury
Hill

Water
Tower

Toll
Gate

Mast

Birnbeck
Island

PC

Spring
Cove

Weston
Woods

Pier

Lifeboat
Station

Worlebury

1 SHRUBBERY TERR
2 SHRUBBERY WLK W
3 SHRUBBERY WLK

RAINHAM
CT
TRINITY
PL

Anchor
Head

PC

CAMP
RD

1 MONPELIER
2 TREWARTHA PARK

CAMP RD N

SOUTH RD

BIRKETT RD

ATLANTIC RD

ST
MATTHEW'S

GROVE PARK RD

QUEEN'S RD

CECIL RD

LEEWOOD

EASTCOMBE
GDNS

1

MADEIRA RD

ATLANTIC
CT

ATLANTIC RD S

SHRUBBERY AVE

TOWER
WLK

ST PETER'S
AVE

TICHBORNE RD

LEEWOOD RD

EASTFIELD PARK

EASTCOMBE RD

MANOR
RD

VICTORIA

CLAREMONT CRES

HAMILTON
RD

MARINE
PL

SHRUBBERY RD

VICTORIA
PARK

ST JOHN'S
CL

ST JOHN'S RD

ST JOSEPH'S RD

ARUNDELL RD

LANDEMANN CIRC

Hospl

1 MONPELIER

PC

BRISTOL RD LOWER

62

BIRNBECK RD

PC

NIGHTSTONE RD

P

UPPER CHURCH RD

PC

COOMBE RD

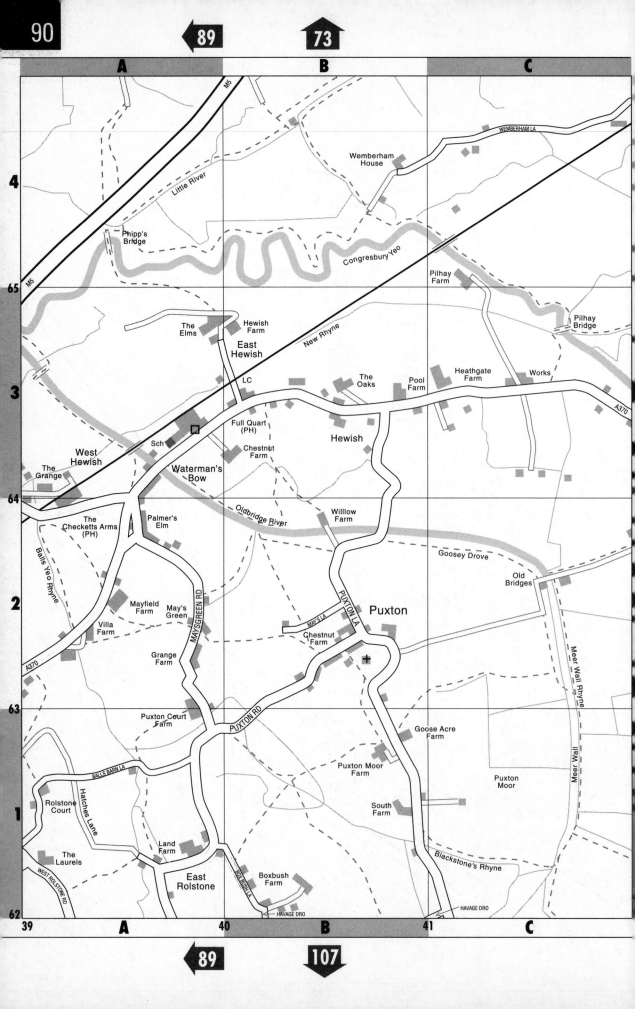

A B C

4

Little River

M5

Phipp's
Bridge

Wemberham
House

WEMBERHAM LA

65

M5

Congresbury Yeo

Pilhay
Farm

Pilhay
Bridge

The Elms

Hewish
Farm

East
Hewish

New Rhyne

3

LC

The
Oaks

Pool
Farm

Heathgate
Farm

Works

A370

Full Quart
(PH)

Hewish

West
Hewish

Sch

Chestnut
Farm

The
Grange

Waterman's
Bow

Oldbridge River

Willlow
Farm

64

The Checketts Arms
(PH)

Palmer's
Elm

Goosey Drove

Old
Bridges

Balls Yeo Rhyne

MAYSGREEN RD

Mayfield
Farm

May's
Green

PUXTON LA

Puxton

Meer Wall Rhyne

2

Villa
Farm

MAY'S LA

Chestnut
Farm

A370

Grange
Farm

Meer Wall

63

Puxton Court
Farm

PUXTON RD

Goose Acre
Farm

BALLS BARN LA

Puxton Moor
Farm

Puxton
Moor

Rolstone
Court

Hatches Lane

1

Land
Farm

South
Farm

The
Laurels

Blackstone's Rhyne

WEST ROLSTONE RD

BOX BUSH LA

East
Rolstone

Boxbush
Farm

HAVAGE DRO

HAVAGE DRO

62

39 A 40 B 41 C

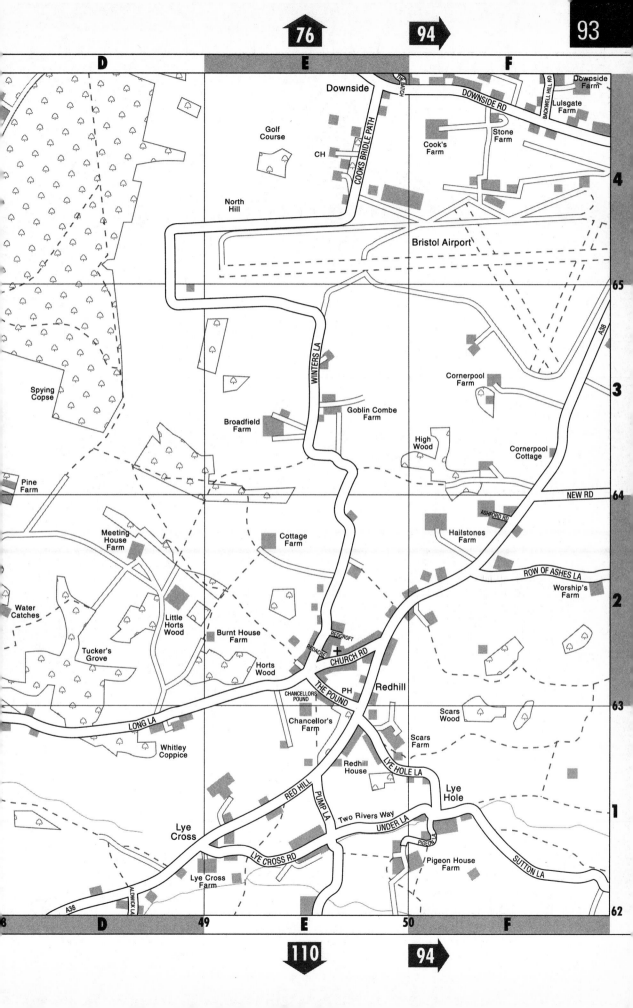

A B C

Hanging Grove Farm

Lulsgate Bottom

Quarry (dis)

St Katherine's Vicarage

CURRELS LA 1
DIAL LA 2

Felton

New Farm

Airport Tavern (PH)

COOMBE DALE

DOWNSIDE RD

A38

SCHOOL LA

NORTH SIDE RD

P

Sch

WEST LA

STANSHALLS RD

STANSHALLS CL

STANSHALLS DR

FROG LA

Upper Town

UPPER TOWN LA

ORCHARD CL

VEE LA

Hospl

KINGSTON LA

P

P

BARROW LA

B3130

Winford

George and Dragon (PH)

FELTON ST

Felton Hill

Felton Common

LONG CROSS

Long Cross

RAGLAN LA

FELTON LA

MARKET

BRINMARSIDE

KINGSTON MEAD

THE CLASS

HIGH ST

4

65

A38

Oxhouse Lane

Hayes Cottage

HAY LA

OXHOUSE LA

OLD HILL

Oldhill Farm

Old Hill

PARSONAGE CL

PARSONAGE LA

Glenmore House

Prospect House

Froglane Farm

FROG LA

3

Hunters Hall

OLD BARN LA

LONG LA

Kingdown Lane

Winford Manor

GREATSTONE LA

The Bungalow Inn (PH)

Kingdown

Redhouse Farm

Quarry (dis)

REDDING PIT LA

CROWN HILL

64

Thrubwell Farm

THRUBWELL LA

Butcombe Court

GREEN LA

FEATHERBED LA

Myrtle House Farm

REGIL LA

BROAD MEAD L

ROW OF ASHES LA

2

Merry Hill Farm

Row of Ashes Farm

BENDHES LA

HEN LA

63

Rusling House

Regilbury Court

Ridgehil Farm

Ruslin Farm

Bicknell Farm

Regilbury Farm

Regil

1

YEWTREE BATCH

THE STREET

POOL LA

SUTTON LA

Howgrove Farm

THE BATCH

Regilbury Park Farm

62

51 A 52 B 53 C

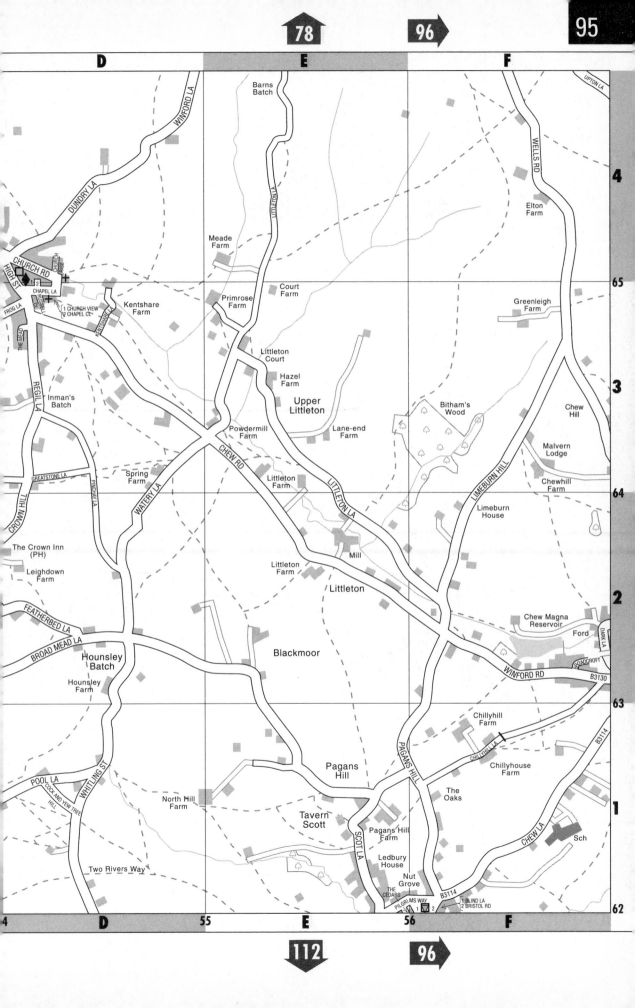

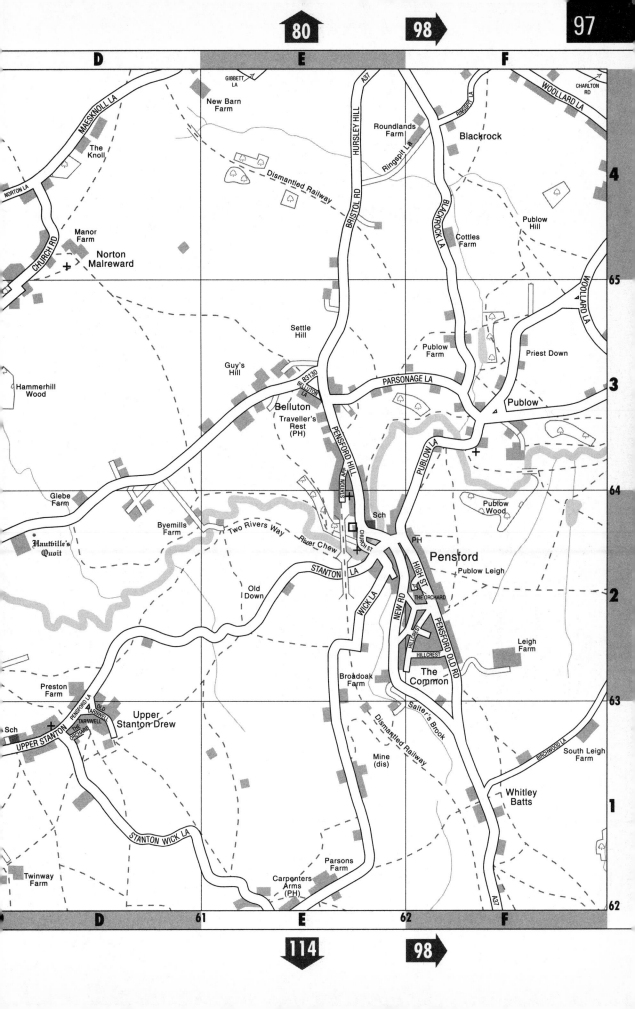

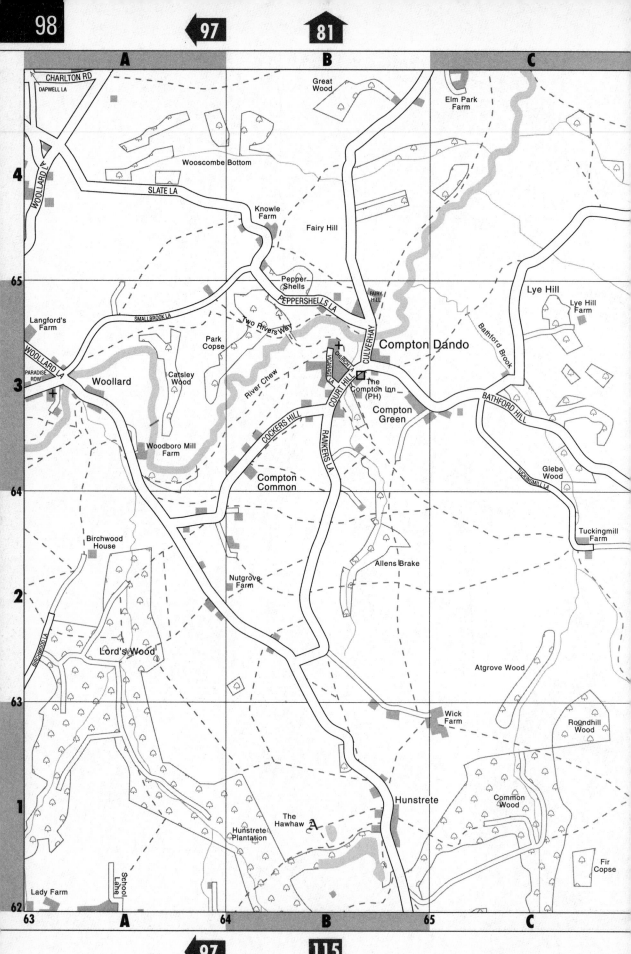

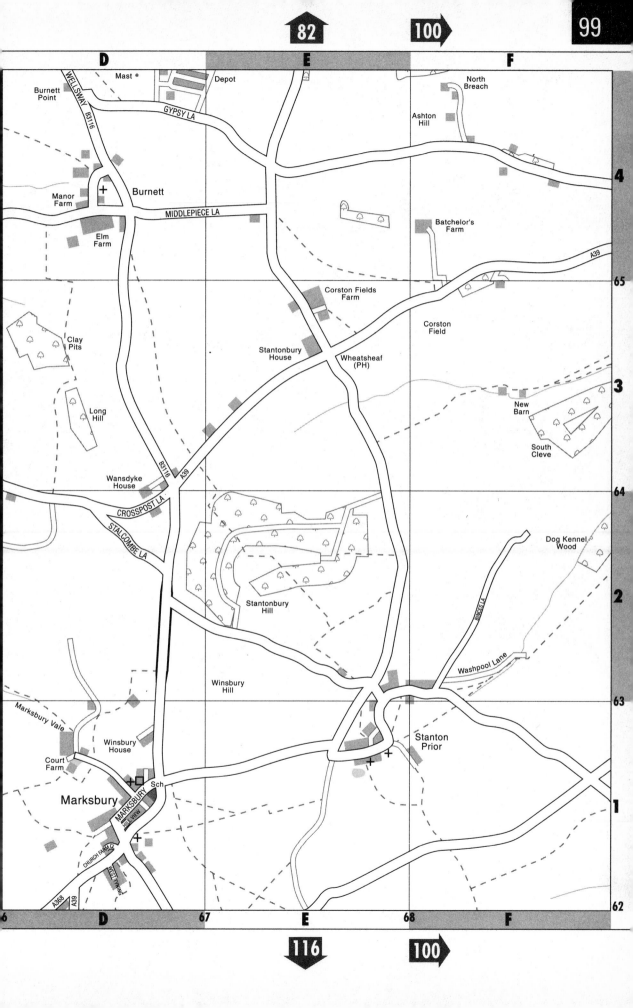

Burnett Point
WELLSWAY B3116
Mast
Depot
GYPSY LA
North Breach
Ashton Hill

Manor Farm
Burnett
4

Elm Farm
MIDDLEPIECE LA
Batchelor's Farm
A39

Clay Pits
65
Corston Fields Farm
Corston Field

Long Hill
Stantonbury House
Wheatsheaf (PH)
3
New Barn
South Cleve

B3116
A39
Wansdyke House
64

CROSSPOST LA
STALCOMBE LA
Dog Kennel Wood

Stantonbury Hill
2
BINCES LA
Washpool Lane

Winsbury Hill
63
Marksbury Vale

Winsbury House
Stanton Prior

Court Farm
Sch
Marksbury
MARKSBURY
HILL VIEW
1

CHURCH FARM CL
WEST ING
A368
A39
62

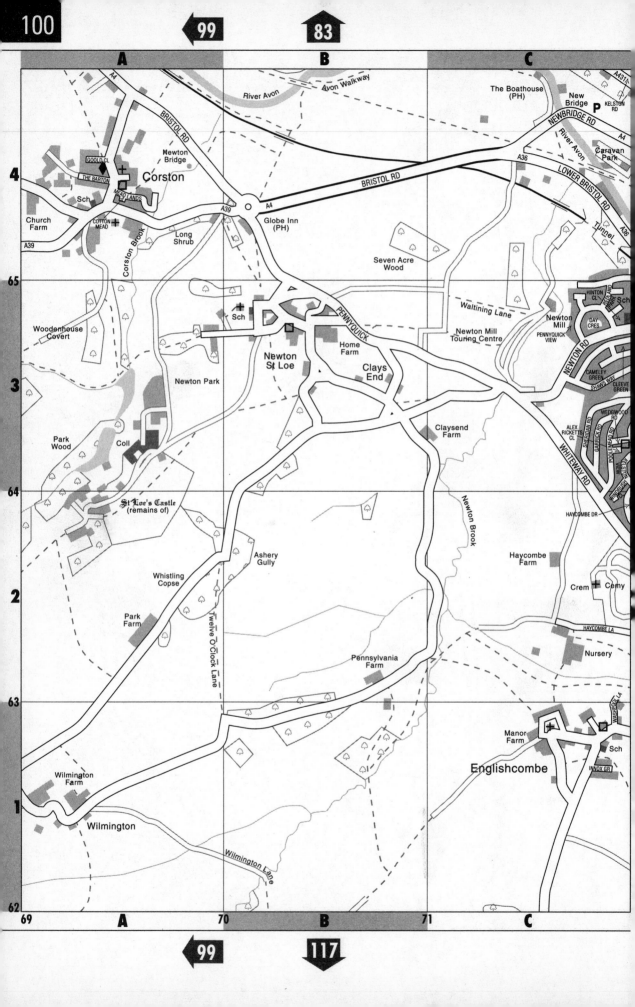

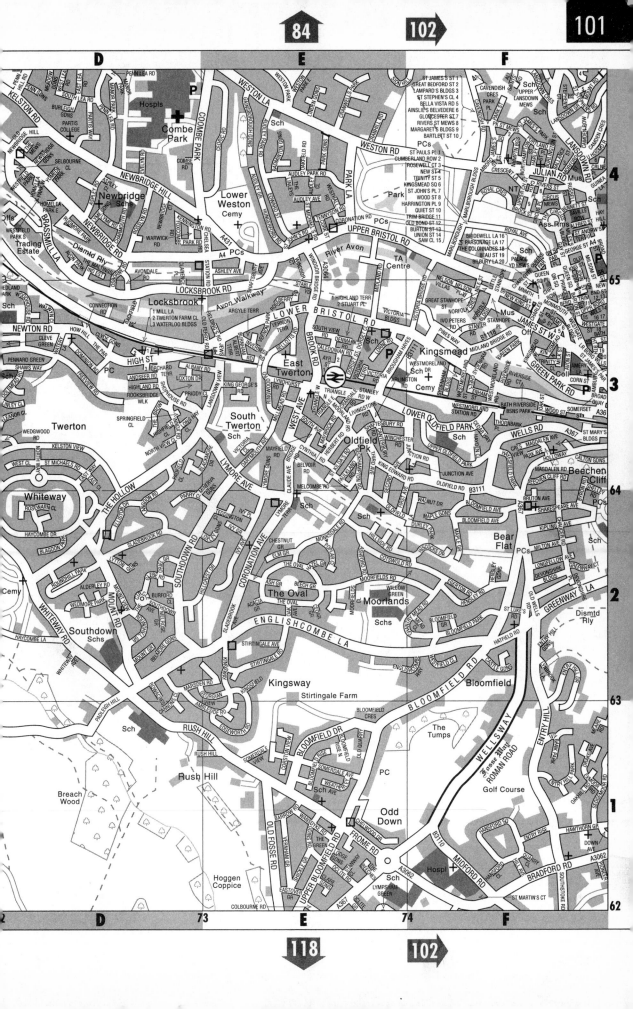

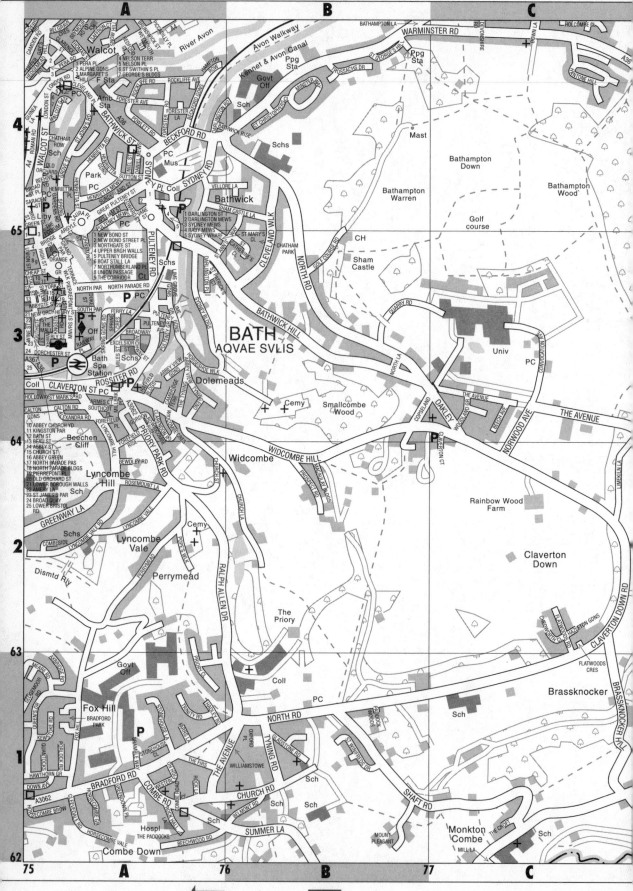

A   B   C

WARMINSTER RD

BATHAMPTON LA

Avon Walkway

Kennet & Avon Canal

Walcot

River Avon

Mast

Bathampton Down

Bathampton Warren

Bathampton Wood

Golf course

Sham Castle

BATHWICK HILL

Bathwick

Sham Castle La

Cleveland Wlk

Chatham Park

St Mary's Cl

Univ

1 DARLINGTON ST
2 DARLINGTON MEWS
3 SYDNEY MEWS
4 RABY MEWS
5 SYDNEY WHARF

1 NEW BOND ST
2 NEW BOND STREET PL
3 NORTHGATE ST
4 UPPER BRGH WALLS
5 PULTENEY BRIDGE
6 BOAT STALL LA
7 NORTHUMBERLAND PL
8 UNION PASSAGE
9 THE CORRIDOR

BATH
AQVAE SVLIS

Bath Spa Station

Dolemeads

Smallcombe Wood

Cemy

10 ABBEY CHURCH YD
11 KINGSTON PAR
12 BATH ST
13 BEAU ST
14 ABBEY ST
15 CHURCH ST
16 ABBEY GREEN
17 NORTH PARADE PAS
18 NORTH PARADE BLDGS
19 PIERPONT PL
20 OLD ORCHARD ST
21 LOWER BOROUGH WALLS
22 AMERY LA
23 ST JAMES'S PAR
24 BROAD QUAY
25 LOWER BRISTOL RD

Lyncombe Hill

Widcombe

WIDCOMBE HILL

Beechen Cliff

THE AVENUE

Rainbow Wood Farm

Lyncombe Vale

Cemy

Claverton Down

Perrymead

The Priory

Dismtd Rly

Govt Off

Coll

Brassknocker

PC

Fox Hill

Bradford Park

NORTH RD

Sch

BRASSKNOCKER HILL

THE FIRS

WILLIAMSTOWE

THE AVENUE

Stonehouse

CHURCH RD

Sch   Sch

BRADFORD RD

COMBE RD

Sch

Hospl
THE PADDOCKS

SUMMER LA

BEECHWOOD RD

MOUNT PLEASANT

Monkton Combe

Sch

Combe Down

SHAFT RD

WESTON-SUPER-MARE

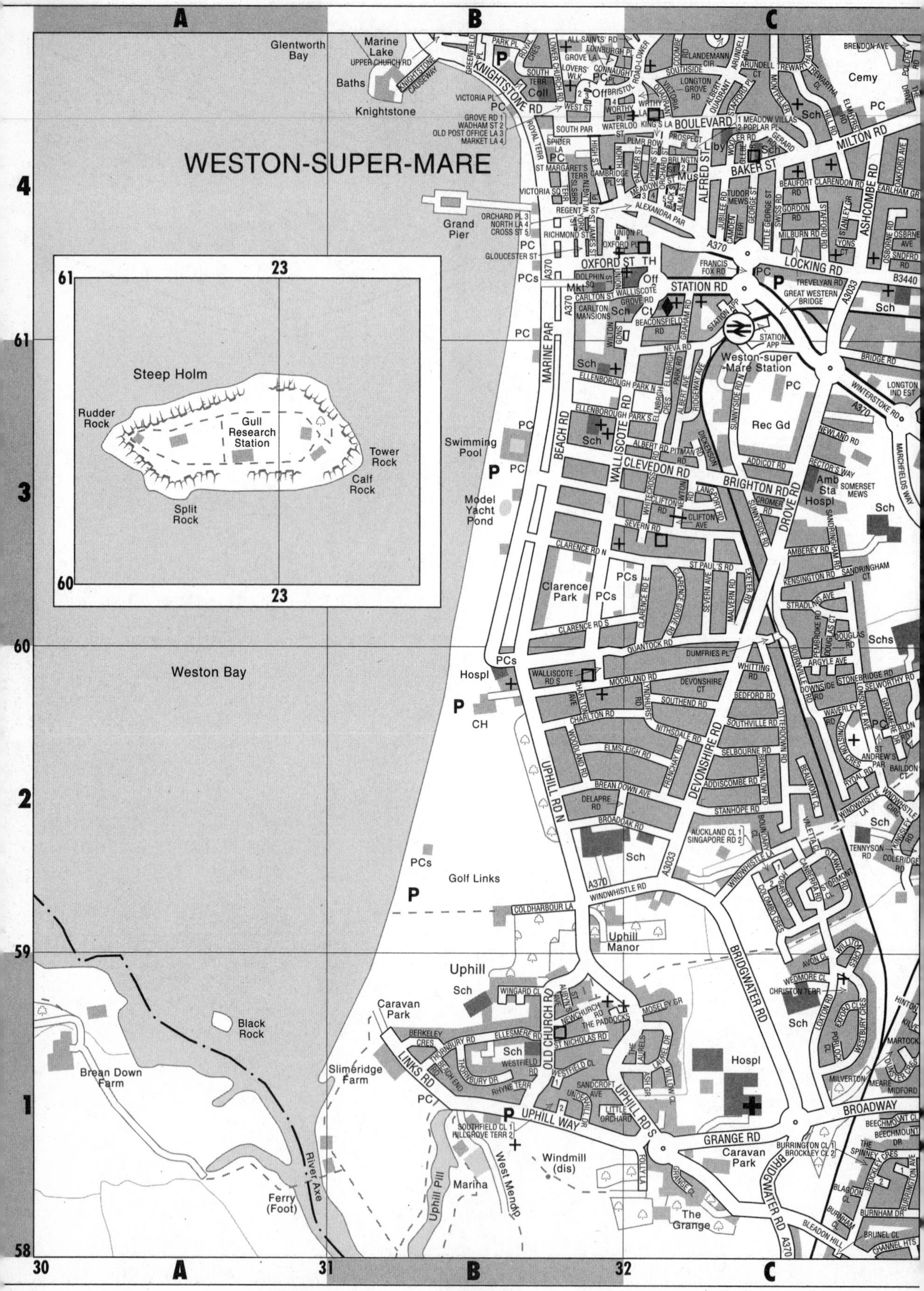

Glentworth Bay

Marine Lake

Baths

Knightstone

Grand Pier

Weston Bay

Steep Holm

Rudder Rock

Gull Research Station

Tower Rock

Calf Rock

Split Rock

Swimming Pool

Model Yacht Pond

Clarence Park

Hospl

Golf Links

Uphill Manor

Uphill

Caravan Park

Black Rock

Brean Down Farm

Slimeridge Farm

River Axe

Ferry (Foot)

Mariha

Windmill (dis)

West Mendip

Uphill Pill

The Grange

Caravan Park

Weston-super-Mare Station

Rec Gd

Amb Sta Hospl

Somerset Mews

Hospl

BAKER ST

MILTON RD

LOCKING RD

OXFORD ST

STATION RD

BRIGHTON RD

DEVONSHIRE RD

UPHILL RD N

BEACH RD

MARINE PAR

CLEVEDON RD

WALLISCOTE

BRIDGWATER RD

OLD CHURCH RD

UPHILL WAY

GRANGE RD

BROADWAY

LINKS RD

← 105
89 ↑

A **B** **C**

West Wick
A370
WEST WICK
Westacres Farm
Waywick Farm
Waterloo Farm

MOOR LA
Lypstone Farm
SUMMER LA
Ivy Cottage
Cannaway's Farm
Old Yeo Rhyne
West Moor Rhyne

4

A370
Locking Head Cottages
ETON LA
Ivy House Farm
SILVER MOOR LA
WOLVERS HILL RD

LOCKING HEAD RD
Locking Head Farm
Wolvershill Manor
Woolvers Hill

61

Pool Farm

Woolvershill Batch

3

Locking Farm Ind Est
RAF Locking
Laurel Farm
Court Farm

A371
Park Farm

HOMEFIELD CL
HOMEFIELD
THE ORCHARD
BEECHWOOD AVE
MANOR GDNS
PH
60
B3368
ELM TREE RD
LEAFY WAY DR
Sch
SUMMER LA
Stonebridge
RYDAL AVE
PYCROFT
GRENVILLE AVE
MEADOW
FAIRACRES
LIME CL
MENDIP RISE
BIRCH CL
WHITECROSS LA
BYRON
SOUTH LAWN
THE GREEN
OLD BANWELL RD
B3368
HILLMEAD
Cave View
Caravan Park
LYCHGATE PARK

2
Locking
THE BURY
Church Farm
Knightcott
KNIGHTCOTT RD
A371
CHESTERFIELD CL
KNIGHTCOTT GDNS
WILLIAM DAW
BANWELL RD
Perries
Wingfield House
Elborough
Works
KNIGHTCOTT IND EST
HIGH ST
NORTH VIEW DR

59
Lower Canada
Hillend
The Caves
Banwell Hill
Mast
Manor Farm
Mon
Whitley Head

WINDMILL HILL
Benthills Wood
1
CANADA
COOMBE
Windmill Farm
Elborough Hill
Upper Canada
BRIDEWELL LA
CHRISTON RD
Christon Hill
Christon Plantation
M5
Yarberry

58
36 **A** 37 **B** 38 **C**

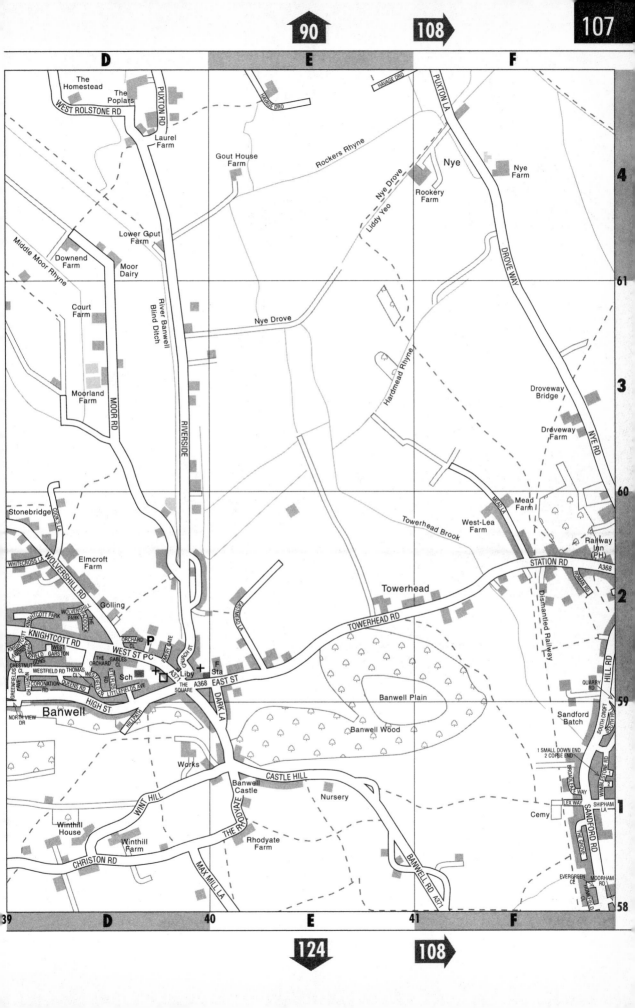

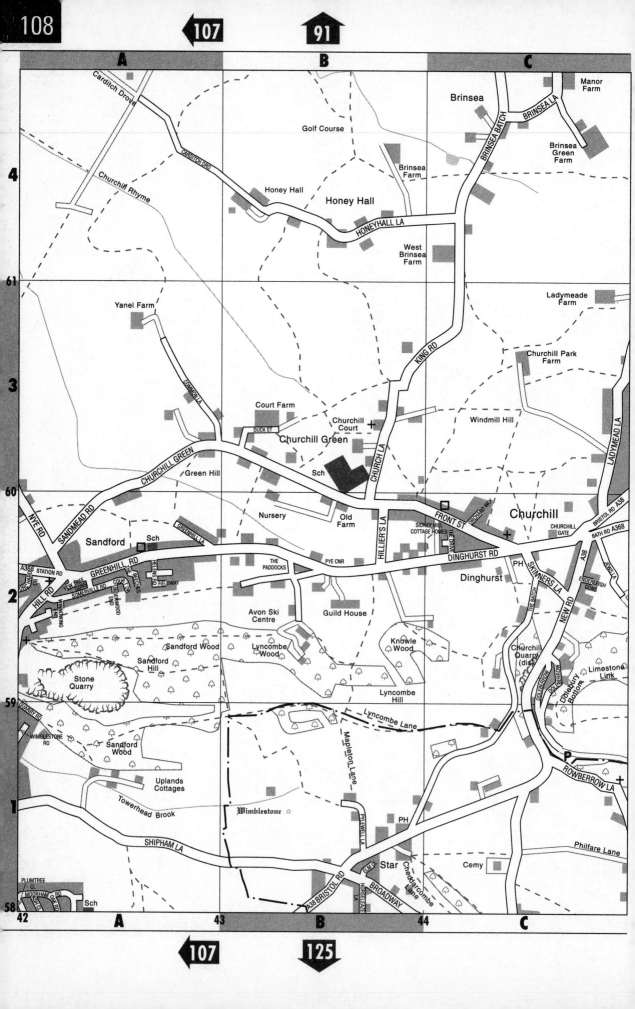

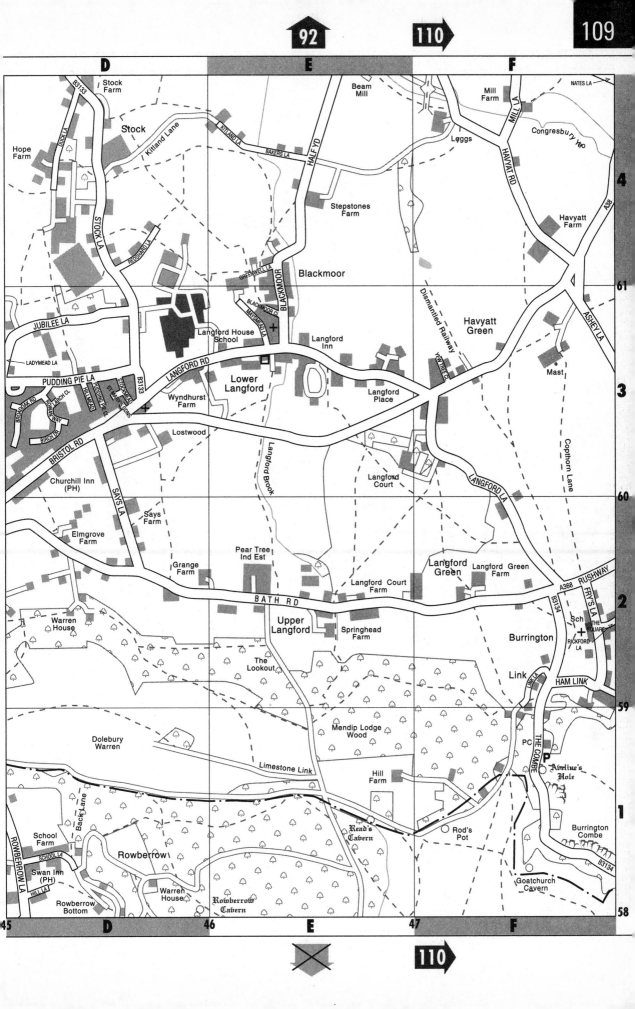

109
93

A   B   C

NATES LA

Caravan and Camping Site

Cowslip Green

Cribb's Farm

Paradise Farm

Sutton Farm

A38

4

Perry Bridge

Aldwick Court

Aldwick Wood

Woodlands

Hanging Wood

Long Wood

Round Wood

ALDWICK LA

Aldwick

61

BLAGDON LA

Aldwick Court Farm

Butcombe Farm

EMLEY LA

ASHLEY LA

3

Congresbury Yeo

Uxford Bridge

Dismantled Railway

Bourne

Emley Farm

60

Wadley Farm

Sewage Works

BOURNE LA

HOOKS BATCH

Coombe Lodge Farm

BOURNE LA

Home Bay Point

A368 RUSHWAY

Ridge Farm

LAYS LA

Ford

Coombe Lodge (Coll)

STATION RD

DARK LA

PARK LA

2

THE BATCH

RICKFORD RISE

Rickford

PH

Wks

MENLEA

CLANDERS

Home Farm

Ridgeon Wood

Blagdon Coombe

GARSTON A

West End

Burrington Lane

RICKFORD LA

HIGH ST

Fire Sta

P

BELL SQ

HAM LINK

THE COOMBE

The Park

Rickford Rising

POST OFFICE

MEAD

PARK BATCH

The New Inn (PH)

59

Street End Inn

STREET END

LIBERTY LA

OLD WATER GDNS

GRUB LA

PC

The Hill Gardens

Cemy

Fuller's Hay

Coll

RHODYATE

The Grove

BLADACRE LA

SWANCOMBE LA

EASTCH

CHURCH ST

BATH RD

PH

Sch

East End

WESTCROFT

Lower Hill Farm

Burrington Ham

STREET END LA

BELLOW

THE SCORE

EASTCROFT CL

DIPLAND GR

1

Blagdon

A368

Burrington Coombe

Toad's Hole

LUVERS LA

Swancombe Wood

B3134

Lower Ellick Wood

THE COMBE

Lower Ellick Farm

ELLICK RD

TWO TREES

Rhodyate Hill Farm

B3134

NEWFIELDS

58

48   A   49   B   50   C

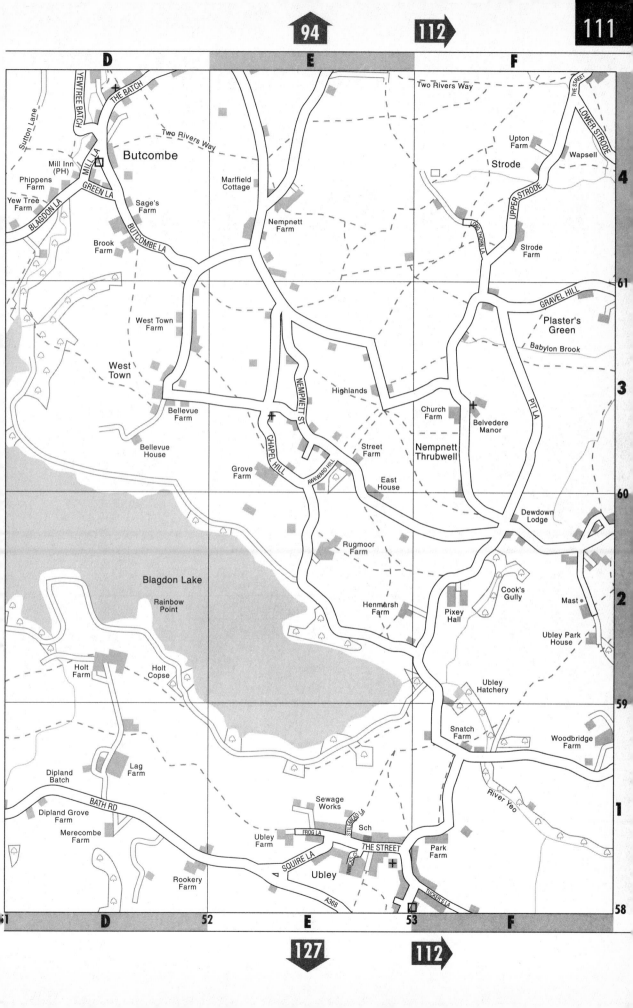

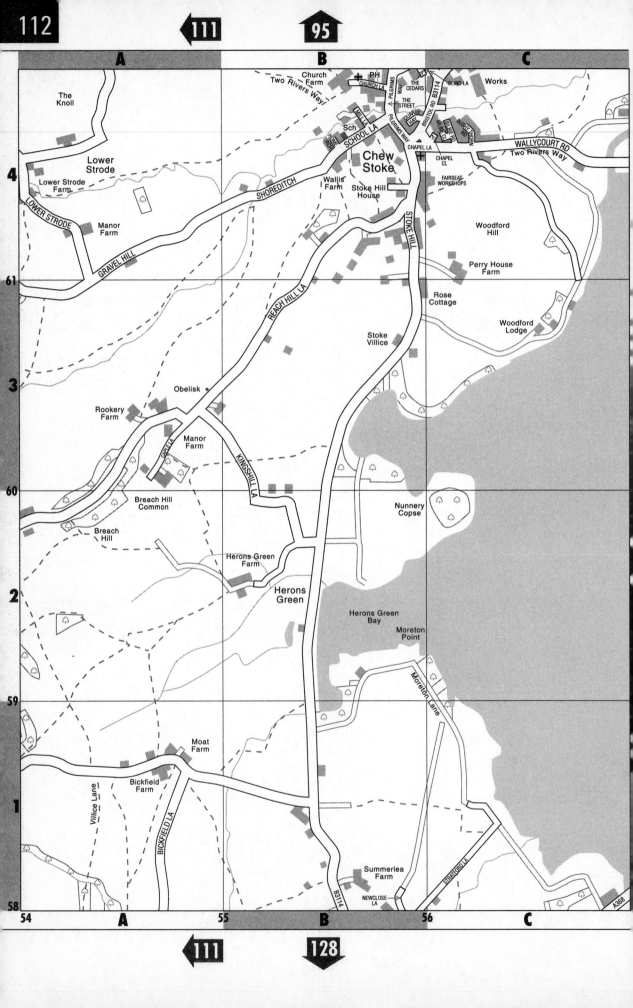

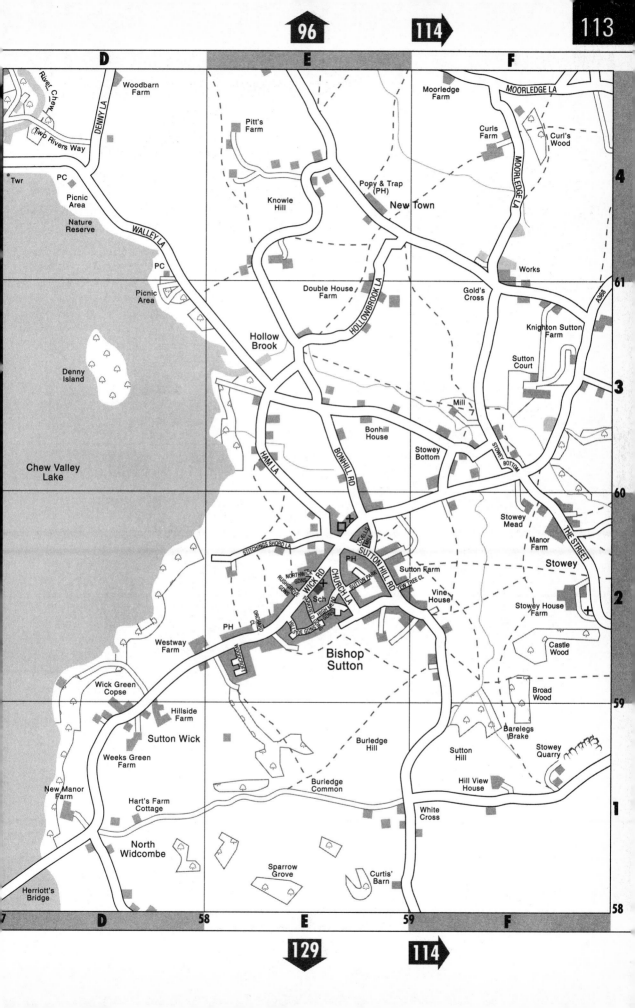

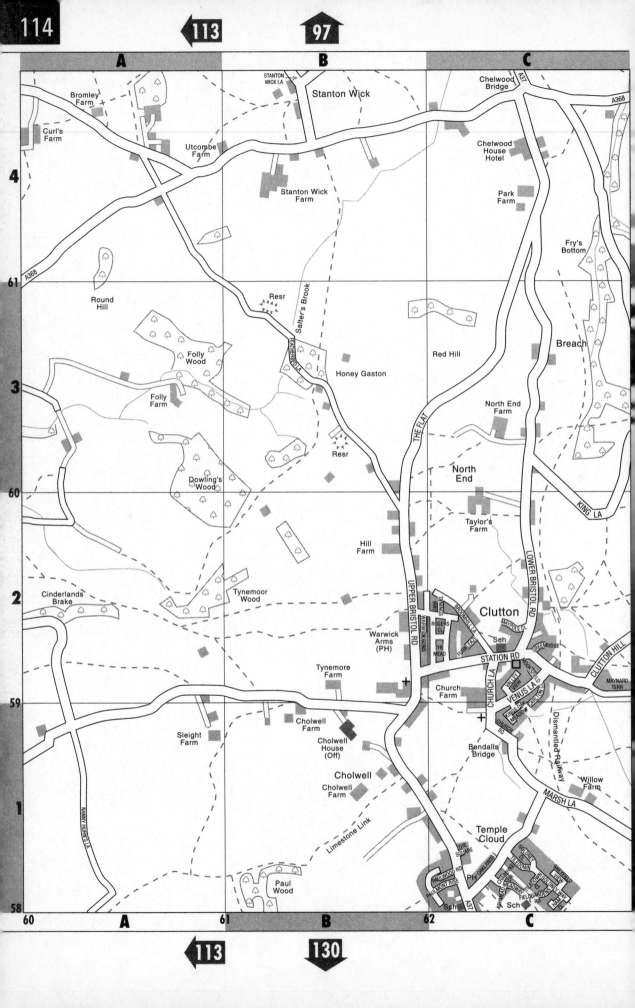

A   **B**   **C**

Bromley Farm

Curl's Farm

STANTON WICK LA

Stanton Wick

Chelwood Bridge

A368

A37

Utcombe Farm

Stanton Wick Farm

Chelwood House Hotel

Park Farm

4

Fry's Bottom

A368

Round Hill

Resr

Salter's Brook

Red Hill

Breach

61

Folly Wood

FEATHERBED LA

Honey Gaston

3

Folly Farm

North End Farm

Resr

North End

Dowling's Wood

THE FLAT

KING LA

60

Taylor's Farm

LOWER BRISTOL RD

Hill Farm

Cinderlands Brake

Tynemoor Wood

Clutton

UPPER BRISTOL RD

MAYPOLE CL

WARWICK GDNS

TINING'S WAY

ROGERS CL

BROCKLANDS

THE MEAD

Sch

GREENRIDGE

2

Warwick Arms (PH)

FURNLEAZE

STATION RD

CLUTTON HILL

MAYNARD TERR

Tynemore Farm

Church Farm

CHURCH LA

VENUS LA

VALLEY VIEW

MOORSIDE

Sleight Farm

Cholwell Farm

KINGS OAK MEADOW

CARLINGCOTT LA

Dismantled Railway

59

Cholwell House (Off)

CHURCH SQ

Bendalls Bridge

Willow Farm

Cholwell

NANNY HURN'S LA

Cholwell Farm

MARSH LA

1

Limestone Link

Temple Cloud

THE SQUARE

GOLD DRY

TILEDOWN

GREENFIELD VIEW

PH

OAKLANDS

Paul Wood

PAULWOOD RD

PAULMONT RISE

A37

ASHMEAD

MEADWAY

GREENWAY

GOLDNEY WAY

HAY?

58

Sch

FIELDGARDENS RD

Sch

60   **A**   **61**   **B**   **62**   **C**

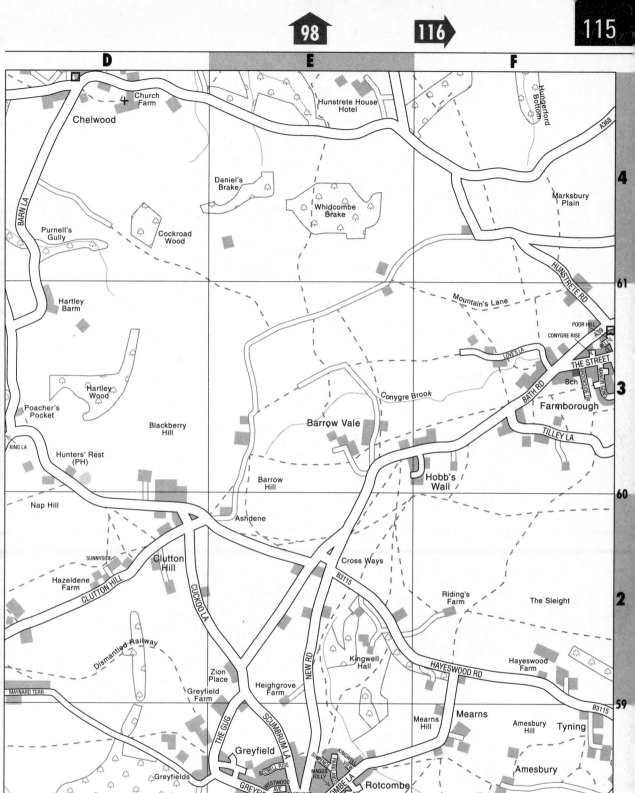

D
E
F

4

Chelwood
Church Farm
Hunstrete House Hotel
Hungerford Bottom
A368
Marksbury Plain

BARN LA

Daniel's Brake
Whidcombe Brake

Purnell's Gully
Cockroad Wood

61

HUNSTRETE RD

Mountain's Lane

POOR HILL
A39
CONYGRE RISE

Hartley Barm

THE STREET

Hartley Wood

Conygre Brook

BATH RD
Sch
BROOKSIDE DR
MANOR FORD

3

Poacher's Pocket

Barrow Vale

Farmborough

KING LA

Blackberry Hill

TILLEY LA

Hunters' Rest (PH)

Hobb's Wall

Nap Hill

Barrow Hill

60

Ashdene

SUNNYSIDE
Clutton Hill

Cross Ways
B3115

Riding's Farm

The Sleight

2

Hazeldene Farm
CLUTTON HILL

CUCKOO LA

Dismantled Railway

Kingwell Hall

Hayeswood Farm

HAYESWOOD RD

MAYNARD TERR

Zion Place

Greyfield Farm

NEW RD

Heighgrove Farm

59
B3115

THE GUG

SCUMBRUM LA

Greyfield

Mearns Hill
Mearns

Amesbury Hill
Tyning

Greyfields

SCOBELL RISE

KINGWELL VIEW
PARKLANDS

Amesbury

WESTWOOD AVE
EASTWOOD CL

MAGGS FOLLY

ROTCOMBE LA

Rotcombe

GREYFIELD RD
GREYFIELD COMM

ROTCOMBE VALE

Greyfield Wood Farm

LANSDOWN PL

Rugbourne Farm

1

Greyfield Wood

HIGH ST

PH
SOUTHOVER RD
EASTOVER RD

Long Lands
Limestone Link

High Littleton

Timsbury Bottom Farm

Timsbury Bottom

PRIORS HILL

MARSH LA

BUTLASS CL

BUNGAY'S HILL

BROOM HILL LA

Sch
TIMSBURY RD
GOOSARD LA
A39
LANGFORD'S LA

58

63
D
64
E
65
F

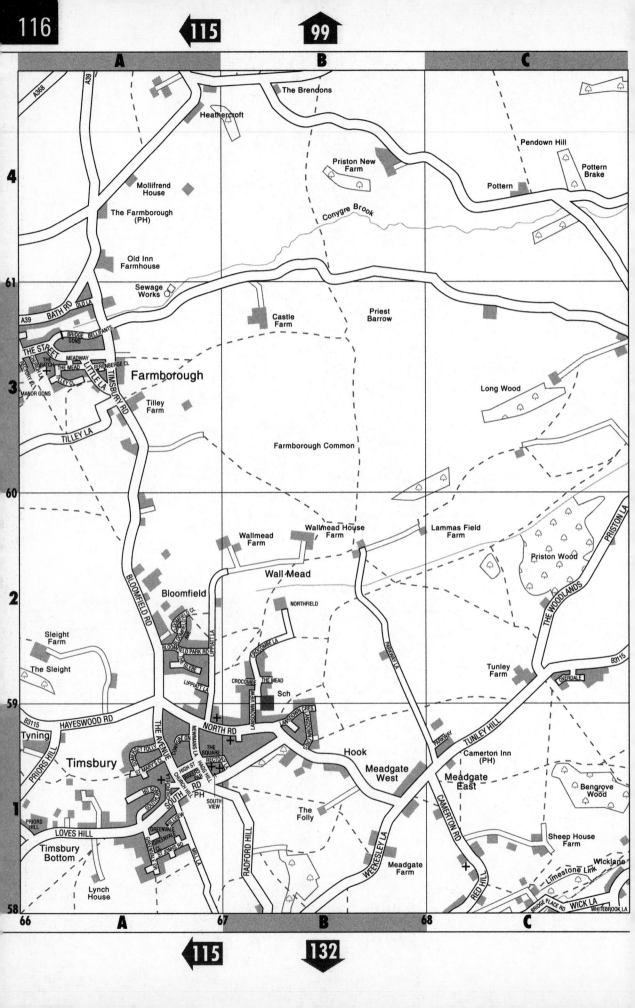

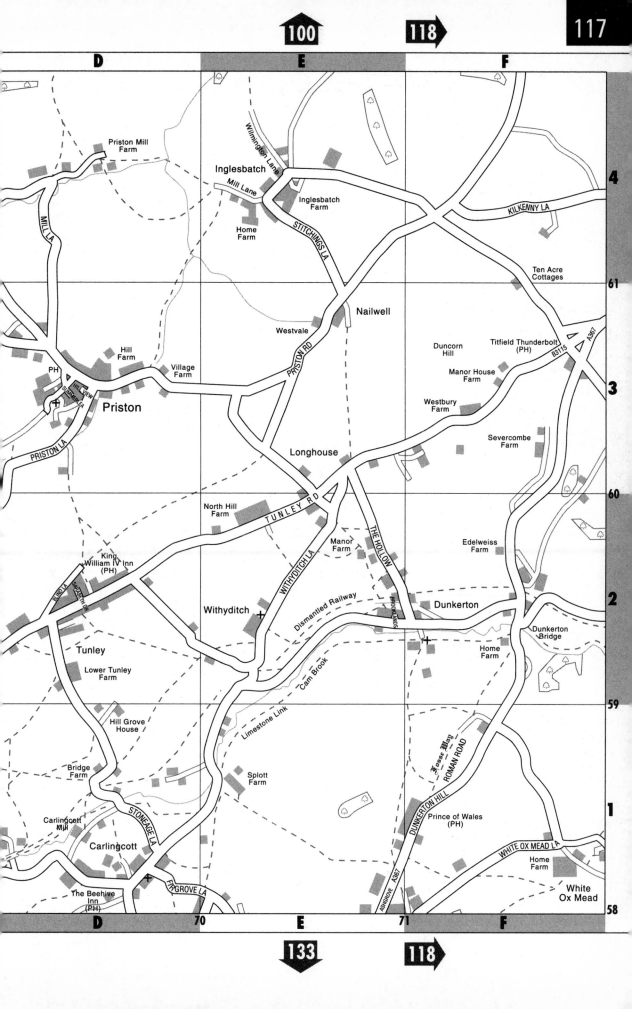

4

61

3

60

2

59

1

58

Priston Mill Farm

Inglesbatch

Wilmington Lane

Mill Lane

Inglesbatch Farm

Home Farm

STITCHINGS LA

KILKENNY LA

Ten Acre Cottages

Nailwell

Westvale

PRISTON RD

MILL LA

Hill Farm

PH

HILL VIEW

SILVER LEA

Village Farm

Priston

PRISTON LA

Longhouse

North Hill Farm

TUNLEY RD

Manor Farm

THE HOLLOW

Duncorn Hill

Titfield Thunderbolt (PH)

B3115

A367

Manor House Farm

Westbury Farm

Severcombe Farm

Edelweiss Farm

Dunkerton

BROOKLANDS

Dunkerton Bridge

King William IV Inn (PH)

BUND LA

SADGETH DR

Withyditch

WITHYDITCH LA

Dismantled Railway

Tunley

Lower Tunley Farm

Cam Brook

Home Farm

Limestone Link

Hill Grove House

Bridge Farm

STONEAGE LA

Splott Farm

ROMAN ROAD

Roman Road

DUNKERTON HILL

Prince of Wales (PH)

WHITE OX MEAD LA

Home Farm

Carlingcott Mill

Carlingcott

FIRGROVE LA

ASHGROVE A367

White Ox Mead

The Beehive Inn (PH)

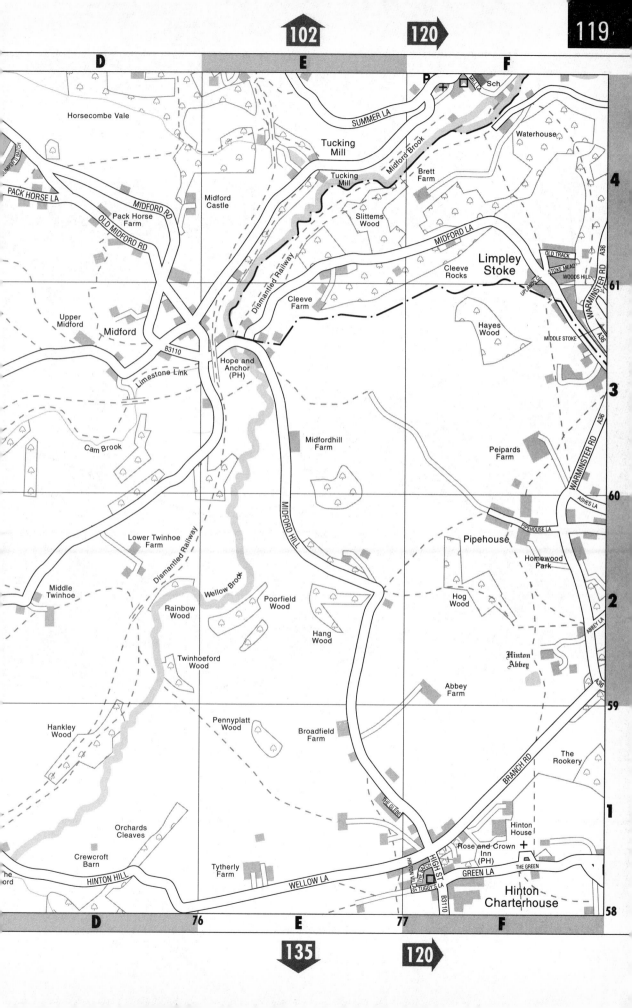

A
B
C

TOTTERDOWN LA

PURN RD
BLEADON HILL
LEIGHTON LA
SOUTHRIDGE HTS

Hillcote
Estate

Bleadon
Hill

Bleadon Hill

West Mendip Way
ROMAN ROAD

Purn Hill

Coombe
Farm

4

Purn Lane

Purn

Hellenge
Hill

CELTIC WAY

A370

Purn
Farm

PURN WAY

MANOR GRANGE

PH

PH

ACCOMMODATION RD

CHESTNUT LA

PINE TEA

BLEADON RD

AMESBURY RD

TENTERK CL

57

South Combe 1
Fern Lea 2
Whitegate Cl 3

BRIDGE RD

OLD SCHOOL LA

CORONATION RD

PC

MULBERRY LA

THE BARTON

ASH RD
BIRCH AVE
WILLOW DR

THE VEALE

Wonderstone

SHIPLATE RD

Shiplate

MEGROMBE LA

Caravan
Park

Bleadon

Quarries
(dis)

South Hill

South Hill
Farm

Shiplate
Manor
Farm

3

River Axe

Lake
Farm

Batch Rhyne

Boat Rhyne

Bleadon
Bridge

THE CRESCENT

56

Hobbs Boat
Inn
(PH)

BRIDGWATER RD

BOAT LA

Rhynemoor
Farm

North Farm
House

2

Batch
Farm

STEVENS LA

Wrentmoor Rhyne

Batch Rhyne

Honeymeade
Farm

Appledore

55

Garage

Chestnut
Farm

Eastertown
Farm

WORTH RD

RECTORY WAY

Rectory
Farm

COPPICE END
CNR

Eastertown

EASTERTOWN

WHITE HOUSE LA

1

Holm
Farm

THE BOUNDARIES

LYMPSHAM RD

NORTH STREET

THE WORTHIES

Sch

CHURCH LA

SLADE LA

CHURCH RD

Stonebow
Farm

PURLING ROW

PURLING ROW

A370

Poplar
Farm

Lympsham

WEST RD

SOUTH RD

54

D E F

4

Yarberry Farm
Yarberry

CANADA COOMBE
Christon Plantation
Barleycombe Lodge
Keeper's Cottage
BANWELL RD
M5

Bleadon Hill
Manor Farm
FLAGSTAFF RD

57

Hamwood
Christon

Loxton Hill
NEARCOMBE LA
Shiplate Slait
Loxton Wood
Oakes Farm
Lox Yeo River
Long Acre

3

Shiplate Wood
West Mendip Way
BARTON RD

The Paddock

56

The Lodge
Crook Peak

Shiplate House Farm
HILLVIEW RD
Loxton
CHURCH LA
The Webbington Hotel
Webbington

SHIPLATE RD
Museum
KENNEL LA
WEBBINGTON RD

2

SEVIER RD COWSLIP LA
Old Lox Yeo

White House Farm
WHITE HOUSE LA
River Axe
HAMS LA

55

Crab Hole
Poplar Farm

Riverside Farm
BIDDISHAM LA

1

North Yeo Farm
Mark Yeo
Old River Axe
The House Farm

Badgworth

M5

54

123
107

A **B** **C**

Lox Yeo River

Sewage Works

MAX MILL LA

Max Mills Farm

Max House Farm

Water Works

Winscombe Brook

BANWELL RD

A371

HOMEFIELD CL

BIGNELL CL

Mooseheart

KNAPPS CL

Sta Sch

Dismd Rly

SANDFORD RD

PC

Nut Tree Farm

WOODBOROUGH RD A371

THE LYNCH

LYNCH CRES

LYNCHMEAD

CHURCH RD

4

57 BARTON RD

Barton Farm

Laurel Farm

Barton

Willow Farm

PARSONS WAY

Winscombe Orchard

CHURCH LA

THE SQUARE

Winscombe Brook

Eastwell Lane

Broad Knoll

Church Knoll

WINSCOMBE HILL

3

Barton Hill

Old Quarry Farm

BARTON DRO

Saw Mill

Resr

Hill Farm

Winscombe Hill

The Hall

Compton Hill

56 West Mendip Way

Coombe Cottage

Wavering Down

Cross Plain

King's Wood

Compton Bishop

COOMBE LA

Bourton Coombe

2

BUTTS BATCH

CHURCH LA

VICARAGE LA

VERNON LA

BIG TREE CL

Caves

WEBBINGTON RD

Compton Farm

BOURTON LA

Bourton Farm

55 P

RACKLEY LA

Dunnett Farm

New Town

Resr

Cross

White Hart (PH)

A38

CROSS LA

Old River Axe

Rackley

COACH RD

OLD

P

River Axe

Cheddar Yeo

Bow Bridge

Stock's Rhyne

Compton Bishop Farm

Cross Culvert

Yeo Bridge

CROSS MOOR DRO

Middle Rhyne

1

TURNPIKE RD

A38

54

39 **A** **40** **B** **41** **C**

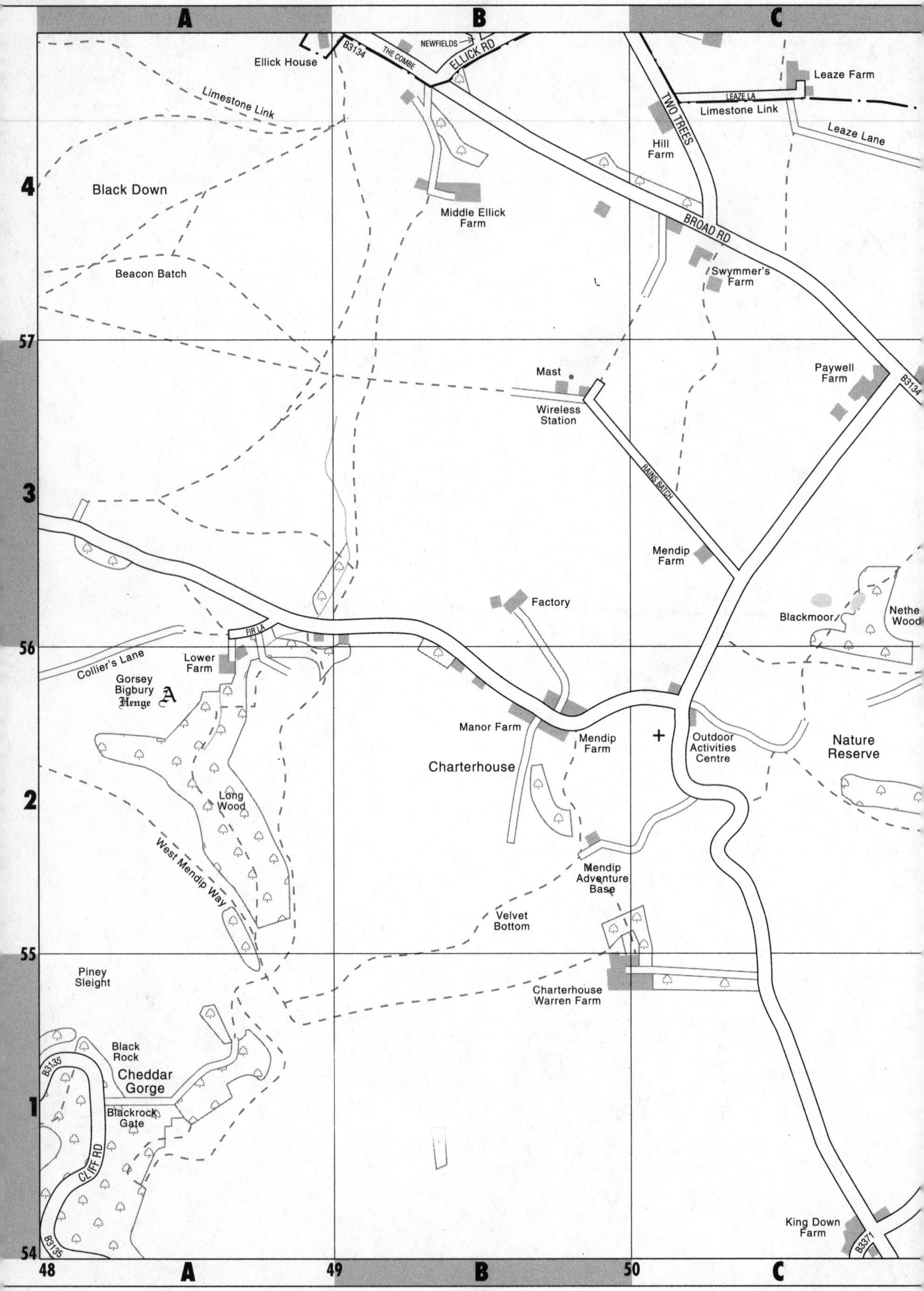

110

A B C

4

Black Down

Ellick House

Limestone Link

NEWFIELDS

ELLICK RD

THE COMBE

B3134

Leaze Farm

LEAZE LA

Limestone Link

Leaze Lane

TWO TREES

Hill
Farm

BROAD RD

Middle Ellick
Farm

Swymmer's
Farm

Beacon Batch

Paywell
Farm

B3134

57

Mast

Wireless
Station

3

RAINS BATCH

Mendip
Farm

Nethe
Wood

Factory

Blackmoor

56

FIR LA

Collier's Lane

Lower
Farm

Gorsey
Bigbury
Henge

Manor Farm

Charterhouse

Mendip
Farm

Outdoor
Activities
Centre

Nature
Reserve

Long
Wood

2

West Mendip Way

Mendip
Adventure
Base

Velvet
Bottom

55

Piney
Sleight

Charterhouse
Warren Farm

Black
Rock

Cheddar
Gorge

B3135

1

CLIFF RD

Blackrock
Gate

King Down
Farm

B3371

B3135

54

48 A 49 B 50 C

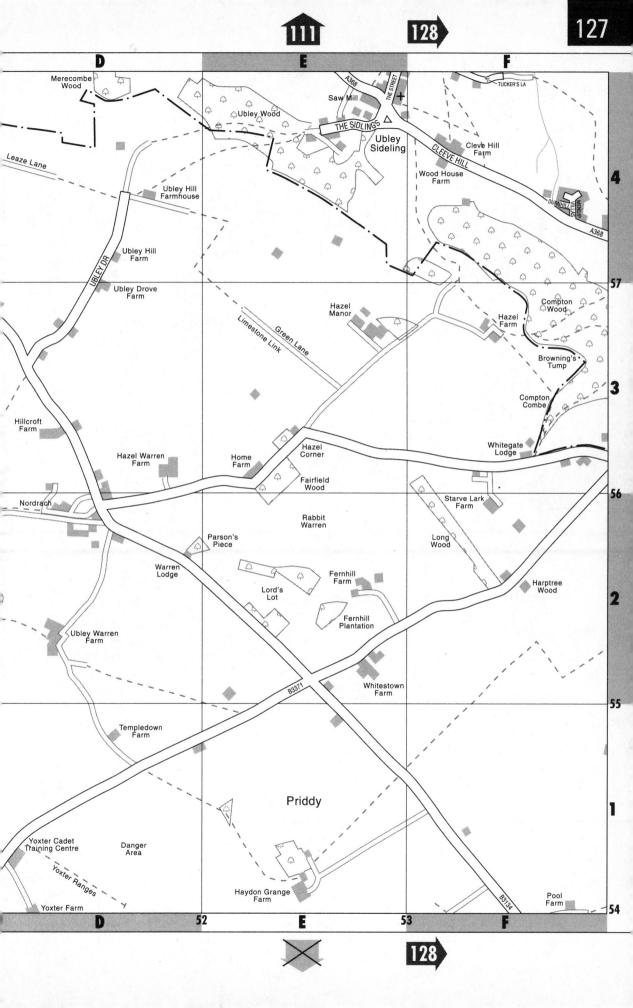

D E F

Merecombe
Wood

Leaze Lane

Ubley Wood

Saw Mill

THE STREET

A368

THE SIDLINGS

Ubley
Sideling

CLEVE HILL

Cleve Hill
Farm

TUCKER'S LA

Wood House
Farm

MENDIP VILLAS

DURSHILL

A368

4

Ubley Hill
Farmhouse

UBLEY DR

Ubley Hill
Farm

Ubley Drove
Farm

Limestone Link

Green Lane

Hazel
Manor

Hazel
Farm

Compton
Wood

57

Browning's
Tump

Compton
Combe

3

Hillcroft
Farm

Hazel Warren
Farm

Home
Farm

Hazel
Corner

Fairfield
Wood

Whitegate
Lodge

Nordrach

Rabbit
Warren

Starve Lark
Farm

56

Parson's
Piece

Long
Wood

Warren
Lodge

Lord's
Lot

Fernhill
Farm

Harptree
Wood

2

Ubley Warren
Farm

B3371

Fernhill
Plantation

Whitestown
Farm

55

Templedown
Farm

Priddy

1

Yoxter Cadet
Training Centre

Danger
Area

Yoxter Ranges

Yoxter Farm

Haydon Grange
Farm

B3134

Pool
Farm

54

A B C

4

Greenacres Farm

Blckfield House Farm

NEWCLOSE LA

B3114

STRATFORD LA

Blue Bowl Inn (PH)

Lower Gurney Farm

A368

River Yeo

VILLICE LA

YEW TREE LA

BICKFIELD LA

White Cross Farm

UNDERTOWN LA

THE REDDINGS

MILL LA

UNDERTOWN

A368

Ring of Bells (PH)

THE COOMBE

THE BATCH

RECTORY LA

THE STREET

TINKER'S LA

Compton Martin

ROMAN ROAD (course of)

Fairash Poultry Farm

Tilly Manor Farm

B3114

NEWTON CL

WHISTLEY LA

West Harptree

57

RIDGE CRES

RIDGEWAY CL

B3114

3

HIGHFIELD LA

The Wrangle

HARPTREE HILL

Beaconsfield Farm

Limestone Link

COW LANE LA

Bungalow Farm

Cemy

Molly Brook

TOWNSEND

B3114 COLE RD

BELLHORSE LA

RIDGE LA

Ridge

High St

Harptree Court

56

Harptree Hill Farm

The Wellsway Inn (PH)

Shortcombe Farm

Waldegrave Arms (PH)

Sch

THE CROSS

ASH LA

WHITECROSS RD

East Harptree

CHURCH LA

MIDDLE ST

GREY HOLLOW

ORCHARD END

WATER ST

2

OLD BRISTOL RD

WESTERN LA

Harptree Combe

Proud Cross

Wallace

CULVER LA

WALLACE LA

HIGHFIELD LA

Newhouse

Garrow Bottom

GIBBETS BROW

Lamb Leer Cavern

Garrow

Garrowpipe Spring

Smitham Hill

The Grove

MORGAN'S LA

Morgan's Cottage

1

Lamb Bottom

OLD BRISTOL RD

East Harptree Woods

Chy

The Belt

Pitt Farm

Spring Farm

54

A B C

54 55 56

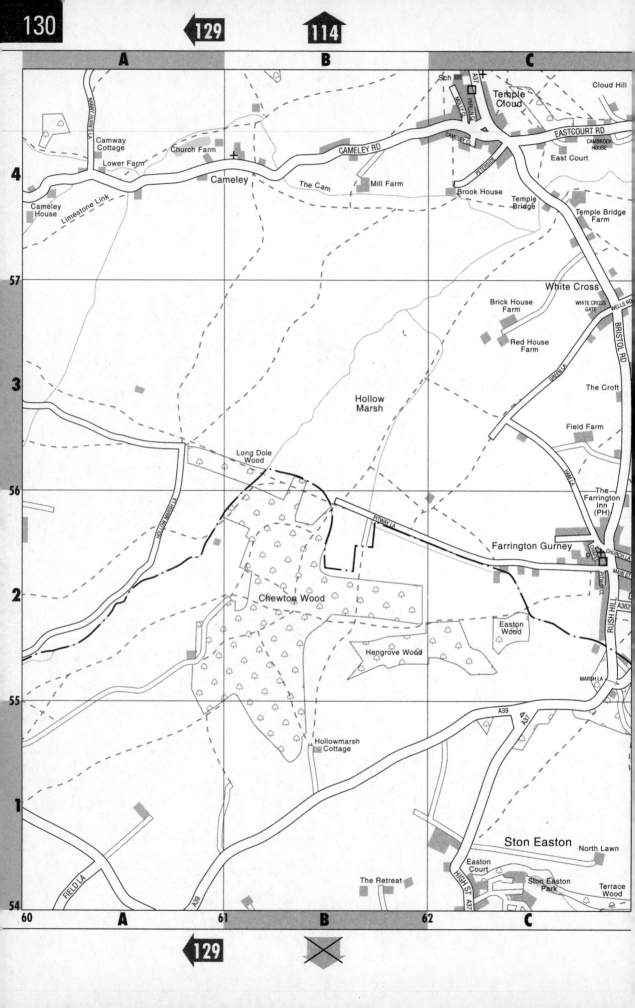

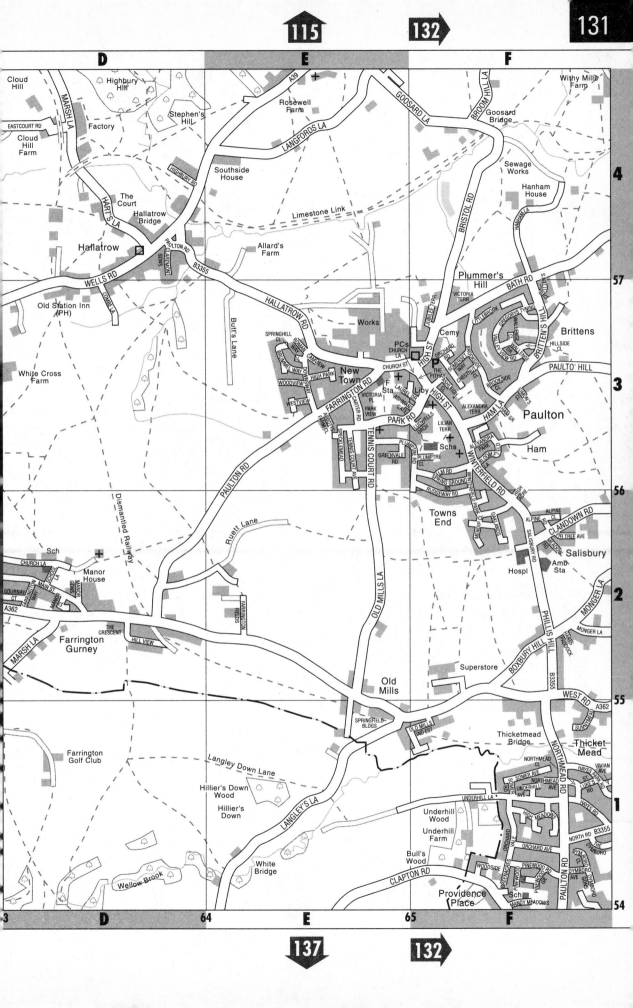

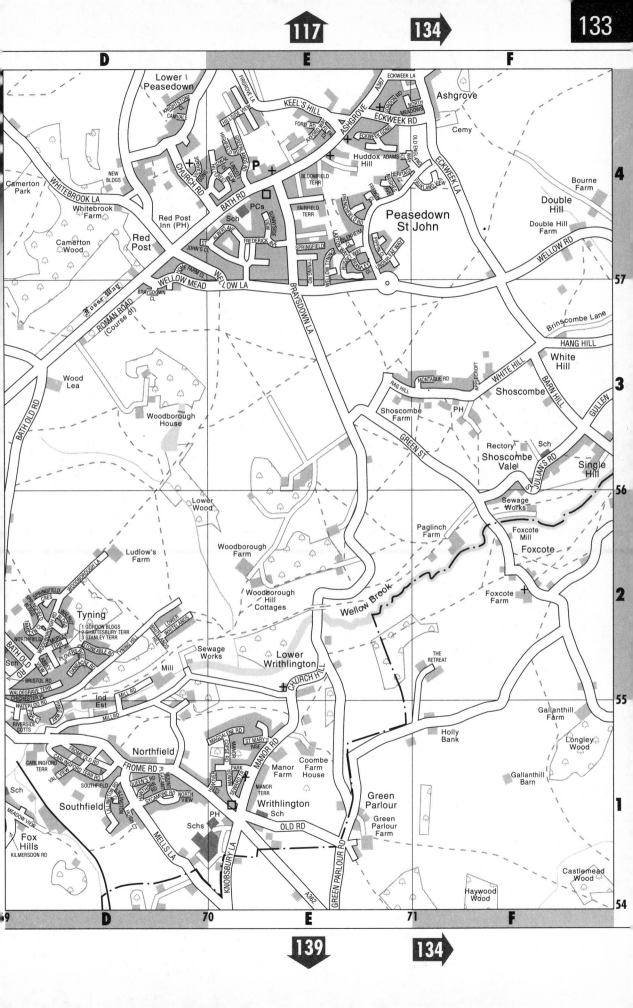

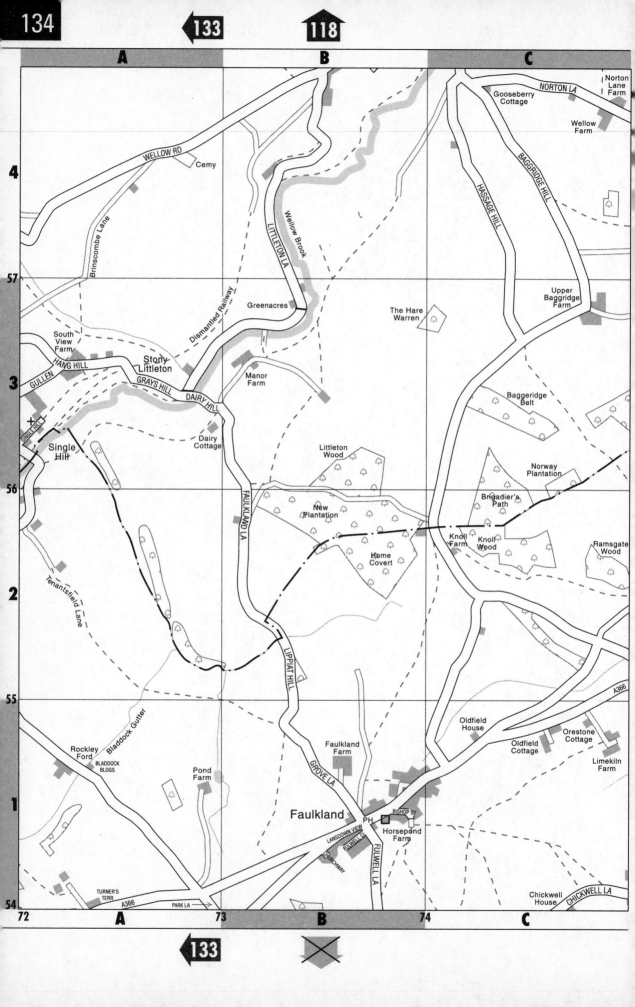

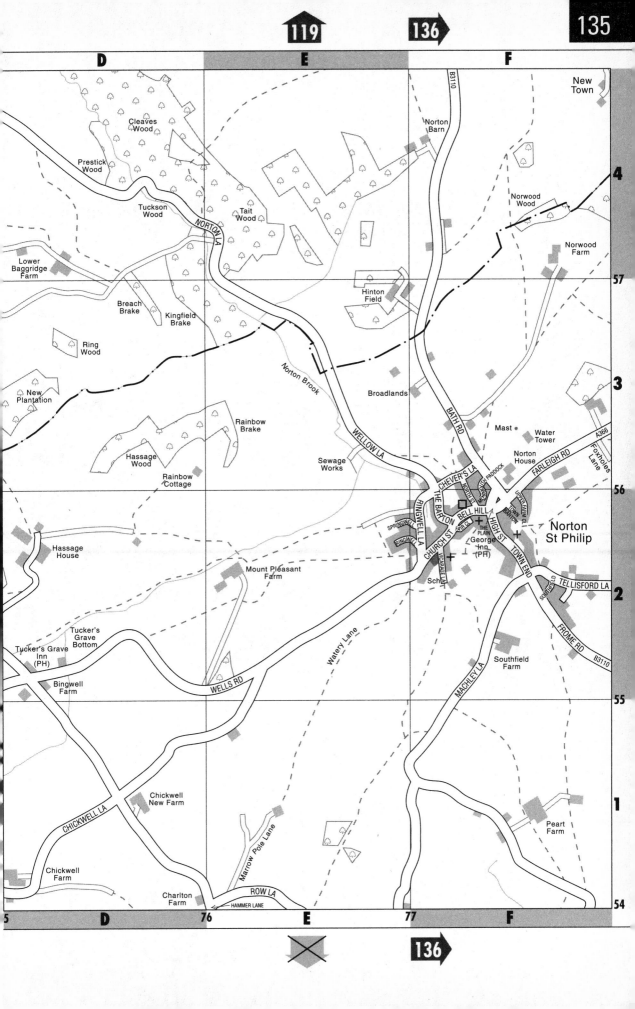

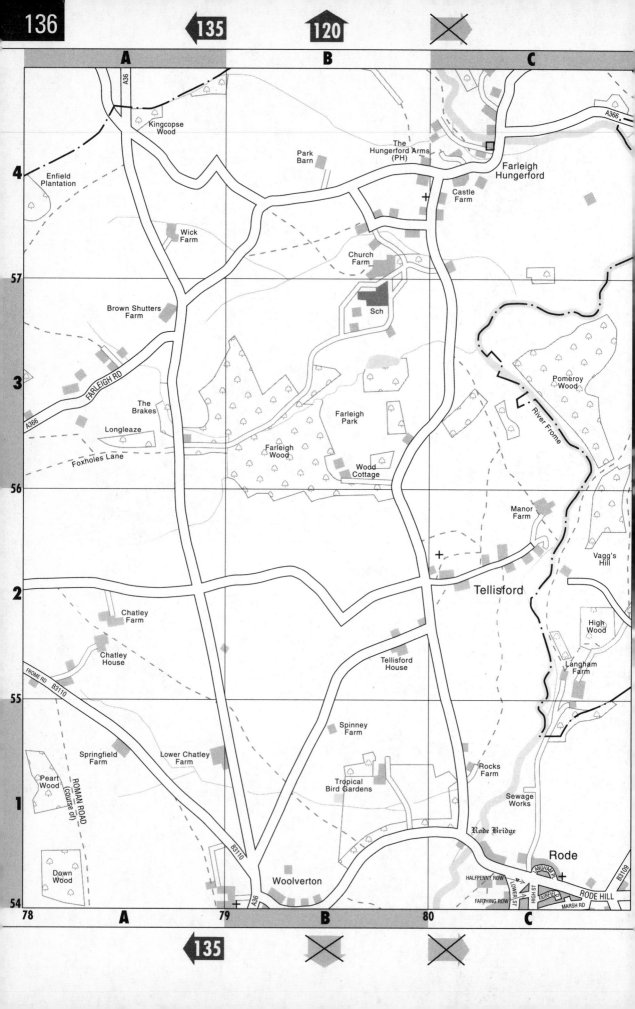

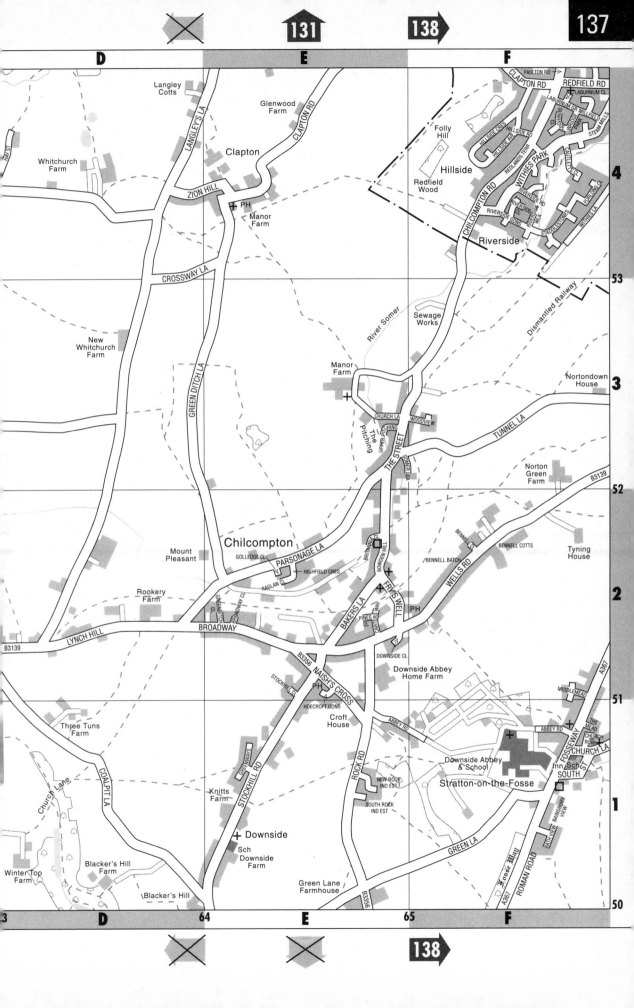

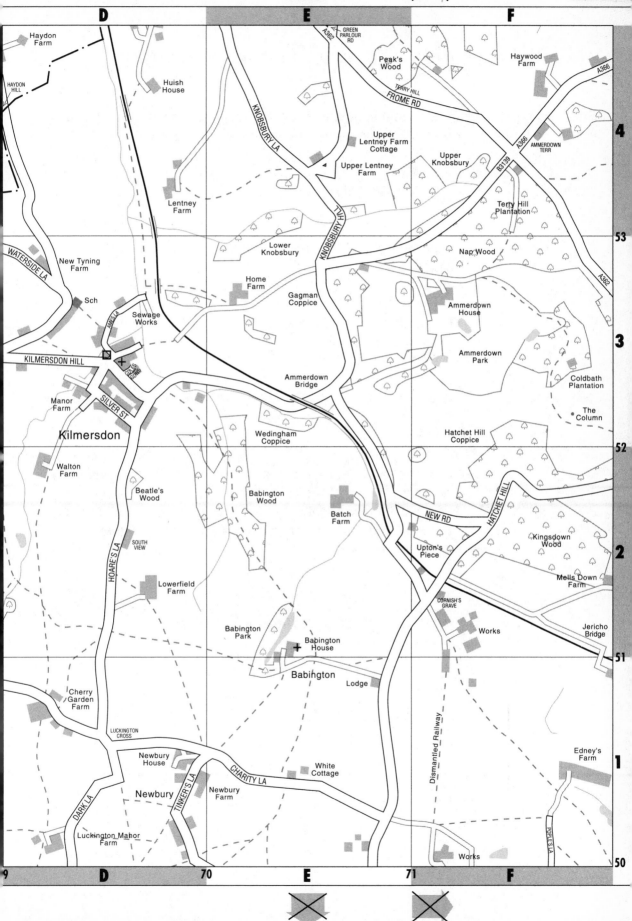

Haydon Farm

HAYDON HILL

Huish House

WATERSIDE LA

New Tyning Farm

Sch

AMB LA

Sewage Works

KILMERSDON HILL

Manor Farm

SILVER ST

Kilmersdon

Walton Farm

Beatle's Wood

HOARE'S LA

SOUTH VIEW

Lowerfield Farm

Cherry Garden Farm

LUCKINGTON CROSS

Newbury House

DARK LA

TINKER'S LA

Newbury

Newbury Farm

Luckington Manor Farm

CHARITY LA

White Cottage

KNOBSBURY LA

A362

GREEN PARLOUR RD

Peak's Wood

TERRY HILL

FROME RD

Upper Lentney Farm Cottage

Upper Lentney Farm

Lentney Farm

Lower Knobsbury

Home Farm

Gagman Coppice

KNOBSBURY HILL

Ammerdown Bridge

Wedingham Coppice

Babington Wood

Batch Farm

Babington Park

Babington House

Babington

Lodge

Upper Knobsbury

Nap Wood

Ammerdown House

Ammerdown Park

Hatchet Hill Coppice

NEW RD

Upton's Piece

HATCHET HILL

Kingsdown Wood

CORNISH'S GRAVE

Works

Haywood Farm

A366

A366

AMMERDOWN TERR

B3139

Terry Hill Plantation

Coldbath Plantation

The Column

A362

Mells Down Farm

Jericho Bridge

Dismantled Railway

Edney's Farm

Works

POPLES LA

4

53

3

52

2

51

1

50

9

D

70

E

71

F

EXPLANATION OF THE STREET INDEX REFERENCE SYSTEM

Street names are listed alphabetically and show the locality, the page number and a reference to the square in which the name falls on the map page.

Example: Hill View Rd. Puck..53 E3

Hill View Rd   This is the full street name, which may have been abbreviated on the map.

Puck   This is the abbreviation for the town, village or locality in which the street falls.

53   This is the page number of the map on which the street name appears.

E3   The letter and figure indicate the square on the map in which the centre of the street falls. The square can be found at the junction of the vertical column carrying the appropriate letter and the horizontal row carrying the appropriate figure.

ABBREVIATIONS USED IN THE INDEX
Road Names

Approach	App	Grove	Gr
Arcade	Arc	Heights	Hts
Avenue	Ave	Industrial Estate	Ind Est
Boulevard	Bvd	Junction	Junc
Buildings	Bldgs	Lane	La
Business Park	Bsns Pk	North	N
Broadway	Bwy	Orchard	Orch
By-Pass	By-Ps	Parade	Par
Causeway	Cswy	Passage	Pas
Circle	Circ	Place	Pl
Circus	Cir	Pleasant	Plea
Close	Cl	Precinct	Prec
Common	Comm	Promenade	Prom
Corner	Cnr	Road	Rd
Cottages	Cotts	South	S
Court	Ct	Square	Sq
Courtyard	Ctyd	Stairs	Strs
Crescent	Cres	Steps	Stps
Drive	Dri	Street, Saint	St
Drove	Dro	Terrace	Terr
East	E	Walk	Wlk
Embankment	Emb	West	W
Esplanade	Espl	Yard	Yd
Gardens	Gdns		

Key to abbreviations of Town, Village and Rural locality names used in the index of street names.

Abbots Leigh	Ab Lei	62	A4	
Acton Turville	A Tur	42	C3	
Almondsbury	Alm	24	A3	
Alveston	Alve	15	D2	
Aust	Aust	13	D3	
Avonmouth	Avon	33	E1	
Axbridge	Axb	125	D1	
Backwell	Back	76	A3	
Badgworth	Badg	123	F1	
Banwell	Ban	107	D1	
Barrow Gurney	Ba Gu	77	F3	
Bath	Bath	102	B3	
Batheaston	Bathe	85	F2	
Bathford	Bathf	86	B1	
Berrow	Berr	121	D1	
Bishop Sutton	Bi Sut	113	E2	
Bitton	Bitt	82	C4	
Blagdon	Blag	110	C1	
Bleadon	Blea	122	B3	
Box	Box	86	C2	
Bristol	Bris	63	E3	
Brockley	Brock	75	E1	
Burton	Burt	43	D2	
Butcombe	But	111	D4	
Charfield	Char	11	D3	
Charlcombe	Charl	84	C2	
Cheddar	Ched	125	F2	
Chew Magna	Ch Mag	96	B2	
Chew Stoke	Ch St	112	B4	
Chilcompton	Chil	137	E2	
Chipping Sodbury	Ch Sod	28	B1	
Churchill	Chur	108	C2	
Clevedon	Cleve	57	D2	
Clutton	Clut	114	C2	
Cold Ashton	Co Ash	68	C3	
Colerne	Col	70	C2	
Compton Bishop	Co Bi	124	A2	
Compton Dando	Co Dan	98	B3	
Compton Martin	Co Mar	128	A3	
Congresbury	Cong	91	F2	
Corston	Cor	100	A4	
Cromhall	Crom	10	A1	
Didmarton	Did	20	C3	
Dodington	Dod	41	D2	
Doynton	Doyn	54	A1	
Dundry	Dun	78	B1	
Dyrham	Dyrh	54	B2	
East Harptree	E Harp	128	C2	
Easton in Gordano	E in G	47	D2	
Englishcombe	Engl	100	C1	
Falfield	Falf	9	F4	
Farmborough	Farm	116	A3	
Faulkland	Faulk	134	B1	
Frampton Cotterell	Fr Cot	38	A4	
Great Badminton	Gr Bad	30	C1	
Grittleton	Grit	43	F3	
Hawkesbury Upton	H Up	20	A1	
Hillesley	Hill	19	E4	
Hinton Blewett	Hin Ble	129	F3	
Hinton Charterhouse	Hin Cha	119	F1	
Holcombe	Hol	138	B1	
Horton	Hort	29	E3	
Iron Acton	Ir Act	26	B2	
Kelston	Kel	83	E2	
Keynsham	Keyn	81	F2	
Kilmersdon	Kilm	139	D3	
Kingston Seymour	K Sey	73	E1	
Kingswood	Kings	11	F2	
Kingswood	Kingsw	65	E4	
Limpley Stoke	Li St	119	F4	
Litton	Litt	129	F1	
Locking	Lock	106	A2	
Long Ashton	Lo Ash	62	A1	
Luckington	Luck	31	F2	
Lympsham	Lymp	122	A1	
Mangotsfield	Mang	51	F4	
Marksbury	Marks	99	D1	
Marshfield	Marsh	69	F4	
Midsomer Norton	Mid No	132	A2	
Monkton Farleigh	Mon Far	103	F4	
Nailsea	Nail	59	E2	
Newport	Newp	4	A4	
North Nibley	N Nib	5	E2	
North Wraxall	N Wrax	56	C2	
Norton St Philip	N St P	135	F2	
Oldbury-on-Severn	O-on-S	7	E3	
Olveston	Olve	14	A2	
Paulton	Paul	131	F3	
Peasedown St John	P St J	133	E4	
Pensford	Pens	97	F2	
Pilning	Piln	22	B4	
Portbury	Portb	46	B2	
Portishead	Portis	45	D2	
Priddy	Priddy	127	E1	
Priston	Pris	117	D3	
Pucklechurch	Puck	53	D3	
Puxton	Pux	90	B2	
Radstock	Rad	132	C1	
Rockhampton	Rock	8	C4	
Rode	Rode	136	C1	
Shipham	Ship	125	F4	
Siston	Sist	52	C2	
Southstoke	Sosto	118	C4	
Stinchcombe	Stin	5	D4	
Ston Easton	Ston E	130	C1	
Stone	Stone	3	F2	
Stoke Gifford	St Gif	36	C2	
Tellisford	Tell	136	C2	
Thornbury	Thorn	8	C1	
Timsbury	Tims	116	A1	
Tormarton	Tor	41	F1	
Tytherington	Tyth	16	B3	
Wellow	Well	118	B1	
Westerleigh	West	39	D2	
Weston in Gordano	W in G	44	C1	
Weston-Super-Mare	W-S-M	104	B4	
Westwood	Westw	120	C2	
Whitchurch	Whit	80	B2	
Wick	Wick	67	E3	
Wick St Lawrence	W St L	89	D4	
Wickwar	Wickw	18	A3	
Winford	Win	94	C4	
Winscombe	Winsc	125	D4	
Winsley	Winsl	120	C4	
Winterbourne	Wint	37	F3	
Wotton-under-Edge	W-u-E	11	F4	
Wraxall	Wrax	60	B2	
Wrington	Wring	92	C1	
Yate	Yate	27	E1	
Yatton	Yatt	91	E4	

5c Bsns Centre. Cleve

5c Bsns Centre. Cleve 57 D1
Abbey Church Yd. Bath 102 A3
Abbey Cl. Keyn 81 F3
Abbey Green. Bath 102 A3
Abbey La. Hi Cha 120 A2
Abbey Park. Keyn 81 F3
Abbey Rd. Bris 48 C4
Abbey Rd. Chil 137 E1
Abbey Rd. Chil 137 F1
Abbey St. Bath 102 A3
Abbey St. Kings 11 F3
Abbey View Gdns. Bath ... 102 A3
Abbey View. Bath 102 A3
Abbey View. Mid No 133 D2
Abbeydale. Wint 37 D3
Abbeygate St. Bath 102 A3
Abbeywood Dr. Bris 48 B3
Abbot's Cl. W-S-M 89 D2
Abbots Ave. Kingsw 65 E2
Abbots Cl. Bris 80 A2
Abbots Horn. Nail 59 E1
Abbots Leigh Rd. Ab Lei .. 62 B4
Abbots Leigh Rd. Lo Ash .. 62 B4
Abbots Rd. Kingsw 65 E1
Abbots Way. Bris 49 F3
Abbotsbury Rd. Nail 59 E1
Abbotsford Rd. Bris 49 D1
Abbotswood. Kingsw 65 E4
Abbotswood. Yate 39 E4
Abbott Rd. Piln 22 A3
Abbotts Farm Cl. Paul 131 E4
Aberdeen Rd. Bris 63 D4
Abingdon Gdns. Bath 118 B4
Abingdon Rd. Bris 51 D2
Ableton La. Avon 33 F4
Ableton La. Piln 22 A3
Ableton Wlk. Bris 48 B3
Abraham Cl. Bris 64 A3
Abson Rd. Wick 53 E2
Acacia Ave. Kingsw 51 E2
Acacia Cl. Kingsw 51 E2
Acacia Ct. Keyn 81 E2
Acacia Gr. Bath 101 E2
Acacia Rd. Kingsw 51 E2
Acacia Rd. Rad 132 C1
Accommodation Rd. Blea .. 121 F3
Acid Rd. Avon 33 E2
Acorn Gr. Bris 78 C3
Acraman's Rd. Bris 63 E2
Acrebush Cl. Bris 79 D3
Acton Rd. Bris 51 D2
Adams Cl. P St J 133 E4
Addicot Rd. W-S-M 104 C4
Addiscombe Rd. Bris ... 80 A3
Addiscombe Rd. W-S-M . 104 C2
Addison Rd. Bris 63 F2
Adelaide Pl. Bris 50 C2
Adelaide Pl. Bris 64 A4
Admiral's Wlk. Portis ... 45 D3
Agate St. Bris 63 D2
Aiken St. Bris 64 A3
Ainslie's Belvedere. Bath .. 101 F4
Aintree Dr. Mang 37 F1
Air Balloon Rd. Bris 65 D4
Airport Rd. Bris 80 A4
Aisecombe Way. W-S-M . 105 E3
Akeman Way. Avon 47 E4
Alard Rd. Bris 79 F4
Albany Gate. St Gif 36 C3
Albany Rd. Bath 101 E3
Albany Rd. Bris 49 F1
Albany St. Bris 65 E4
Albany Way. Kingsw ... 66 B3
Albermarle Row. Bris .. 62 C3
Albert Ave. P St J 133 E4
Albert Ave. W-S-M 104 C4
Albert Cres. Bris 64 A3
Albert Gr. Bris 64 B4
Albert Par. Bris 64 B4
Albert Park Pl. Bris 49 F1
Albert Park. Bris 49 F1
Albert Pl. Bris 49 D4
Albert Pl. Bris 63 E2
Albert Quadrant. W-S-M . 104 C4
Albert Rd. Bris 64 A2
Albert Rd. Cleve 57 E2
Albert Rd. Keyn 81 F3
Albert Rd. Kingsw 65 E4
Albert Rd. Mang 51 F2
Albert Rd. Piln 22 A3
Albert Rd. Portis 45 E3
Albert Rd. W-S-M 104 C3
Albert St. Bris 64 B4
Albert Terr. Bath 101 E3
Albert Terr. Bris 50 C4
Alberton Rd. Bris 50 C3
Albion Cl. Mang 51 F3
Albion Pl. Bris 50 A1
Albion St. Bris 64 B4
Alburys. Wring 92 B2
Alcove Rd. Bris 50 C2
Alder Dr. Bris 50 C1
Alder Terr. Rad 132 C1
Aldercombe Rd. Bris .. 48 B4
Alderdown Cl. Bris ... 48 A4
Alderley Rd. Bath 101 D2

Alderley Rd. Hill 19 E4
Aldermoor Way. Kingsw .. 65 F2
Aldernay Ave. Bris 64 C2
Alders The. Bris 37 D1
Alderton Rd. Grit 43 E3
Alderton Rd. Bris 49 F4
Aldwick Ave. Bris 79 E2
Aldwick La. Blag 110 B4
Aldwick La. But 110 B4
Aldwick La. Wring 110 B4
Alex Ricketts Cl. Bath .. 100 C3
Alexander Way. Yatt 91 D4
Alexandra Cl. Kingsw ... 51 E2
Alexandra Gdns. Kingsw . 51 E2
Alexandra Par. W-S-M .. 104 C4
Alexandra Park. Bris ... 49 E1
Alexandra Park. Bris ... 50 C2
Alexandra Park. Paul ... 131 F3
Alexandra Pl. Kingsw ... 51 E2
Alexandra Rd. Bath 102 A3
Alexandra Rd. Bris 49 E4
Alexandra Rd. Bris 63 D4
Alexandra Rd. Bris 78 C4
Alexandra Rd. Cleve ... 57 E2
Alexandra Rd. Fr Cot ... 38 B4
Alexandra Rd. Kingsw .. 65 E3
Alexandra Terr. Paul ... 131 F3
Alexandra Way. Thorn .. 8 A2
Alford Rd. Bris 64 B1
Alfred Hill. Bris 63 E4
Alfred Lovell Gdns. Kingsw 66 A2
Alfred Par. Bris 63 E4
Alfred Pl. Bris 63 E4
Alfred Rd. Bris 49 D2
Alfred Rd. Bris 63 E2
Alfred St. Bath 101 F4
Alfred St. Bris 64 A3
Alfred St. Bris 64 B4
Alfred St. W-S-M 104 C4
Algars Dr. Ir Act 26 C2
Algiers St. Bris 63 E2
Alison Gdns. Back ... 76 A4
All Hallows Rd. Bris .. 64 A4
All Saints' La. Bris ... 63 E4
All Saints' Rd. Bath .. 101 F4
All Saints' Rd. Bris ... 49 D1
All Saints' Rd. W-S-M . 87 F1
All Saints' St. Bris ... 63 E4
Allanmead Rd. Bris ... 80 A4
Allengrove La. Luck ... 31 E2
Allens La. Wins 125 F4
Aller Par. W-S-M 105 D1
Aller. W-S-M 105 D1
Allfoxton Rd. Bris ... 50 A2
Allington Dr. Kingsw .. 65 F2
Allington Gdns. Nail .. 75 E4
Allington Rd. Bris ... 63 E3
Allison Ave. Bris 64 C2
Allison Rd. Bris 64 C2
Alma Cl. Kingsw 65 F4
Alma Pl. Well 118 B1
Alma Rd. Bris 63 D4
Alma Rd. Kingsw ... 51 F1
Alma Road Ave. Bris . 63 D4
Alma St. Bris 49 D1
Alma St. W-S-M ... 104 C4
Alma Vale Rd. Bris .. 63 D4
Almeda Rd. Bris ... 65 D3
Almond Cl. W-S-M .. 89 D1
Almond Way. Mang .. 51 F3
Almondsbury Bsns Centre.
   St Gif 24 B2
Almorah Rd. Bris .. 63 F2
Alpha Centre The. Yate . 27 E2
Alpha Rd. Bris 63 E2
Alpine Cl. Paul ... 131 F2
Alpine Gdns. Bath .. 102 A4
Alpine Rd. Bris ... 50 B1
Alpine Rd. Paul ... 131 F2
Alsop Rd. Kingsw .. 51 E1
Alton Rd. Bris 49 F3
Altringham Rd. Bris . 64 B4
Alverstoke. Bris ... 79 F4
Alveston Hill. Thorn .. 15 D3
Alveston Rd. Olve ... 14 B2
Alveston Wlk. Bris .. 48 A4
Alwins Ct. Kingsw .. 65 F2
Amberey Rd. W-S-M . 104 C3
Amberlands Cl. Back . 76 A4
Amberley Cl. Keyn .. 81 F2
Amberley Cl. Mang .. 51 E4
Amberley Gdns. Nail . 59 E1
Amberley Rd. Mang . 51 E4
Amberley Rd. St Gif . 36 A4
Amberley Way. Wickw . 18 A2
Amble Cl. Kingsw ... 65 F4
Ambleside Ave. Bris . 35 D1
Ambleside Rd. Bath .. 101 E1
Ambra Vale E. Bris .. 63 D3
Ambra Vale S. Bris .. 63 D3
Ambra Vale W. Bris .. 63 D3
Ambra Vale. Bris ... 63 D3
Ambrose Rd. Bris .. 63 D3
Ambury. Bath 101 F3

Amercombe Wlk. Bris ... 80 B4
Amery La. Bath 102 A3
Ames La. Kilm 139 D3
Amesbury Dr. Blea 122 A3
Ammerdown Terr. Faulk . 139 F4
Anchor La. Bris 63 E3
Anchor Rd. Bath 84 A1
Anchor Rd. Bris 63 E3
Anchor Rd. Kingsw .. 52 A1
Anchor Way. E in G . 47 E2
Andereach Cl. Bris .. 80 A4
Andover Rd. Bris ... 63 F1
Andruss Dr. Dun ... 78 B1
Angers Rd. Bris 64 A2
Anglesea Pl. Bris ... 49 D1
Annandale Ave. W-S-M . 88 C1
Anson Cl. Keyn 82 B1
Anstey St. Bris 50 B1
Anstey's Rd. Kingsw . 65 E3
Anthea Rd. Bris ... 50 C1
Antona Ct. Bris ... 47 E4
Antona Dr. Bris ... 47 E4
Antrim Rd. Bris ... 49 D3
Anvil Rd. Yatt 74 C1
Anvil St. Bris 63 F3
Apex Ct. St Gif ... 24 B2
Apperley Cl. Yate .. 39 E4
Apple Tree Dr. Wins . 125 D4
Appleby Wlk. Bris .. 79 E4
Applecroft. Well ... 133 F3
Appledore Cl. Bris . 80 A4
Applegate. Bris ... 35 D2
Appletree Ct. W-S-M . 89 D1
Apseleys Mead. St Gif . 24 B1
Apsley Cl. W-S-M ... 88 B1
Apsley Rd. Bris ... 49 D1
Apsley St. Bris ... 50 B2
Arbutus Dr. Bris .. 48 B4
Arcade The. Bris .. 63 F4
Arch Cl. Lo Ash ... 61 F1
Archer Cl. Kingsw .. 65 F2
Archer Wlk. Bris .. 80 C3
Archfield Rd. Bris . 49 E1
Archgrove. Lo Ash . 61 F1
Archway St. Bath .. 102 A3
Arden Cl. St Gif .. 36 C3
Arden Cl. W-S-M .. 88 C2
Ardenton Wlk. Bris . 35 D2
Ardern Cl. Bris ... 48 A4
Argus Rd. Bris ... 63 E2
Argyle Ave. Bris .. 50 B1
Argyle Ave. W-S-M . 104 C2
Argyle Dr. Yate ... 27 F2
Argyle Pl. Bris ... 63 D3
Argyle Rd. Bris ... 51 D1
Argyle Rd. Bris ... 63 F4
Argyle Rd. Cleve .. 57 E3
Argyle St. Bath ... 102 A3
Argyle St. Bris ... 50 B1
Argyle St. Bris ... 63 E2
Argyle Terr. Bath .. 101 E3
Arley Cotts. Bris .. 49 E1
Arley Hill. Bris ... 49 E1
Arley Park. Bris .. 49 E1
Arley Terr. Bris ... 50 C1
Arlingham Way. Bris . 23 F1
Arlington Rd. Bath . 101 E3
Arlington Rd. Bris . 64 B3
Arlington Villas. Bris . 63 D4
Armada Pl. Bris ... 49 F1
Armes Ct. Bath ... 102 A3
Armidale Ave. Bris . 49 F1
Armoury Sq. Bris .. 64 A4
Armstrong Ct. Yate . 27 E2
Armstrong Way. Yate . 27 D2
Arnall Dr. Bris ... 34 C1
Arneside Rd. Bris .. 35 E1
Arno's St. Bris ... 64 A2
Arnold Ct. Ch Sod . 28 A1
Arnor Cl. W-S-M .. 89 D2
Arrowfield Cl. Bris . 80 A1
Arthur Skemp Cl. Bris . 64 A4
Arthur St. Bris ... 64 A3
Arthur St. Bris ... 64 B4
Arthurswood Rd. Bris . 79 D2
Arundel Cl. Bris .. 79 D3
Arundel Rd. Bath . 85 D1
Arundel Rd. Bris .. 49 E2
Arundel Rd. Cleve . 57 E2
Arundel Wlk. Keyn . 81 E3
Arundell Ct. W-S-M . 104 C4
Arundell Rd. W-S-M . 87 F1
Ascot Cl. Bris ... 35 F1
Ascot Cl. Mang .. 37 F1
Ash Cl. St Gif ... 36 B4
Ash Cl. Wins 108 A1
Ash Cl. Yate 27 E2
Ash Gr. Bath ... 101 E2
Ash Gr. Bris 51 E2
Ash Gr. Cleve ... 57 F2
Ash Gr. W-S-M .. 104 C1
Ash Hayes Dr. Nail . 59 F1
Ash Hayes Rd. Nail . 59 F1
Ash La. Alm 23 E1
Ash Rd. Bris 49 F3
Ash Ridge Rd. St Gif . 24 A2
Ash Tree Cl. Blea .. 122 B3
Ash Tree Ct. Rad .. 132 C1

Ash Wlk. Bris 35 D2
Ashbourne Cl. Kingsw .. 66 B3
Ashburton Rd. Bris 35 E1
Ashbury Dr. W-S-M 88 A1
Ashcombe Cres. Kingsw . 66 B3
Ashcombe Gdns. W-S-M . 105 D4
Ashcombe Park Rd. W-S-M 88 A1
Ashcombe Rd. W-S-M .. 104 C4
Ashcott. Bris 79 F4
Ashcroft Ave. Keyn ... 81 E3
Ashcroft Rd. Bris 48 B4
Ashcroft. W-S-M 105 D1
Ashdene Ave. Bris ... 50 B2
Ashdene Rd. W-S-M .. 105 D4
Ashdown Rd. Portis .. 45 D3
Ashel's Batch. Litt .. 129 E1
Asher La. Bris 63 F4
Ashes La. Hi Cha ... 120 A2
Ashfield Pl. Bris ... 49 F1
Ashfield Rd. Bris ... 63 D2
Ashford Dr. W-S-M .. 105 D1
Ashford Rd. Bath ... 101 E2
Ashford Rd. Bris ... 36 A4
Ashford Rd. Wring .. 93 F2
Ashford Way. Kingsw . 66 A4
Ashgrove Ave. Ab Lei . 62 A4
Ashgrove Ave. Bris .. 49 F2
Ashgrove Rd. Bris ... 49 D1
Ashgrove Rd. Bris ... 49 F2
Ashgrove Rd. Bris ... 63 D2
Ashgrove. P St J ... 133 E4
Ashgrove. Thorn ... 8 B1
Ashland Rd. Bris ... 79 D2
Ashleigh Cl. Paul ... 131 F3
Ashleigh Cl. W-S-M .. 105 D4
Ashleigh Cres. Yatt .. 91 D4
Ashleigh Rd. W-S-M .. 105 D4
Ashleigh Rd. Yatt ... 91 D4
Ashley Ave. Bath ... 101 E4
Ashley Cl. Bris 49 F2
Ashley Court Rd. Bris . 49 F1
Ashley Down Rd. Bris . 49 F1
Ashley Grove Rd. Bris . 49 F1
Ashley Grove Rd. Bris . 50 A1
Ashley Hill. Bris ... 49 F1
Ashley La. Blag 110 A3
Ashley La. Winsl ... 120 C4
Ashley La. Wring ... 110 A3
Ashley Par. Bris ... 49 F1
Ashley Park. Bris ... 49 F2
Ashley Rd. Bathf ... 86 B1
Ashley Rd. Bris 49 F1
Ashley Rd. Cleve ... 57 D1
Ashley St. Bris 50 A1
Ashley Trading Est. Bris . 49 F1
Ashley. Kingsw 65 F4
Ashman Cl. Bris ... 64 A4
Ashmans Gate. Paul . 131 F3
Ashmead Rd Ind Est. Keyn . 82 A3
Ashmead Rd. Keyn .. 82 A3
Ashmead Way. Bris . 62 C3
Ashmead. Clut 114 C1
Ashton Ave. Bris .. 63 D3
Ashton Cl. Cleve ... 57 D1
Ashton Cres. Nail .. 59 E1
Ashton Dr. Bris ... 62 C1
Ashton Gate Rd. Bris . 63 D2
Ashton Gate Terr. Bris . 63 D2
Ashton Rd. Bris ... 62 C2
Ashton Rd. Lo Ash .. 62 C2
Ashton Vale Rd. Bris . 62 C2
Ashton Way. Keyn .. 81 F3
Ashton. Bris 37 E1
Ashvale Cl. Nail ... 60 A1
Ashville Rd. Bris .. 63 D2
Ashwell Cl. Bris ... 80 C3
Ashwicke Rd. Marsh . 70 A2
Ashwicke. Bris 80 A3
Ashwood. E Harp .. 128 C2
Aspen Cl. Col 70 C3
Aspley Cl. Bris ... 101 D4
Aspley Rd. Bath ... 101 D4
Assembly Rooms La. Bris . 63 E3
Aston Gate Underpass. Bris 62 C2
Astry Cl. Bris 34 A1
Atchley St. Bris ... 64 A4
Atherston. Kingsw .. 66 B3
Athlone Wlk. Bris .. 63 F1
Atholl Cl. W-S-M .. 88 C2
Atkins Cl. Bris ... 80 C3
Atlantic Ct. W-S-M . 87 E1
Atlantic Rd S. W-S-M . 87 E1
Atlantic Rd. Avon .. 47 E4
Atlantic Rd. W-S-M . 87 E1
Atlas Cl. Bris 51 D1
Atlas Rd. Bris 63 F2
Atlas St. Bris 64 A3
Atwell Dr. St Gif .. 24 A1
Atwood Dr. Bris ... 34 A1
Aubrey Meads. Bitt . 82 C4
Aubrey Rd. Bris ... 63 D2
Auburn Ave. Kingsw . 66 A2
Auburn Rd. Bris ... 49 D1
Auckland Cl. W-S-M . 104 C2
Audley Ave. Bath .. 101 E4
Audley Cl. Bath ... 101 E4
Audley Gr. Bath ... 101 E4
Audley Park Rd. Bath . 101 E4

Audrey Wlk. Bris 49 E1
Aust Rd. Aust 13 F3
Aust Rd. Olve .... 13 F
Aust Rd. Piln .... 12 B
Austen Dr. W-S-M .... 89 D
Austen Gr. Bris ..... 50 A
Avalon Cl. Yatt ..... 74 A
Avalon House. Nail .. 59 E
Avalon Rd. Bris ..... 65 C
Avebury Rd. Bris .... 62 C
Avening Cl. Nail .... 75 F
Avening Green. Char .. 10 B
Avening Rd. Bris .... 65 C
Avenue The. Back ... 76 A
Avenue The. Bath ... 102 B
Avenue The. Bath ... 102 C
Avenue The. Bris .... 48 C
Avenue The. Bris .... 49 D
Avenue The. Bris .... 64 C
Avenue The. Cleve ... 57 F
Avenue The. Keyn ... 81 F
Avenue The. St Gif .. 24 A
Avenue The. St Gif .. 36 B
Avenue The. Tims ... 116 A
Avenue The. Wins ... 125 E
Avenue The. Yate ... 27 E
Avenue The. Yatt ... 91 D
Averay Rd. Bris .... 50 B
Avon Bsns Pk. Bris .. 51 D
Avon Cl. Keyn ..... 81 F
Avon Cl. W-S-M .... 104 C
Avon Cres. Bris .... 63 D
Avon Cres. Wickw .. 18 A
Avon Ct. Bathe .... 86 A
Avon Gorge Ind Est. Avon . 47 E
Avon Gr. Bris ..... 48 B
Avon La. Keyn ..... 82 C
Avon Mill La. Keyn .. 81 F
Avon Park. Bath ... 101 D
Avon Park. Bris ... 64 B
Avon Rd. Char .... 11 D
Avon Rd. E in G ... 47 E
Avon Rd. Keyn .... 81 F
Avon Rise. Luck ... 31 F
Avon Riverside Est. Avon .. 47 E
Avon St. Bath .... 101 F
Avon St. Bris .... 63 F
Avon Trading Est. Bris .. 64 A
Avon Vale. Bris ... 48 B
Avon Valley Bsns Pk. Bris . 64 C
Avon View. Kingsw .. 65 D
Avon Way. Bris ... 48 B
Avon Way. Portis .. 45 C
Avon Way. Thorn .. 15 E
Avon Wlk. Bris ... 79 D
Avonbank Ind Centre. Avon 47 E
Avonbridge Trading Est.
   Avon .... 33 E
Avondale Bldgs. Bath .. 85 D
Avondale Pl. Bathe ... 85 E
Avondale Rd. Bath ... 101 D
Avondale Rd. Bris ... 64 B
Avondown Cl. Bris ... 35 E
Avondown Ct. Bris ... 63 E
Avonlea. Kingsw .... 65 E
Avonleaze. Bris .... 48 A
Avonleigh Ct. Bris .. 63 D
Avonleigh Rd. Bris .. 63 D
Avonmouth Rd. Avon . 47 E
Avonmouth Way. Avon . 33 E
Avonside Rd. Bris ... 64 B
Avonside Way. Bris .. 64 B
Avonsmere Residential Pk.
   Bris .... 36 B
Avonwood Cl. Bris .. 47 F
Awdelett Cl. Bris ... 34 A
Awkley La. Olve .... 13 F
Awkward Hill. But ... 111 E
Axbridge Cl. Nail ... 75 F
Axbridge Moor Dro. Axb . 125 D
Axbridge Rd. Bath .. 102 A
Axbridge Rd. Bris ... 63 F
Axbridge Rd. Ched .. 125 F
Axe Cl. W-S-M .... 105 E
Axford Way. P St J .. 133 E
Axis. Bris ...... 79 E
Aycote Cl. W-S-M .. 88 B
Ayford La. Marsh ... 69 F
Aylesbury Cres. Bris . 63 D
Aylesbury Rd. Bris .. 63 D
Aylmer Cres. Bris .. 80 A
Aylminton Wlk. Bris . 34 A
Ayr St. Bath ..... 101 E
Aztec Centre The. St Gif . 24 A
Aztec West. St Gif .. 24 A

Back La. Axb ..... 125 E
Back La. E in G ... 47 E
Back La. K Sey ... 73 D
Back La. Litt .... 129 D
Back La. Litt .... 129 F
Back La. Marsh ... 69 F
Back La. Wickw ... 18 A
Back Of Kingsdown Par. Bris 63 E
Back Rd. Bris .... 63 D
Back St. H Up .... 20 A

Back St. W-S-M 104 C4
Back Stoke La. Bris 48 C3
Backfields La. Bris 63 F4
Backfields. Bris 63 F4
Backwell Bow. Back 60 B1
Backwell Comm. Back 76 A4
Backwell Hill Rd. Back ... 76 C2
Backwell Wlk. Bris 78 C4
Baden Hill Rd. Tyth 16 B3
Baden Rd. Bris 64 B4
Baden Rd. Kingsw 66 A4
Badenham Gr. Bris 47 F4
Bader Cl. Yate 27 E2
Badger's La. Alm 23 E1
Badgers Cl. St Gif 24 B2
Badgers Rise. Portis 44 C2
Badminton Wlk. Bris 64 B1
Badgeworth. Yate 39 E3
Badminton Centre The. Yate 27 E1
Badminton Ct. Yate 27 E1
Badminton Gdns. Bath ... 101 E4
Badminton Rd. Bris 49 F1
Badminton Rd. Ch Sod ... 40 C4
Badminton Rd. Fr Cot 38 B3
Badminton Rd. Mang 51 F4
Badminton Rd. West 38 B3
Badminton Rd. Yate 27 D1
Badminton Trading Est. Yate 27 D1
Badminton Wlk. Mang ... 51 F4
Badminton. Bris 37 E1
Baggridge Hill. Well 134 C4
Baglyn Ave. Kingsw 51 F2
Bagnell Cl. Bris 80 C3
Bagnell Rd. Bris 80 C3
Bagstone Rd. Wickw 16 C2
Bailbrook Gr. Bath 85 E2
Bailbrook La. Bath 85 E2
Baildon Cres. W-S-M 105 D2
Baildon Ct. W-S-M 104 C2
Baildon Rd. W-S-M 105 D2
Baileys Court Rd. St Gif .. 36 C3
Baileys Ct Rd. St Gif 37 D3
Baileys Ct. St Gif 36 C3
Bailiffs Cl. Axb 125 E1
Bailiffs' Wall. Axb 125 E1
Bainsbury View. 137 F1
Baker Cl. Cleve 73 D4
Baker St. W-S-M 104 C4
Baker's Bldgs. Wring 92 B1
Bakers Par. Tims 116 A1
Bakers La. Chil 137 E2
Bakers La. Wring 109 E4
Bakersfield. Kingsw 66 A2
Balaclava Rd. Bris 50 C2
Baldwin St. Bris 63 E3
Balfour Rd. Bris 63 D2
Ballance St. Bath 101 F4
Ballast La. Avon 33 F1
Balls Barn La. Ban 90 A1
Balmain St. Bris 64 A2
Balmoral Cl. St Gif 36 B2
Balmoral Ct. Mang 52 A3
Balmoral Rd. Bris 49 F1
Balmoral Rd. Keyn 81 F2
Balmoral Rd. Kingsw 65 F1
Balmoral Way. W-S-M ... 88 B1
Baltic Pl. E in G 47 E2
Bamfield. Bris 80 A3
Bampton Cl. Bris 79 D4
Bampton. W-S-M 88 C2
Banfield Cl. Bris 48 A4
Bangor Gr. Bris 64 C3
Bangrove Wlk. Bris 47 F4
Banister Gr. Bris 79 E4
Bank Pl. E in G 47 E2
Bank Rd. Avon 33 E4
Bank Rd. Kingsw 65 E4
Bank Rd. Piln 22 C3
Banks Cl. Cleve 73 E4
Bankside Rd. Bris 64 B2
Bankside. Mang 51 F2
Banner Rd. Bris 49 F1
Bannerdown Cl. Bathe ... 86 A2
Bannerdown Dr. Bathe ... 86 A2
Bannerdown Rd. Bathe .. 86 B3
Bannerleigh La. Lo Ash .. 62 C3
Bannerleigh Rd. Lo Ash . 62 C3
Bannerman Rd. Bris 64 A4
Bannetts Tree Cres. Alve 15 D4
Bantock Cl. Bris 79 E3
Bantry Rd. Bris 79 F4
Banwell Cl. Keyn 82 A1
Banwell Rd. Ban 123 F4
Banwell Rd. Bath 118 B4
Banwell Rd. Bris 63 D2
Banwell Rd. Lock 106 A2
Banwell Rd. Wins 123 F4
Banwell Rd. Wins 124 C4
Baptist St. Bris 50 A1
Barberry Farm Rd. Yatt . 74 A1
Barbour Gdns. Bris 79 E2
Barbour Rd. Bris 79 E2
Barcroft Cl. Bris 65 E4
Barker Wlk. Bris 50 A1
Barley Cl. Fr Cot 38 B4
Barley Cl. Mang 52 A3
Barley Croft. Bris 48 C3

Barn End. Marsh 70 A4
Barn Hill. Well 133 F3
Barn La. Pens 115 D4
Barn Owl Way. St Gif 36 C3
Barn Pool. Ship 125 F4
Barnabas St. Bris 49 F1
Barnaby Cl. Mid No 132 A1
Barnack Trading Est. Bris ... 63 E1
Barnard Wlk. Keyn 81 E2
Barnard's Cl. Yatt 91 E4
Barnes St. Bris 64 B4
Barnfield Way. Bathe 86 A2
Barnhill Rd. Ch Sod 28 A1
Barns Cl. Ba Gu 77 F2
Barns Cl. Nail 59 F1
Barnstable House. Bris .. 63 F4
Barnstaple Rd. Bris 79 F4
Barnstaple Wlk. Bris 79 F4
Barnwood Rd. Yate 39 E4
Barossa Pl. Bris 63 E3
Barrack's La. Bris 47 E4
Barratt St. Bris 50 B1
Barrington Cl. Kingsw ... 51 F1
Barrington Ct. Bris 63 F2
Barrington Ct. Kingsw ... 51 F1
Barrow Court La. Ba Gu . 77 D3
Barrow Court La. Back ... 77 D3
Barrow Hill Cres. Bris ... 47 E4
Barrow Hill Rd. Bris 47 E3
Barrow Hill. Wick 67 D3
Barrow La. Ba Gu 77 F1
Barrow La. Win 94 C4
Barrow Rd. Bath 101 E1
Barrow Rd. Bris 64 A4
Barrow Rd. Lock 105 F1
Barrow St. Ba Gu 77 E3
Barrow St. Lo Ash 77 E3
Barrowmead Dr. Bris 47 F4
Barrows The. Bris 79 D2
Barrows The. W-S-M 105 E4
Barrs Court Ave. Kingsw 66 A3
Barrs Court Rd. Kingsw . 66 A3
Barrs Court Rd. Kingsw . 66 A3
Barrs La. N Nib 5 F2
Barry Cl. Kingsw 66 B1
Barry Cl. W-S-M 105 D1
Bartlett St. Bath 101 F4
Bartlett's Rd. Bris 63 E1
Bartley St. Bris 63 E2
Barton Cl. Alve 15 D3
Barton Cl. Bris 64 C3
Barton Cl. Wint 37 F3
Barton Dro. Wins 124 B3
Barton Green. Bris 64 A4
Barton Hill Rd. Bris 64 A4
Barton Manor. Bris 64 A3
Barton Rd. .... 124 ""
Barton Rd. Bris 63 F3
Barton Rd. Co Bi 123 F3
Barton St. Bath 101 F3
Barton St. Bris 63 E4
Barton The. Blea 122 B3
Barton The. Cor 100 A4
Barton The. Kingsw 65 E2
Barton The. N St P 135 F2
Barton Vale. Bris 63 F3
Bartonia Gr. Bris 64 B1
Barwood Cl. Kingsw 65 F4
Batch La. Lymp 121 F2
Batch The. Blag 110 A2
Batch The. But 111 D4
Batch The. Ch Mag 96 A2
Batch The. Chur 108 C2
Batch The. Co Mar 128 A4
Batch The. Farm 116 A3
Batch The. Hin Cha 119 F1
Batch The. Wring 93 E4
Batch The. Yatt 91 D4
Batches The. Bris 63 D1
Batchfield La. West 53 E4
Bates Cl. Bris 64 A4
Bath Bldgs. Bris 49 F1
Bath Hill. Keyn 81 F3
Bath Hill. Well 118 B1
Bath New Rd. Mid No ... 132 C2
Bath Old Rd. Mid No 132 C2
Bath Rd. Bitt 82 B4
Bath Rd. Bitt 82 C4
Bath Rd. Blag 109 E2
Bath Rd. Blag 110 C1
Bath Rd. Box 86 C3
Bath Rd. Bris 64 B2
Bath Rd. Ch Sod 41 E2
Bath Rd. Chur 109 E2
Bath Rd. Col 70 C1
Bath Rd. Doyn 67 F2
Bath Rd. Farm 115 F3
Bath Rd. Keyn 82 B2
Bath Rd. Kingsw 65 F2
Bath Rd. Kingsw 66 B3
Bath Rd. N St P 135 F3
Bath Rd. P St J 133 E4
Bath Rd. Paul 131 F3
Bath Rd. Sist 66 B3
Bath Rd. Thorn 15 D4
Bath Rd. Tor 41 E2
Bath Rd. Wick 67 F2
Bath Riverside Bsns Park.

Bath 101 F3
Bath St. Bath 101 F3
Bath St. Bris 63 D2
Bath St. Bris 63 F3
Bath St. Kingsw 51 F2
Bath View. Chil 137 F1
Bathampton La. Bath ... 85 F1
Bathford Hill. Bathf 86 A1
Bathford Hill. Co Dan ... 98 C3
Bathurst Par. Bris 63 E3
Bathurst Rd. W-S-M 105 E4
Bathwell Rd. Bris 64 A2
Bathwick Hill. Bath 102 B3
Bathwick Rise. Bath 102 A4
Bathwick St. Bath 102 A4
Batley Ct. Kingsw 66 B2
Batstone Cl. Bath 85 D1
Batten Cl. Ch Sod 28 A1
Batten's La. Bris 65 D3
Battenburg Rd. Bris 65 D4
Battens Rd. Bris 65 D4
Battersby Way. Bris 34 C1
Battersea Rd. Bris 64 B4
Battery La. Portis 45 D4
Battery Rd. Portis 45 E3
Battle La. Ch Mag 96 A2
Battson Rd. Bris 80 C2
Baugh Gdns. Mang 37 F1
Baugh Rd. Mang 37 F1
Bay Gdns. Bris 50 B1
Bay Rd. Cleve 57 E3
Bay Tree Cl. Bris 35 F4
Bay Tree Rd. Bath 85 D1
Bay Tree Rd. Cleve 57 F1
Bayleys Dr. Kingsw 65 E3
Baynham Ct. Kingsw 65 D3
Baynton Rd. Bris 63 D2
Bayswater Ave. Bris 49 D2
Bayswater Rd. Bris 49 F4
Baytree Rd. W-S-M 88 B1
Baytree View. W-S-M ... 88 B1
Beach Ave. Cleve 57 E1
Beach Ave. Piln 22 A4
Beach End Rd. W-S-M ... 104 B1
Beach Hill. Bitt 66 C2
Beach Hill. Portis 45 E3
Beach La. Bitt 67 E1
Beach Rd E. Portis 45 E3
Beach Rd W. Portis 45 E3
Beach Rd. Piln 21 F4
Beach Rd. W St L 88 A3
Beach Rd. W-S-M 88 A2
Beach The. Cleve 57 E2
Beachgrove Gdns. Bris . 51 E2
Beachgrove Rd. Bris ... 51 D2
Beachley Wlk. Bris 47 E4
Beacon La. Wint 37 E3
Beacon Rd. Bath 85 D1
Beaconlea. Kingsw 65 E3
Beaconsfield Rd. Bris .. 49 D1
Beaconsfield Rd. Bris .. 64 A2
Beaconsfield Rd. Bris .. 64 C4
Beaconsfield Rd. Cleve . 57 F2
Beaconsfield Rd. W-S-M 104 C4
Beaconsfield St. Bris ... 64 A3
Beale Cl. Bris 80 C3
Beam St. Bris 64 B4
Bean Acre The. Bris 47 E4
Bean St. Bris 50 A1
Beanhill Cres. Alve 15 D3
Bearbridge Rd. Bris 78 C2
Beau St. Bath 101 F3
Beauchamp Rd. Bris ... 49 E2
Beauchamps Dr. Chil .. 138 A3
Beauford Sq. Bath 101 F3
Beaufort Ave. Mid No .. 132 A1
Beaufort Ave. Yate 27 E1
Beaufort Cl. Bris 64 B4
Beaufort Cres. St Gif ... 36 C2
Beaufort East. Bath 85 E1
Beaufort Hts. Bris 64 C4
Beaufort Park St Gif 24 B2
Beaufort Pl. Bath 85 E1
Beaufort Pl. Bris 37 D1
Beaufort Pl. Bris 64 A4
Beaufort Rd. Bris 49 D1
Beaufort Rd. Bris 49 F3
Beaufort Rd. Bris 51 E1
Beaufort Rd. Bris 64 C4
Beaufort Rd. Fr Cot 38 A4
Beaufort Rd. Mang 51 F3
Beaufort Rd. Mang 52 A4
Beaufort Rd. W-S-M 104 C4
Beaufort Rd. Yate 27 E1
Beaufort St. Bris 63 E1
Beaufort St. Bris 64 A4
Beaufort. Bris 37 E1
Beauley Rd. Bris 63 D2
Beaumont Cl. Bris 66 A2
Beaumont Cl. W-S-M ... 104 C2
Beaumont St. Bris 64 A4
Beaumont Terr. Bris ... 64 A4
Beaver Cl. Wint 37 F4
Beazer Cl. Kingsw 51 E2
Becket Ct. Puck 53 D3
Becket Dr. W-S-M 89 D2

Becket Rd. W-S-M 89 D2
Becket's La. Nail 75 F4
Beckford Gdns. Bath ... 102 A4
Beckford Gdns. Bris 80 A2
Beckford Rd. Bath 102 A4
Beckhampton Rd. Bath 101 E3
Beckington Rd. Bris 63 F1
Beckington Wlk. Bris ... 63 F1
Beckington. W-S-M 105 D1
Beckspool Rd. Bris 51 E4
Bedford Cres. Bris 49 F3
Bedford Rd. W-S-M 104 C2
Bedford St. Bath 102 A4
Bedminster Down Rd. Bris .. 63 D1
Bedminster Par. Bris ... 63 E2
Bedminster Pl. Bris 63 E2
Bedminster Rd. Bris ... 63 E1
Bedwin Cl. Portis 44 C2
Beech Ave. Bath 102 C3
Beech Cl. Alve 15 D3
Beech Cl. Kingsw 66 A3
Beech Cl. Ship 125 F4
Beech Dr. Nail 60 A2
Beech Dr. Ship 125 F4
Beech Gr. Bath 101 E2
Beech Leaze. Alve 15 D3
Beech Rd. Bris 49 F3
Beech Rd. Keyn 82 C2
Beech Rd. Ship 125 F4
Beech Rd. Yatt 91 E4
Beech Terr. Rad 132 B1
Beechcroft Wlk. Bris ... 50 A4
Beechcroft. Dun 78 B1
Beechen Cliff Rd. Bath 101 F3
Beechen Dr. Bris 51 D2
Beeches Gr. Bris 64 B1
Beeches Ind Est. Ir Act 27 D1
Beeches The. Bath 101 E1
Beeches The. Kingsw .. 66 B1
Beeches The. Wins 108 A2
Beechfield Cl. Lo Ash .. 62 B1
Beechmont Cl. W-S-M .. 105 D1
Beechmont Dr. W-S-M .. 105 D1
Beechmount Gr. Bris ... 80 A4
Beechwood Ave. Kingsw 65 E3
Beechwood Ave. Lock .. 106 A2
Beechwood Cl. Bris 80 B4
Beechwood Dr. Portis .. 44 C3
Beechwood Rd. Bath ... 102 A1
Beechwood Rd. Bris 51 D2
Beechwood Rd. E in G 47 D2
Beechwood Rd. Nail 59 E1
Beechwood Rd. Portis .. 44 C3
Beehive Yd. Bath 102 A4
Beek's La. Marsh 69 E3
Begbrook Dr. Bris 50 C3
Begbrook La. Bris 50 C3
Begbrook Park. Bris ... 51 D4
Beggar Bush La. Lo Ash 61 F2
Beggar Bush La. Wrax 61 F2
Beggars Bush La. Ab Lei 62 A3
Beggarswell Cl. Bris ... 63 F4
Belfast Wlk. Bris 79 F4
Belfry Ave. Bris 65 D4
Belfry. Kingsw 66 A3
Belgrave Cres. Bath ... 85 D1
Belgrave Hill. Bris 49 D1
Belgrave Pl. Bris 63 D4
Belgrave Rd. Bath 85 D1
Belgrave Rd. Bris 63 D4
Belgrave Rd. W-S-M ... 105 D4
Bell Barn Rd. Bris 48 B3
Bell Cl. Farm 115 F3
Bell Hill Rd. Bris 65 D4
Bell Hill. Bris 50 B2
Bell Hill. N St P 135 F2
Bell La. Bris 63 E4
Bell Rd. Fr Cot 38 B3
Bell Sq. Blag 110 C2
Bell Sq. Marsh 70 A4
Bell Wlk. Wring 92 C1
Bella Vista Rd. Bath ... 101 F4
Bellamy Ave. Bris 79 E2
Bellamy Cl. Bris 65 D3
Belland Dr. Bris 79 F2
Belle Vue Rd. Bris 50 B1
Bellevue Cl. Kingsw ... 65 F4
Bellevue Cotts. Bris ... 63 D3
Bellevue Cres. Bris 63 D3
Bellevue Pk. Bris 64 B1
Bellevue Rd. Bris 63 F2
Bellevue Rd. Cleve 57 E2
Bellevue Rd. Kingsw .. 65 F4
Bellevue Terr. Bris 63 D4
Bellevue Terr. Bris 63 F2
Bellevue Terr. Bris 64 B1
Bellevue. Bris 63 D3
Bellhorse La. E Harp ... 128 B3
Bellhouse Wlk. Bris ... 34 A1
Bellifants. Farm 116 A3
Bellotts Rd. Bath 101 E3
Belluton La. Pens 97 E3
Belluton Rd. Bris 64 A2
Belmont Dr. St Gif 36 C3
Belmont Dr. Wrax 61 D2
Belmont Hill. Wrax 61 D1

Belmont Rd. Bath 102 B1
Belmont Rd. Bris 49 F2
Belmont Rd. Bris 64 B2
Belmont Rd. Wins 125 D4
Belmont St. Bris 50 A1
Belmore Gdns. Bath ... 101 D2
Beloe Rd. Bris 49 F3
Belroyal Ave. Bris 64 C2
Belstone Wlk. Bris 79 E4
Belton Ct. Bath 84 A1
Belton Rd. Bris 64 A4
Belton Rd. Portis 45 D3
Belvedere Cres. W-S-M 88 B1
Belvedere Rd. Bris 49 D2
Belvoir Rd. Bath 101 E3
Belvoir Rd. Bris 49 F1
Benches La. But 94 B2
Benford Cl. Bris 51 E3
Bennell Batch. Chil 137 F2
Bennell Cotts. Chil 137 F2
Bennett La. Bath 85 D1
Bennett Rd. Bris 64 C4
Bennett St. Bath 101 F4
Bennett Way. Bris 62 C3
Bennett's Ct. Yate 28 A1
Bennett's Rd. Bath 85 E2
Bennetts Way. Cleve . 57 F3
Bensaunt Gr. Bris 35 E2
Bentley Cl. Bris 79 F2
Bentley Rd. W-S-M 89 D2
Benville Ave. Bris 48 B4
Berenda Dr. Kingsw ... 66 A2
Beresford Cl. Keyn 82 C1
Beresford Gdns. Bath . 84 A2
Berkeley Ave. Bris 49 E2
Berkeley Ave. Bris 63 E4
Berkeley Ave. Mid No . 132 A1
Berkeley Cl. Char 11 D3
Berkeley Cl. Mang 52 A4
Berkeley Cres. W-S-M 104 C3
Berkeley Gdns. Keyn .. 81 F2
Berkeley Gr. Bris 50 B1
Berkeley Green Rd. Bris 50 B1
Berkeley Green. Bris .. 37 D1
Berkeley Mead. St Gif 37 D3
Berkeley Pl. Bris 63 D4
Berkeley Rd. Bris 49 D4
Berkeley Rd. Bris 49 E2
Berkeley Rd. Bris 51 D1
Berkeley Rd. Kingsw .. 65 E4
Berkeley Rd. Mang 51 E3
Berkeley Sq. Bris 63 E4
Berkeley St. Bris 50 B2
Berkshire Rd. Bris 49 E2
Berlington Ct. Bris 63 E3
Berners Cl. Bris 79 E4
Berrow Wlk. Bris 63 F1
Berrows Mead. Wickw . 27 D4
Berry La. Bris 49 F3
Berwick La. Alm 34 B4
Berwick Rd. Bris 50 A1
Beryl Gr. Bris 80 B4
Beryl Rd. Bris 63 D2
Besom La. West 39 E3
Bethel Rd. Bris 64 C4
Betjeman Ct. Kingsw .. 66 A3
Bevan Ct. Bris 35 F1
Beverley Ave. Mang ... 37 F1
Beverley Cl. Bris 65 D3
Beverley Gdns. Bris ... 48 B4
Beverley Rd. Bris 49 F4
Beverston Gdns. Bris . 34 A1
Beverstone. Kingsw ... 65 E4
Bevington Cl. Bris 23 F1
Bevington La. Stone ... 2 C4
Bevington Wlk. Bris ... 23 F1
Bewley Rd. Bath 102 A2
Bexley Rd. Bris 51 D2
Bibstone. Kingsw 66 A4
Bibury Ave. St Gif 36 A4
Bibury Cl. Bris 49 E4
Bibury Cl. Nail 60 A1
Bibury Cres. Bris 49 E4
Bibury Cres. Kingsw .. 65 E3
Bickerton Cl. Bris 34 C2
Bickfield La. Co Mar .. 128 A4
Bickford Cl. Kingsw ... 66 A3
Bickley Cl. Kingsw 65 E1
Biddeston Rd. Bris 49 F4
Biddisham Cl. Nail 59 F1
Biddle St. Yatt 91 D4
Bideford Cres. Bris ... 79 F4
Bideford Rd. W-S-M ... 88 C1
Bidwell Cl. Bris 35 D2
Bifield Cl. Bris 80 C3
Bifield Gdns. Bris 80 C3
Bifield Rd. Bris 80 C3
Big Tree Cl. Co Bi 124 B2
Bignell Cl. Wins 124 C4
Bigwood La. Bris 63 E3
Bilberry Cl. Bris 48 B4
Bilbie Cl. Bris 49 F4
Bilbie Cl. Ch St 112 C4
Bilbie Rd. Ch St 112 C4
Bilbury La. Bath 101 F3

144

Billand Cl. Bris — Brockley Rd. Keyn

Billand Cl. Bris 78 C2
Bilsham La. Piln 12 C1
Bince's Lodge La. Mid No 132 A2
Binces La. Marks 99 F2
Bindon Dr. Bris 35 E2
Binhay Rd. Yatt 91 E4
Binley Gr. Bris 80 B2
Binmead Gdns. Bris 79 D2
Birbeck Rd. Bris 48 C3
Birch Ave. Blea 122 B3
Birch Ave. Cleve 57 F2
Birch Cl. Bris 35 F4
Birch Cl. Lock 106 A2
Birch Croft. Bris 80 A2
Birch Ct. Keyn 81 E2
Birch Dr. Alve 14 C2
Birch Dr. Chur 109 D3
Birch Dr. Puck 53 D3
Birch Gr. Portis 45 E2
Birch Rd. Bris 63 D2
Birch Rd. Kingsw 51 F2
Birch Rd. Rad 132 C1
Birch Rd. Yate 27 E1
Birchall Rd. Bris 49 E2
Birchdale Rd. Bris 80 A4
Birchdene. Nail 60 A1
Birches The. Nail 60 A1
Birchwood Ave. W-S-M 105 D4
Birchwood Dr. Wrax 61 D2
Birchwood La. Pens 97 F1
Birchwood Rd. Bris 64 C2
Birdale Cl. Bris 34 C2
Birdcombe Cl. Nail 59 F2
Birdlip Cl. Nail 76 A4
Birdwell La. Lo Ash 61 F1
Birdwell Rd. Lo Ash 61 F1
Birdwood. Kingsw 65 E3
Birgage Rd. H Up 19 F1
Birkdale. Kingsw 66 A3
Birkdale. Yate 39 F4
Birkett Rd. W-S-M 87 D1
Birkin St. Bris 64 A3
Birnbeck Rd. W-S-M 87 E1
Bisdee Rd. Lock 105 E1
Bishop Ave. W-S-M 89 D2
Bishop Manor Rd. Bris 49 E4
Bishop Rd. Bris 49 E2
Bishop St. Bris 63 F4
Bishop St. Faulk 134 B1
Bishop's Wood. Alm 24 B3
Bishops Cl. Bris 48 C2
Bishops Cove. Bris 78 C3
Bishops Mead. Brock 92 A4
Bishops Rd. Brock 92 A4
Bishopsworth Rd. Bris 79 D4
Bishopthorpe Rd. Bris 49 F4
Bishport Ave. Bris 79 E2
Bishport Cl. Bris 79 D2
Bisley. Yate 39 E4
Bittern Cl. W-S-M 88 C1
Bitterwell Cl. West 38 B2
Bittlemead. Bris 79 F2
Black Boy Hill. Bris 49 D1
Blackacre. Whit 80 B2
Blackberry Ave. Bris 50 C3
Blackberry Dr. W-S-M 89 D1
Blackberry Hill. Bris 50 C3
Blackberry La. Winsl 120 B4
Blackbird Cl. Rod 138 A4
Blackdown Ct. Bris 80 A3
Blackdown Rd. Portis 45 D3
Blackfriars Rd. Nail 59 D1
Blackfriars. Bris 63 E4
Blackhorse Hill. Alm 35 D4
Blackhorse La. Mang 52 A4
Blackhorse Pl. Mang 52 A3
Blackhorse Rd. Kingsw 65 E4
Blackhorse Rd. Mang 52 A4
Blackmoor Cl. Chur 109 E3
Blackmoor Rd. Ab Lei 47 F1
Blackmoor. Chur 109 E3
Blackmoor. Cleve 57 E1
Blackmoor. W-S-M 88 C1
Blackmoors La. Bris 62 C2
Blackmore Dr. Bath 101 E3
Blackrock La. Pens 97 F4
Blacksmith La. Bathe 85 D3
Blacksmith's La. Kel 83 D2
Blackswarth Rd. Bris 64 B4
Blackthorn Cl. Bris 79 E3
Blackthorn Dr. St Gif 36 B4
Blackthorn Gdns. W-S-M 89 D1
Blackthorn Rd. Bris 79 E3
Blackthorn Sq. Cleve 57 E1
Blackthorn Terr. W-S-M 89 D1
Blackthorn Way. Nail 60 A1
Blackthorn Wlk. Kingsw 51 F1
Bladdock Bldgs. Faulk 134 A1
Bladen Cl. Portis 45 F2
Blagdon Cl. Bris 63 F1
Blagdon Cl. W-S-M 104 C1
Blagdon La. Blag 110 C3
Blagdon La. But 110 C3
Blagdon Park. Bath 101 D2
Blagrove Cl. Bris 79 E2
Blagrove Cres. Bris 79 E2
Blaisdon Cl. Bris 34 C1
Blaisdon. Yate 39 F4
Blaise Hamlet. Bris 34 B1
Blaise Wlk. Bris 48 B4
Blake End. W-S-M 88 C2
Blake Rd. Bris 50 A3
Blakeney Gr. Nail 75 E4
Blakeney Mills. Yate 27 E1
Blakeney Rd. Bris 23 F1
Blakeney Rd. Bris 50 A4
Blakes Rd. Thorn 8 A1
Blanchards. Ch Sod 40 B4
Blandford Cl. Bris 49 D3
Blandford Cl. Nail 59 F1
Bleadon Hill. W-S-M 122 A4
Bleadon Rd. Blea 122 A3
Blenheim Cl. P St J 133 E4
Blenheim Cl. W-S-M 89 D1
Blenheim Dr. Bris 36 A2
Blenheim Dr. Yate 27 E2
Blenheim Gdns. Bath 85 D1
Blenheim St. Bris 50 A1
Blenheim Way. Portis 45 F3
Blenhiem Rd. Bris 49 D2
Blenman Cl. Bris 51 D4
Blind La. Bath 84 B1
Blind La. Ch St 112 C4
Blind La. Cong 91 F3
Blind La. Pris 117 D2
Bloomfield Ave. Bath 101 F2
Bloomfield Ave. Tims 116 A2
Bloomfield Cl. Tims 116 A2
Bloomfield Cres. Bath 101 E1
Bloomfield Dr. Bath 101 E1
Bloomfield Gr. Bath 101 F2
Bloomfield La. Paul 131 F3
Bloomfield Park Rd. Tims 116 A2
Bloomfield Park. Bath 101 F2
Bloomfield Rd. Bath 101 F2
Bloomfield Rd. Bris 64 B2
Bloomfield Rd. Tims 116 A2
Bloomfield Rise N. Bath 101 E1
Bloomfield Rise. Bath 101 E1
Bloomfield Terr. P St J 133 E4
Bloomfield. W-S-M 105 D1
Bloy St. Bris 50 B1
Bluebell Cl. Thorn 8 B1
Bluebells The. St Gif 36 C4
Blueberry Way. W-S-M 88 C1
Blythe Gdns. W-S-M 89 D2
Boat La. Lymp 122 B2
Boat Stall La. Bath 102 A3
Bobbin La. Westw 120 C2
Bobbin Parr. Westw 120 C2
Bockenem Cl. Thorn 15 E4
Bodey Cl. Kingsw 66 A3
Bodmin Wlk. Bris 79 F4
Bodyce Rd. Alve 15 D3
Boiling Wells La. Bris 50 A2
Bolton Rd. Bris 49 F2
Bond St. Bris 63 F4
Bond's La. Marsh 55 F1
Bonhill Rd. Bi Sut 113 E3
Bonnington Wlk. Bris 50 A4
Boot La. Bris 63 E2
Booth Rd. Bris 63 E2
Bordesley Rd. Bris 80 A2
Borgie Pl. W-S-M 88 C2
Borleyton Wlk. Bris 78 C2
Borver Gr. Bris 79 D2
Boscombe Cres. Mang 51 F4
Boston Rd. Bris 49 F4
Boswell Rd. Westw 120 C2
Boswell St. Bris 50 B1
Botham Cl. W-S-M 89 D2
Botham Dr. Bris 64 B1
Boucher Pl. Bris 50 A1
Boulevard. W-S-M 104 C4
Boulters Rd. Bris 79 E2
Boulton's La. Bris 65 E4
Boulton's Rd. Kingsw 65 E4
Boundaries The. Lymp 122 A1
Boundary Cl. Rod 138 A4
Boundary Cl. W-S-M 104 C2
Boundary Rd. Avon 33 E2
Boundary Rd. Fr Cot 38 B4
Bourchier Gdns. Bris 79 D2
Bourne Cl. Bris 65 D4
Bourne Cl. Wint 37 F4
Bourne La. Blag 110 A2
Bourne La. Bris 50 A1
Bourne Rd. Bris 65 D4
Bourneville Bsns Centre.
Bris 64 C1
Bourneville Rd. Bris 64 B4
Bournville Rd. Bris 64 C1
Bournville Rd. W-S-M 104 C2
Boursland Cl. St Gif 24 B1
Bourton Ave. St Gif 36 B4
Bourton Cl. St Gif 36 B4
Bourton Combe. Back 76 C4
Bourton La. Co Bi 124 C2
Bourton La. Lock 89 E2
Bourton Mead. Back 76 C4
Bourton Mead. Lo Ash 62 A1
Bourton Wlk. Bris 79 D4
Bouverie St. Bris 64 A4
Boverton Rd. Bris 36 A2
Bowden Cl. Bris 48 B4
Bowden Hill. Chil 137 E2
Bowden Pl. Mang 51 F4
Bowden Rd. Bris 64 C4
Bowden Way. Wrax 61 D2
Bower Rd. Bris 63 D2
Bower Wlk. Bris 63 F2
Bowerleaze. Bris 48 B3
Bowlditch La. Mid No 132 A2
Bowling Hill Bsns Pk.
Ch Sod 28 A1
Bowling Hill. Ch Sod 28 A1
Bowling Rd. Ch Sod 40 A4
Bowood. Bris 37 E1
Bowring Cl. Bris 79 E2
Bowsland Way. St Gif 24 B1
Bowstreet La. Alm 35 D4
Box Bush La. Ban 90 B1
Box Rd. Bathe 86 B2
Box Rd. Bathf 86 B2
Box Wlk. Keyn 81 E2
Boxbury Hill. Paul 131 F2
Boxhedge Farm La. West 38 C2
Boyce Dr. Bris 50 A1
Boyce's Ave. Bris 63 D4
Boyd Cl. Wick 67 D4
Boyd Rd. Keyn 82 B2
Brabazon Rd. Bris 36 A1
Bracewell Gdns. Bris 35 E2
Bracey Dr. Bris 51 E3
Brackenbury Dr. St Gif 36 C3
Brackendean. St Gif 24 B1
Brackenwood Rd. Cleve 57 F3
Bracton Dr. Bris 80 A3
Bradeston Gr. Bris 51 D4
Bradford Cl. Cleve 57 E1
Bradford Park. Bath 102 A1
Bradford Rd. Bath 102 A1
Bradford Rd. Bathf 86 A1
Bradford Rd. Winsl 120 C4
Bradhurst St. Bris 64 A3
Bradley Ave. Wint 37 F3
Bradley Cres. Bris 47 F3
Bradley Rd. Bris 23 F1
Bradley Stoke Way. St Gif 24 B1
Bradley Stoke Way. St Gif 37 D3
Bradstone Rd. Wint 37 E3
Bradville Gdns. Lo Ash 77 F4
Bradwell Gr. Bris 49 E4
Brae Rd. Wins 125 D4
Brae Rise. Wins 125 D4
Braemar Ave. Bris 35 F1
Braemar Cres. Bris 35 F1
Bragg's La. Bris 63 F4
Braikenridge Cl. Cleve 57 E1
Braikenridge Rd. Bris 64 B2
Brainsfield. Bris 48 C3
Brake Cl. Kingsw 65 F4
Brake Cl. St Gif 36 C3
Brake The. Fr Cot 38 B3
Brake The. Yate 27 F3
Brakewell Gdns. Bris 80 A2
Bramble Dr. Bris 48 B2
Bramble La. Bris 48 B2
Bramble Rd. W-S-M 88 C2
Bramble Way. Bath 102 A1
Brambles The. Keyn 81 E2
Brambling Wlk. Bris 50 C3
Bramley Cl. E in G 47 E2
Bramley Cl. Kings 11 F2
Bramley Cl. Olve 14 A2
Bramley Cl. P St J 133 E4
Bramley Cl. Yatt 91 D4
Bramley Ct. Kingsw 65 F2
Bramley Dr. Back 76 A3
Bramley Sq. Cong 91 F2
Bramleys The. Nail 75 D4
Brampton Way. Portis 45 F2
Bramshill Dr. W-S-M 88 C2
Branch Rd. Hin Cha 119 F1
Branche Gr. Bris 79 E2
Brandash Rd. Ch Sod 28 A1
Brandon St. Bris 63 E3
Brandon Steep. Bris 63 E3
Brangwyn Gr. Bris 50 A3
Brangwyn Sq. W-S-M 88 C1
Branksome Cres. Bris 36 A2
Branksome Dr. Bris 36 A2
Branksome Dr. Wint 37 F3
Branksome Rd. Bris 49 D2
Branscombe Rd. Bris 48 B2
Branscombe Way. Portis 44 C2
Branscombe Wlk. Portis 44 C2
Branwhite Cl. Bris 50 A4
Brassknocker Hill. Bath 102 C1
Brassmill La. Bath 101 D4
Bratton Rd. Bris 79 E4
Braunton Rd. Bris 63 E2
Braydon Ave. St Gif 36 B4
Brayne Ct. Kingsw 65 F2
Braysdown Cl. P St J 133 D3
Braysdown La. P St J 133 E3
Braysdown La. P St J 133 E4
Breach La. Nail 74 C4
Breach Rd. Bris 63 D2
Breaches Gate. St Gif 36 C3
Breaches La. Keyn 82 A2
Breaches The. E in G 47 D3
Brean Down Ave. Bris 49 D2
Brean Down Ave. Bris 49 D3
Brean Down Ave. W-S-M 104 B2
Brean Rd. Lymp 121 F1
Brecknock Rd. Bris 64 A2
Brecon Rd. Bris 49 D3
Brecon View. W-S-M 105 D1
Bredon Cl. Kingsw 65 F4
Bredon Nook Rd. Bris 49 E4
Bredon. Yate 39 E4
Bree Cl. W-S-M 89 D2
Brendon Ave. W-S-M 104 C4
Brendon Cl. Kingsw 66 B2
Brendon Gdns. Nail 59 F1
Brendon Rd. Bris 63 E2
Brendon Rd. Portis 45 D3
Brenner St. Bris 50 A1
Brent Cl. W-S-M 105 D1
Brent Rd. Bris 49 F3
Brentry Ave. Bris 64 A4
Brentry Hill. Bris 35 D1
Brentry La. Bris 35 D2
Brentry Rd. Bris 50 C2
Brereton Way. Kingsw 66 A2
Brewerton Cl. Bris 35 E2
Brewery Hill. Bitt 82 C4
Brewery La. Hol 138 B1
Briar Cl. Nail 60 A1
Briar Cl. Rod 138 B4
Briar Mead. Yatt 74 A1
Briar Rd. Lock 105 F2
Briar Way. Bris 51 E2
Briar Wlk. Bris 51 E2
Briarfield Ave. Kingsw 65 E3
Briarleaze. Alve 14 C1
Briars The. Back 75 F4
Briarside Rd. Bris 35 E2
Briarwood. Bris 48 C3
Briary Rd. Portis 45 E3
Briavels Gr. Bris 49 F1
Brick St. Bris 63 F4
Bridewell La. Bath 101 F3
Bridewell La. Lock 106 B1
Bridewell St. Bris 63 E4
Bridge Cl. Whit 80 B2
Bridge Farm Cl. Bris 80 A2
Bridge Farm Sq. Cong 91 E2
Bridge Gdns. Farm 116 A3
Bridge Place Rd. Tims 132 C4
Bridge Rd. Bath 101 E3
Bridge Rd. Blea 122 A3
Bridge Rd. Bris 50 A2
Bridge Rd. Ir Act 27 D1
Bridge Rd. Kingsw 52 A2
Bridge Rd. Lo Ash 62 C3
Bridge Rd. Sist 52 B2
Bridge St. Bath 102 A3
Bridge St. Bris 50 B1
Bridge St. Bris 63 E3
Bridge Valley Rd. Bris 62 C4
Bridge Way. Fr Cot 38 A4
Bridge Wlk. Bris 50 A4
Bridgeleap Rd. Mang 51 F4
Bridges Dr. Bris 51 E3
Bridgman Gr. Bris 36 A2
Bridgwater Ct. W-S-M 105 D2
Bridgwater Rd. Ba Gu 77 F1
Bridgwater Rd. Blea 122 B2
Bridgwater Rd. Bris 78 B3
Bridgwater Rd. Dun 78 B3
Bridgwater Rd. Lymp 122 B2
Bridgwater Rd. W-S-M 104 C1
Bridgwater Rd. Wins 125 D3
Bridle Way. Alve 14 C2
Briercliffe Rd. Bris 48 B4
Brierly Furlong. St Gif 36 C2
Briery Leaze Rd. Bris 80 A3
Bright St. Bris 64 A4
Bright St. Kingsw 65 E4
Brighton Cres. Bris 63 E1
Brighton Mews. Bris 63 D4
Brighton Pl. Kingsw 51 E1
Brighton Rd. Bris 35 F4
Brighton Rd. Bris 49 E1
Brighton Rd. W-S-M 104 C3
Brighton St. Bris 63 F4
Brighton Terr. Bris 63 D1
Brigstocke Rd. Bris 63 F4
Brimbles. Bris 36 A1
Brimbleworth La. Lock 89 E2
Brimridge Rd. Wins 125 D4
Brinkmarsh La. Falf 9 E1
Brinkworthy Rd. Bris 50 C3
Brinmead Wlk. Bris 78 C2
Brins Cl. St Gif 36 C2
Brinsea Batch. Cong 108 C4
Brinsea La. Cong 108 C4
Brinsea Rd. Cong 91 F1
Brinsham La. Yate 28 A3
Briscoes Ave. Bris 79 E2
Brislington Hill. Bris 64 C1
Brislington Trading Est. Bris 64 C1
Bristol And Exeter Mews.
Bris 63 F3
Bristol Gate. Bris 62 C3
Bristol Hill. Bris 64 B1
Bristol Phoenix. Bris 63 D1
Bristol Rd Lower. W-S-M 87 F1
Bristol Rd. Bris 37 D1
Bristol Rd. Ch St 112 C4
Bristol Rd. Chur 109 D
Bristol Rd. Co Dan 81 F
Bristol Rd. Cong 91 E
Bristol Rd. Cor 100 B
Bristol Rd. Crom 17 D
Bristol Rd. Fr Cot 26 A
Bristol Rd. Ir Act 26 A
Bristol Rd. Lock 89 E
Bristol Rd. Luck 31 F2
Bristol Rd. Mid No 132 C
Bristol Rd. Paul 130 C
Bristol Rd. Paul 131 F4
Bristol Rd. Pens 97 E4
Bristol Rd. Portis 45 F2
Bristol Rd. Ship 108 B
Bristol Rd. Thorn 15 D
Bristol Rd. Whit 80 B
Bristol Rd. Wins 125 E4
Bristol Rd. Wint 37 E
Bristol Rd. Wint 37 F4
Bristol Vale Centre For Industry.
Bris 63 D
Bristol View. Bath 118 B4
Bristowe House. Bris 51 D
Britannia Cl. Chil 137 E
Britannia Cres. St Gif 36 B
Britannia Rd. Bris 35 F4
Britannia Rd. Bris 50 B1
Britannia Rd. Bris 65 E4
Britannia Rd. Kingsw 65 E4
Britannia Way. Cleve 57 E
British Rd. Bris 63 E
Brittan Pl. Portb 46 C
Britten Ct. Kingsw 65 F2
Britten's Cl. Paul 131 F
Britten's Hill. Paul 131 F
Brixham Rd. Bris 63 E
Brixton Rd. Bris 64 A4
Broad Croft. St Gif 24 B1
Broad La. West 38 B
Broad La. West 39 D
Broad La. Yate 27 E
Broad Mead La. Win 95 D
Broad Oak Rd. Bris 78 C
Broad Oaks. Lo Ash 62 C
Broad Plain. Bris 63 F3
Broad Quay. Bath 101 F3
Broad Quay. Bris 63 E
Broad Rd. Bris 51 E
Broad Rd. Priddy 126 C
Broad St. Bath 102 A4
Broad St. Bris 63 E4
Broad St. Cong 91 E
Broad St. Kingsw 51 F2
Broad St. Mang 51 F2
Broad St. Wring 92 B1
Broad Street Pl. Bath 102 A4
Broad Weir. Bris 63 F4
Broad Wlk. Bris 64 A1
Broadbury Rd. Bris 79 F4
Broadcroft Ave. Yatt 74 C1
Broadcroft Cl. Yatt 74 C1
Broadcroft. Ch Mag 95 F2
Broadfield Ave. Bris 51 E
Broadfield Rd. Bris 64 A
Broadlands Ave. Keyn 81 E3
Broadlands Dr. Bris 34 A
Broadlands. Cleve 57 F2
Broadleas. Bris 79 E4
Broadleaze Way. Winsc 107 F1
Broadleys Ave. Bris 49 E4
Broadmead La. Keyn 82 A3
Broadmead. Bris 63 F4
Broadmoor La. Bath 84 A2
Broadmoor La. Charl 83 F2
Broadmoor Park. Bath 84 A
Broadmoor Vale. Bath 84 A2
Broadoak Hill. Bris 78 C2
Broadoak Rd. Chur 109 D3
Broadoak Rd. W-S-M 104 B2
Broadoak Wlk. Bris 51 D2
Broadstone La. K Sey 72 C
Broadstone Wlk. Bris 79 E3
Broadstones. Mon Far 103 F4
Broadway Ave. Bris 49 E3
Broadway Cl. Chil 137 E2
Broadway La. Paul 132 A3
Broadway Rd. Bris 49 E2
Broadway Rd. Bris 78 C3
Broadway. Bath 102 A3
Broadway. Chil 137 E2
Broadway. Keyn 82 B2
Broadway. Ship 125 F4
Broadway. W-S-M 105 D1
Broadway. Yate 27 F1
Broadways Dr. Bris 50 C4
Brock End. Portis 44 C2
Brock St. Bath 101 F4
Brockhurst Gdns. Bris 65 D4
Brockhurst Rd. Bris 65 D4
Brockley Cl. Nail 59 E1
Brockley Cl. St Gif 36 B4
Brockley Cl. W-S-M 104 C1
Brockley Combe Rd. Brock 76 A1
Brockley Combe Rd. Wring 76 A1
Brockley Cres. W-S-M 104 C1
Brockley La. Brock 75 E2
Brockley Rd. Keyn 82 B2

145

Brockley Way. Brock

Chapel Row. Bathf

Brockley Way. Brock 75 D2
Brockley Way. Yatt 75 D2
Brockley Wlk. Bris 79 D4
Brockridge La. Fr Cot 38 B4
Brocks La. Lo Ash 61 F1
Brocks Rd. Bris 79 E2
Brockway. Nail 59 F1
Brockwood. Winsl 120 C4
Brockworth Cres. Bris 50 C3
Brockworth. Yate 39 E3
Bromley Dr. Mang 51 E4
Bromley Heath Ave. Mang 51 E4
Bromley Heath Rd. Mang 37 E1
Bromley Heath Rd. Mang 51 E4
Bromley Rd. Bris 49 F3
Bromley Rd. Pens 96 C1
Brompton Cl. Kingsw 66 A4
Brompton Rd. W-S-M 105 D1
Broncksea Rd. Bris 35 F1
Brook Cl. Lo Ash 62 A1
Brook Gate. Bris 62 C1
Brook Hill. Bris 49 F1
Brook La. Bris 49 F1
Brook La. Bris 50 C3
Brook Lintons. Bris 64 B2
Brook Rd. Bath 101 E3
Brook Rd. Bris 49 F1
Brook Rd. Bris 50 C1
Brook Rd. Bris 51 D2
Brook Rd. Bris 63 E2
Brook Rd. Kingsw 66 A4
Brook Rd. Mang 51 F3
Brook St. Bris 64 B4
Brook St. Ch Sod 28 A1
Brook Way. St Gif 36 B4
Brookcote Dr. St Gif 36 B3
Brookdale Rd. Bris 79 D3
Brookfield Ave. Bris 49 E2
Brookfield Cl. Ch Sod 28 A1
Brookfield La. Bris 49 E1
Brookfield Park. Bath 84 A1
Brookfield Rd. Bris 49 E1
Brookfield Rd. St Gif 36 A4
Brookfield Wlk. Cleve 57 F2
Brookfield Wlk. Kingsw 66 B2
Brookland Rd. Bris 49 E3
Brookland Rd. W-S-M 105 D4
Brooklands. Pris 117 E2
Brooklea. Kingsw 66 A2
Brookleaze Bldgs. Bath 85 D1
Brookleaze. Bris 48 B3
Brooklyn Rd. Bath 85 E1
Brooklyn Rd. Bris 79 D4
Brooklyn. Wring 92 B1
Brookmead. Thorn 15 E4
Brookside Cl. Bathe 85 F3
Brookside Cl. Paul 131 F3
Brookside Dr. Farm 115 F3
Brookside Dr. Fr Cot 38 A4
Brookside House. Bath 84 A1
Brookside Rd. Bris 64 C1
Brookside. E in G 47 E2
Brookside. Paul 131 F3
Brookside. Win 94 C4
Brookthorpe Ave. Bris 34 A1
Brookthorpe. Yate 39 E4
Brookview Wlk. Bris 79 D4
Broom Farm Cl. Nail 75 F4
Broom Hill La. Paul 131 F4
Broom Hill. Bris 50 C3
Broomground. Winsl 120 C4
Broomhill La. Clut 114 C2
Brotherswood Ct. St Gif 24 B2
Brougham Hayes. Bath 101 E3
Brow Hill. Bathe 85 F2
Brow The. Bath 101 D3
Browning Ct. Bris 50 A4
Brownlow Rd. W-S-M 104 C2
Bruce Ave. Bris 50 B1
Bruce Rd. Bris 50 B1
Brummel Way. Paul 131 E3
Brunel Cl. W-S-M 104 C1
Brunel Ct. Yate 27 E1
Brunel Lock Rd. Bris 62 C3
Brunel Rd. Bris 79 D4
Brunel Rd. Nail 59 D1
Brunel Way. Bris 62 C2
Brunel Way. Thorn 15 D4
Brunswick Pl. Bris 62 C3
Brunswick Sq. Bris 63 F4
Brunswick St. Bath 102 A4
Brunswick St. Bris 63 F4
Brunswick St. Bris 64 B4
Bruton Ave. Bath 101 F2
Bruton Ave. Portis 45 D3
Bruton Cl. Nail 75 F4
Bruton. W-S-M 105 D1
Bryansons Cl. Bris 50 B3
Bryant Ave. Rad 132 B1
Bryant Gdns. Cleve 57 E1
Bryant's Hill. Bris 65 D3
Bryants Cl. Bris 37 E1
Brynland Ave. Bris 49 F2
Bsns Pk The. Bris 79 F2
Buckingham Dr. St Gif 36 B3
Buckingham Gdns. Mang 51 F3
Buckingham Pl. Bris 63 D4
Buckingham Pl. Mang 51 F3
Buckingham Rd. Bris 64 B3
Buckingham Rd. W-S-M 105 D1
Buckingham St. Bris 63 E1
Buckingham Vale. Bris 63 D4
Buckland Green. W-S-M 89 D3
Bucklands Batch. Nail 75 F4
Bucklands Dr. Nail 76 A4
Bucklands End. Nail 75 F4
Bucklands Gr. Nail 75 F4
Bucklands La. Nail 75 F4
Bucklands View. Nail 76 A4
Bude Ave. Bris 65 D4
Bude Cl. Nail 60 A1
Bude Rd. Bris 36 A2
Bull La. Bris 64 C3
Bull La. E in G 47 E2
Bull's Hill. Well 118 C1
Bullens Cl. St Gif 24 B1
Buller Rd. Bris 64 B1
Bullocks La. K Sey 73 E2
Bully La. Yate 17 E1
Bumper's Batch. Sosto 119 D4
Bungay's Hill. Paul 115 F1
Bunting Ct. W-S-M 88 C1
Burbank Cl. Kingsw 66 A2
Burchells Ave. Bris 51 D1
Burchells Green Cl. Bris 51 D1
Burchells Green Rd. Bris 51 D1
Burcott Rd. Avon 33 E3
Burden Cl. St Gif 36 C3
Burfoot Gdns. Bris 80 C2
Burfoot Rd. Bris 80 C2
Burford Cl. Bath 101 D2
Burford Cl. Portis 45 F2
Burford Gr. Bris 47 F3
Burgage Cl. Ch Sod 40 A4
Burgess Green Cl. Bris 64 C4
Burghill Rd. Bris 35 D1
Burghley Rd. Bris 49 F1
Burgis Rd. Bris 80 B3
Burleigh Gdns. Bath 101 D4
Burleigh Way. Wickw 18 A3
Burley Ave. Mang 51 F3
Burley Crest. Mang 51 F3
Burley Gr. Mang 51 F2
Burlington Rd. Bris 49 D1
Burlington Rd. Mid No 132 B1
Burlington St. Bath 101 F4
Burlington St. W-S-M 104 C4
Burnbush Cl. Bris 80 C3
Burnell Dr. Bris 63 F4
Burneside Cl. Bris 35 E1
Burney Way. Kingsw 66 A2
Burnham Cl. Kingsw 51 F1
Burnham Cl. W-S-M 104 C1
Burnham Dr. Kingsw 51 F1
Burnham Dr. W-S-M 104 C1
Burnham Rd. Bath 101 E3
Burnham Rd. Bris 47 E3
Burrington Ave. W-S-M 104 C1
Burrington Cl. Nail 59 F1
Burrington Cl. W-S-M 104 C1
Burrington Wlk. Bris 79 D4
Burrough Way. Wint 37 F3
Burrows La. Hol 138 A1
Burton Cl. Bris 63 F3
Burton Cl. Bris 64 C4
Burton Ct. Bris 63 D4
Burton Rd. A Tur 42 C3
Burton St. Bath 101 F3
Burwalls Rd. Lo Ash 62 C3
Bury Hill La. Yate 28 A4
Bury Hill. Wint 37 F2
Bury La. Doyn 67 F4
Bury The. Lock 106 A2
Burycourt Cl. Bris 34 A1
Bush Ave. St Gif 36 B3
Bushes La. Hort 29 D3
Bushy Park. Bris 63 F2
Bushy Thorn Rd. Ch St 112 C4
Butcombe La. But 111 D4
Butcombe Wlk. Bris 80 A3
Butcombe. W-S-M 105 D1
Butham La. Ch Mag 96 A2
Butlass Cl. Paul 115 E1
Butt's Batch. Wring 92 B1
Butt's La. Mon Far 103 F4
Butt's La. Tor 55 D2
Butterfield Cl. Bris 49 F4
Butterfield Park. Cleve 57 E1
Butterfield Rd. Bris 49 F4
Buttermere Rd. W-S-M 105 D3
Butterworth Ct. Bris 79 E4
Button Cl. Bris 80 A3
Butts Batch. Co Bi 124 A2
Buxton Wlk. Bris 50 A4
Byfields. Cleve 73 E4
Byron Pl. Bris 63 D4
Byron Pl. Kingsw 51 F2
Byron Rd. Bath 101 F2
Byron Rd. Lock 106 A2
Byron Rd. W-S-M 105 D2
Byron St. Bris 50 A1
Byron St. Bris 64 B4

Cabot Cl. Keyn 82 B1
Cabot Cl. Yate 27 F1
Cabot Green. Bris 64 A4
Cabot Rise. Portis 45 D3
Cabot Way. Bris 62 C3
Cabot Way. E in G 47 E2
Cabot Way. W-S-M 89 D2
Cabstand. Portis 45 E3
Cadbury Camp La W. Nail 58 B3
Cadbury Camp La. Nail 59 E3
Cadbury Farm Rd. Yatt 91 E4
Cadbury Halt. W in G 44 C1
Cadbury Heath Rd. Kingsw 66 A3
Cadbury La. W in G 44 C1
Cadbury Rd. Keyn 82 A1
Cadbury Rd. Portis 45 F2
Cadbury Sq. Cong 91 E2
Caddick Cl. Kingsw 51 F1
Cade Cl. Kingsw 65 F3
Cade Cl. St Gif 36 C3
Cadogan Rd. Bris 80 A4
Caen Rd. Bris 63 E2
Caernarvon Rd. Keyn 81 E2
Caine Rd. Bris 49 F4
Cains Cl. Kingsw 65 F3
Cairn Cl. Nail 60 A1
Cairns Rd. Bris 49 E2
Cairns' Cres. Bris 49 F1
Cakenhill Rd. Bris 64 C1
Calcott Rd. Bris 64 A2
Caldbeck Cl. Bris 35 E1
Calder Cl. Keyn 82 A2
Caldicot Cl. Bris 34 B1
Caldicot Cl. Kingsw 66 A1
Caledonia Mews. Bris 62 C3
Caledonia Pl. Bris 62 C4
Caledonian Rd. Bath 101 E3
California Rd. Kingsw 66 A2
Callicroft Rd. Bris 36 A4
Callington Rd. Bris 64 B1
Callowhill Ct. Bris 63 F4
Calton Gdns. Bath 101 F3
Calton Rd. Bath 102 A3
Cam Brook Cl. Tims 132 C4
Camberley Dr. Fr Cot 37 F4
Camberley Rd. Bris 79 E4
Camborne Rd. Bris 50 A4
Cambrian Dr. Yate 27 F2
Cambridge Cres. Bris 49 D4
Cambridge Gr. Cleve 57 E3
Cambridge Park. Bris 49 D2
Cambridge Rd. Bris 49 F2
Cambridge Rd. Cleve 57 F3
Cambridge St. Bris 63 F2
Cambridge st. Bris 64 B4
Cambridge Terr. Bath 102 A3
Cambrook House. Clut 130 C4
Camden Rd. Bath 85 D1
Camden Rd. Bris 63 D3
Camden Row. Bath 101 F4
Camden Terr. Bris 63 D3
Camden Terr. W-S-M 104 C4
Cameley Cl. Clut 130 C4
Cameley Green. Bath 100 C3
Cameley Rd. Clut 130 B4
Camelford Rd. Bris 50 B1
Cameron Wlk. Bris 50 B3
Cameroons Cl. Keyn 81 F2
Camerton Cl. Keyn 82 C2
Camerton Hill. Tims 132 C4
Camerton Rd. Bris 50 B1
Camerton Rd. Tims 116 C1
Camp La. Tor 55 E2
Camp Rd N. W-S-M 87 D1
Camp Rd. Bris 62 C4
Camp Rd. O-on-S 7 D3
Camp Rd. W-S-M 87 E1
Camp View. Nail 59 E1
Campbell Farm Dr. Bris 33 F1
Campbell St. Bris 49 F1
Campion Cl. Thorn 8 B1
Campion Cl. W-S-M 105 E4
Campion Dr. St Gif 24 B1
Campion Wlk. Bris 79 E3
Camplins. Cleve 57 E1
Camvale. P St J 133 D4
Camview. Paul 131 E3
Camwal Rd. Bris 64 A3
Canada Coombe. Blea 106 A1
Canada Coombe. Lock 106 A1
Canada Way. Bris 63 D3
Canberra Gr. Bris 36 A2
Canberra Rd. W-S-M 104 C2
Canford La. Bris 48 C4
Canford La. Bris 49 D4
Canford Rd. Bris 48 C4
Cann La. Bitt 66 C3
Cann La. Sist 66 C3
Cannans Cl. Wint 37 F4
Cannon St. Bris 63 E2
Cannon St. Bris 63 E4
Cannon St. Bris 64 B4
Cannons Gate. Cleve 73 E4
Canon's Rd. Bris 63 E3
Canon's Wlk. Kingsw 51 F1
Canons Wlk. W-S-M 88 B1
Canowie Rd. Bris 49 D2
Cantell Gr. Bris 80 C3
Canterbury Cl. W-S-M 89 D2
Canterbury Cl. Yate 27 F2
Canterbury Rd. Bath 101 E3
Canterbury St. Bris 64 A3
Canters Leaze. Wickw 18 A2
Cantock's Cl. Bris 63 E4
Canvey Cl. Bris 49 F4
Canynge Rd. Bris 62 C4
Canynge Sq. Bris 62 C4
Canynge St. Bris 63 F3
Capel Cl. Kingsw 66 A4
Capel Rd. Bris 34 A1
Capenor Cl. Portis 45 E2
Capgrave Cl. Bris 65 D2
Capgrave Cres. Bris 65 D2
Caple La. Ch St 112 A3
Caraway Gdns. Bris 50 B1
Cardigan Cres. W-S-M 105 E4
Cardigan Rd. Bris 49 D3
Cardill Cl. Bris 79 D4
Carditch Dro. Cong 108 A4
Carey's Cl. Cleve 57 F2
Carice Gdns. Cleve 73 E4
Carisbrooke Rd. Bris 79 E4
Carlingford Terr Rd. Rad 133 D1
Carlingford Terr. Rad 133 D1
Carlisle Rd. Bris 50 B1
Carlow Rd. Bris 79 F4
Carlton Cl. Clut 114 C2
Carlton Ct. Bris 49 D4
Carlton Mansions. W-S-M 104 B4
Carlton Pk. Bris 64 B4
Carlton St. W-S-M 104 B4
Carmarthen Cl. Yate 27 F2
Carmarthen Gr. Kingsw 66 A1
Carmarthen Rd. Bris 49 D3
Carnarvon Rd. Bris 49 E1
Caroline Cl. Keyn 81 E2
Caroline Pl. Bath 101 F4
Carpenters La. Keyn 81 F3
Carre Gdns. W-S-M 88 C2
Carrington Rd. Bris 63 D2
Carroll Ct. Bris 36 C1
Carsons Rd. Sist 52 A1
Carter Rd. Paul 131 E3
Carter's Bldgs. Bris 62 C4
Carters Way. Chil 137 E2
Cartledge Rd. Bris 50 B1
Cashmore Ho. Bris 64 A4
Cassell Rd. Bris 51 E3
Cassey Bottom La. Bris 65 D4
Castle Cl. Back 76 C4
Castle Cl. Bris 34 C1
Castle Ct. Thorn 8 A1
Castle Farm La. Dun 78 A1
Castle Farm Rd. Kingsw 65 E1
Castle Gdns. Bath 101 F2
Castle Hill. Ban 107 E1
Castle La. Marsh 55 F1
Castle Rd. Cleve 57 F3
Castle Rd. Kingsw 51 E1
Castle Rd. Kingsw 66 B2
Castle Rd. Puck 53 E3
Castle Rd. W-S-M 88 C2
Castle St. Bris 63 F4
Castle St. Thorn 8 A1
Castle View Rd. Cleve 57 E3
Castlewood Cl. Cleve 57 E3
Caswell Hill. Portb 46 A1
Caswell La. Portb 46 B1
Catbrain Hill. Bris 35 D3
Catbrain La. Bris 35 D3
Catchpot La. Ch Sod 41 D3
Catemead. Cleve 73 E4
Cater Rd. Bris 79 D3
Catherine Hill. Olve 13 F1
Catherine Mead St. Bris 63 E2
Catherine Pl. Bath 101 F4
Catherine St. Avon 47 E4
Catherine Way. Bathe 86 A3
Catley Gr. Lo Ash 62 A1
Cato St. Bris 50 A1
Catsley Pl. Bath 85 E1
Cattistock Dr. Bris 65 D3
Cattle Market Rd. Bris 63 F3
Cattybrook Rd. Puck 52 B3
Cattybrook St. Bris 64 A4
Caulfield Rd. W-S-M 89 D2
Causeway The. Cong 91 E2
Causeway The. Fr Cot 38 B4
Causeway The. W in G 45 F1
Causeway The. Yatt 91 E4
Causeway View. Nail 59 E1
Causeway. Nail 59 D2
Causley Dr. Kingsw 66 A3
Cautletts Cl. Mid No 137 F4
Cavan Wlk. Bris 63 E1
Cave Ct. Bris 63 F4
Cave Dr. Bris 51 E3
Cave St. Bris 63 F4
Cavell Ct. Cleve 57 E1
Cavendish Cl. Keyn 82 B1
Cavendish Cres. Bath 101 F4
Cavendish Gdns. Bris 48 B2
Cavendish Rd. Bath 101 F4
Cavendish Rd. Bris 35 F4
Cavendish Rd. Bris 49 D3
Caveners Ct. W-S-M 88 A1
Caversham Dr. Nail 60 A1
Cecil Ave. Bris 50 C1
Cecil Rd. Bris 62 C4
Cecil Rd. Kingsw 65 E4
Cecil Rd. W-S-M 87 F1
Cedar Ave. W-S-M 88 B1
Cedar Cl. Bris 35 F4
Cedar Cl. Kingsw 66 A2
Cedar Cl. Lo Ash 61 F1
Cedar Dr. Keyn 81 E2
Cedar Gr. Bath 101 E2
Cedar Gr. Bris 48 B3
Cedar Hall. Bris 51 E4
Cedar Park. Bris 48 B3
Cedar Row. Bris 47 F3
Cedar Terr. Rad 132 B1
Cedar Way. Bath 101 F3
Cedar Way. Nail 60 A1
Cedar Way. Portis 45 E2
Cedar Way. Puck 53 E3
Cedar Way. Wint 37 E3
Cedarhurst Rd. Portis 44 C2
Cedars The. Ch St 95 E1
Cedric Rd. Bath 101 E4
Celandine Cl. Thorn 8 B1
Celestine Rd. Yate 27 E2
Celtic Way. Blea 122 B4
Cemetery Rd. Bris 64 A2
Cennick Ave. Kingsw 51 F1
Centaurus Rd. Bris 35 E4
Central Ave. Avon 22 A2
Central Ave. Kingsw 65 E3
Central Way. Cleve 57 F1
Ceres Cl. Kingsw 65 F1
Cerimon Gate. St Gif 36 C3
Cerney Gdns. Nail 60 A1
Cerney La. Bris 47 F3
Cesson Cl. Ch Sod 40 B4
Chadleigh Gr. Bris 79 E4
Chaffinch Dr. Rod 138 A4
Chaffins The. Cleve 57 F1
Chaingate La. Ir Act 27 D3
Chakeshill Cl. Bris 35 E2
Chakeshill Dr. Bris 35 E2
Chalcombe Cl. St Gif 36 B4
Chalcroft Wlk. Bris 78 C2
Chalfont Rd. W-S-M 105 E4
Chalford Cl. Yate 39 E4
Chalks Rd. Bris 64 B4
Chalks The. Ch Mag 96 A2
Challender Ave. Bris 34 C1
Challoner Ct. Bris 63 E3
Challow Dr. W-S-M 88 A1
Champion Rd. Kingsw 52 A1
Champneys Ave. Bris 34 C2
Chancel Cl. Nail 59 E1
Chancellors Pound. Wring 93 E2
Chancery St. Bris 64 A4
Chandag Rd. Keyn 82 A2
Chandler Cl. Bath 84 A1
Chandos Rd. Bris 49 E1
Chandos Rd. Keyn 81 F4
Chandos Trading Est. Bris 64 A3
Channel Hts. W-S-M 104 C1
Channel Rd. Cleve 57 F3
Channel View Cres. Portis 45 D3
Channel View Rd. Portis 45 D3
Channel's Hill. Bris 49 D4
Channon's Hill. Bris 50 C2
Chantry Cl. Nail 59 E1
Chantry Dr. W-S-M 89 D2
Chantry Gr. Bris 34 B1
Chantry La. Mang 37 F1
Chantry Mead Rd. Bath 101 F2
Chantry Rd. Bris 49 D1
Chantry Rd. Thorn 8 A1
Chapel Barton. Bris 63 D1
Chapel Barton. Nail 59 E1
Chapel Cl. Ch St 112 C4
Chapel Cl. Kingsw 66 A4
Chapel Cl. Nail 59 F1
Chapel Cl. Paul 130 C2
Chapel Cl. Win 95 D3
Chapel Gdns. Bris 35 D1
Chapel Green La. Bris 49 D1
Chapel Hill. Back 76 B4
Chapel Hill. But 111 E3
Chapel Hill. Cleve 57 E2
Chapel Hill. Newp 4 A4
Chapel Hill. Wring 92 B2
Chapel La. A Tur 43 D3
Chapel La. Bris 34 B1
Chapel La. Bris 50 C1
Chapel La. Bris 51 D2
Chapel La. Bris 51 E4
Chapel La. Brock 92 A4
Chapel La. Ch Sod 41 D4
Chapel La. Ch St 112 B4
Chapel La. Dyrh 54 B3
Chapel La. Hill 19 E4
Chapel La. Kingsw 66 A4
Chapel La. Thorn 9 D1
Chapel La. Win 95 D3
Chapel La. Yatt 91 F4
Chapel Rd. Bris 50 A1
Chapel Rd. Bris 79 D3
Chapel Rd. Kingsw 65 E3
Chapel Rd. Mid No 132 C2
Chapel Rd. O-on-S 7 E3
Chapel Row. Bath 101 F3
Chapel Row. Bathf 86 B1

Chapel Row. E in G ... 47 E2
Chapel Row. Luck ... 31 F2
Chapel St. Bris ... 64 A3
Chapel St. Thorn ... 15 D4
Chaplin Rd. Bris ... 50 A1
Chapter St. Bris ... 63 F4
Charbon Gate. St Gif ... 36 C3
Charborough Rd. Bris ... 35 F1
Charbury Wlk. Bris ... 47 F3
Chard Cl. Nail ... 75 F4
Chard Rd. Cleve ... 57 E1
Chardstock Ave. Bris ... 48 B4
Chardyke Dr. Clut ... 114 C1
Charfield Rd. Bris ... 35 E1
Charfield Rd. Kings ... 11 F3
Charfield. Kingsw ... 66 A4
Chargrove. Kingsw ... 66 B3
Chargrove. Yate ... 39 E4
Charis Ave. Bris ... 49 E4
Charity La. Hol ... 139 E1
Charity La. Kilm ... 139 E1
Charlcombe La. Bath ... 84 C2
Charlcombe La. Charl ... 84 C2
Charlcombe Rise. Bath ... 84 C1
Charlcombe View Rd. Bath ... 85 D1
Charlcombe Way. Bath ... 84 C1
Charlcombe Ct. Bris ... 48 C3
Charlecombe Rd. Bris ... 48 C3
Charles Ave. St Gif ... 36 C2
Charles Cl. Thorn ... 8 B2
Charles Pl. Bris ... 63 D3
Charles Rd. Bris ... 36 A2
Charles St. Bath ... 101 F3
Charles St. Bris ... 63 E4
Charlotte St S. Bris ... 63 E4
Charlotte St. Bath ... 101 F3
Charlotte St. Bris ... 63 E4
Charlotte St. Bris ... 63 F4
Charlton Ave. Bris ... 35 F1
Charlton Ave. W-S-M ... 104 C2
Charlton Dr. Wrax ... 60 B4
Charlton Gdns. Bris ... 35 E2
Charlton La. Bris ... 35 D2
Charlton La. Kilm ... 138 B4
Charlton Mead Ct. Bris ... 35 E2
Charlton Mead Dr. Bris ... 35 E2
Charlton Park. Keyn ... 81 E3
Charlton Park. Rod ... 138 A4
Charlton Pl. Bris ... 35 E2
Charlton Rd. Bris ... 35 E2
Charlton Rd. Bris ... 51 D1
Charlton Rd. Co Dan ... 81 E2
Charlton Rd. Hol ... 138 B2
Charlton Rd. Keyn ... 81 E2
Charlton Rd. Kilm ... 138 B2
Charlton Rd. Rod ... 138 A4
Charlton Rd. W-S-M ... 104 B2
Charlton St. Bris ... 64 A4
Charlton View. Portis ... 45 E3
Charminster Rd. Bris ... 51 D2
Charmouth Rd. Bath ... 101 D4
Charnell Rd. Kingsw ... 51 F2
Charnhill Brow. Kingsw ... 52 A2
Charnhill Cres. Kingsw ... 51 F2
Charnhill Dr. Kingsw ... 51 F2
Charnhill Ridge. Kingsw ... 52 A2
Charnhill Vale. Kingsw ... 51 F2
Charnwood. Kingsw ... 52 A2
Charter Rd. W-S-M ... 105 D4
Charter Wlk. Bris ... 80 A3
Charterhouse Cl. Nail ... 59 F1
Charterhouse Rd. Bris ... 64 B4
Chase La. Kings ... 18 B3
Chase La. Wickw ... 18 B3
Chase Rd. Kingsw ... 51 E1
Chase The. Bris ... 51 E2
Chatcombe. Yate ... 39 F4
Chatham Park. Bath ... 102 B3
Chatham Row. Bath ... 102 A4
Chatsworth Pk. Thorn ... 8 B1
Chatsworth Rd. Bris ... 51 D2
Chatsworth Rd. Bris ... 64 B2
Chatterton Green. Bris ... 79 F2
Chatterton Rd. Yate ... 27 E1
Chatterton Sq. Bris ... 63 F3
Chatterton St. Bris ... 63 F3
Chaucer Rd. Bath ... 101 F2
Chaucer Rd. Rod ... 138 A4
Chaucer W-S-M ... 105 D2
Chaucer Wlk. Bris ... 50 A4
Chaundey Gr. Bris ... 79 D3
Chavenage. Kingsw ... 66 A4
Cheap St. Bath ... 102 A3
Cheapside St. Bris ... 63 F2
Cheapside. Bris ... 63 F4
Cheddar Cl. Nail ... 75 F4
Cheddar Gr. Bris ... 79 D4
Cheddar Rd. Axb ... 125 E1
Chedworth Cl. Bath ... 102 C2
Chedworth Rd. Bris ... 50 A3
Chedworth. Kingsw ... 51 F2
Chedworth. Yate ... 39 D4
Cheese La. Bris ... 63 F3
Chelford Gr. St Gif ... 36 A4
Chelmer Gr. Keyn ... 81 F2
Chelmsford Wlk. Bris ... 64 C3
Chelscombe. Bath ... 84 B1
Chelsea Cl. Keyn ... 82 A3

Chelsea Rd. Bath ... 101 E4
Chelsea Rd. Bris ... 50 A1
Chelsea Rd. Bris ... 64 A4
Chelsfield. Back ... 76 A4
Chelston Rd. Bris ... 79 E4
Chelswood Ave. W-S-M ... 105 E4
Chelswood Gdns. W-S-M ... 105 E4
Cheltenham La. Bris ... 49 F1
Cheltenham Rd. Bris ... 49 F1
Cheltenham St. Bath ... 101 F3
Chelvey Batch. Brock ... 75 F2
Chelvey La. Brock ... 75 F2
Chelvey Rd. Nail ... 75 E3
Chelvey Rise. Nail ... 60 A1
Chelvy Cl. Bris ... 79 E2
Chelwood Dr. Bath ... 101 E1
Chelwood Rd. Bris ... 47 E4
Chelwood Rd. Keyn ... 82 C2
Chepstow Park. Mang ... 37 F1
Chepstow Rd. Bris ... 79 E4
Chepstow Wlk. Keyn ... 81 E3
Chequers Cl. Kingsw ... 66 B2
Cherington Rd. Bris ... 49 E4
Cherington Rd. Nail ... 60 A1
Cherington. Kingsw ... 65 D3
Cherington. Yate ... 39 E3
Cheriton Pl. Bris ... 49 D4
Cheriton Pl. Kingsw ... 66 B3
Cherry Ave. Cleve ... 57 F1
Cherry Cl. Yatt ... 91 E1
Cherry Garden La. Kingsw ... 66 A1
Cherry Garden Rd. Kingsw ... 66 B1
Cherry Gdns. Kingsw ... 66 B1
Cherry Gr. Mang ... 52 A3
Cherry Gr. Yatt ... 91 D4
Cherry Hay. Cleve ... 57 E1
Cherry La. Bris ... 63 F4
Cherry Orchard La. Bris ... 64 C4
Cherry Orchard La. Luck ... 31 E3
Cherry Rd. Ch Sod ... 28 A1
Cherry Rd. Lo Ash ... 61 F1
Cherry Rd. Nail ... 59 E1
Cherry Tree Cl. Bris ... 51 E1
Cherry Tree Cl. Keyn ... 81 E2
Cherry Tree Cl. Rad ... 132 C1
Cherry Tree Cres. Bris ... 51 E1
Cherry Wood. Kingsw ... 66 A1
Cherrytree Rd. Bris ... 51 E1
Cherrywood Rd. W-S-M ... 88 C1
Cherrywood Rise. W-S-M ... 88 C1
Chertsey Rd. Bris ... 49 D1
Cherwell Cl. Thorn ... 15 E4
Cherwell Rd. Keyn ... 82 A2
Chescombe Rd. Yatt ... 91 D4
Chesham Road N. W-S-M ... 105 D4
Chesham Road S. W-S-M ... 105 D4
Chesham Way. Kingsw ... 51 E1
Cheshire Cl. Yate ... 27 F2
Chesle Cl. Portis ... 44 C2
Chesle Way. Portis ... 44 C2
Cheslefield. Portis ... 44 C2
Chesley Hill. Wick ... 66 C4
Chessel Cl. St Gif ... 24 B1
Chessel St. Bris ... 63 D2
Chessell Ave. Piln ... 22 B4
Chessington Ave. Bris ... 80 A3
Chester Park Rd. Bris ... 51 D1
Chester Rd. Bris ... 64 C4
Chester St. Bris ... 50 A1
Chesterfield Ave. Bris ... 49 F1
Chesterfield Cl. Ban ... 106 C2
Chesterfield Rd. Bris ... 49 F1
Chesterfield Rd. Mang ... 51 F3
Chestermaster Cl. Alm ... 24 A3
Chesters. Kingsw ... 66 A2
Chesterton Dr. Nail ... 60 A1
Chestnut Ave. Axb ... 125 E1
Chestnut Ave. W-S-M ... 89 D1
Chestnut Cl. Ban ... 107 D2
Chestnut Cl. Bris ... 80 C3
Chestnut Cl. Cong ... 91 D2
Chestnut Cl. Paul ... 131 F3
Chestnut Cl. Rad ... 132 C1
Chestnut Cl. Mang ... 52 A3
Chestnut Dr. Ch Sod ... 28 A1
Chestnut Dr. Thorn ... 8 B1
Chestnut Dr. Yatt ... 74 C1
Chestnut Gr. Bath ... 101 E2
Chestnut Gr. Cleve ... 57 F2
Chestnut Gr. Westw ... 120 C2
Chestnut La. Blea ... 122 A4
Chestnut Park Est. Kings ... 11 F2
Chestnut Rd. Kingsw ... 51 F2
Chestnut Rd. Lo Ash ... 62 A1
Chestnut Rd. Mang ... 51 E3
Chestnut Way. Kingsw ... 51 F2
Chestnut Wlk. Bris ... 79 D3
Chestnut Wlk. Keyn ... 82 C2
Chestnuts The. Wins ... 125 D4
Chetwoode Cl. Bris ... 35 E3
Chevening Cl. St Gif ... 36 B2
Chever's La. N St P ... 135 F1
Cheviot Dr. Thorn ... 15 F4
Cheviot Way. Kingsw ... 66 B3
Chew Hill. Ch Mag ... 96 A2
Chew La. Ch Mag ... 95 F1
Chew La. Ch St ... 95 F1
Chew Rd. Ch Mag ... 95 E3

Chew Rd. Win ... 95 E3
Chew St. Ch Mag ... 96 A2
Chewton Cl. Bris ... 51 D2
Chewton Rd. Co Dan ... 81 F1
Chewton Rd. Keyn ... 81 F1
Cheyne Rd. Bris ... 48 B3
Che Ivey Rd. Brock ... 75 E3
Chichester Pl. Rad ... 133 D1
Chichester Way. Yate ... 27 E2
Chickwell La. Faulk ... 135 D1
Chilcompton Rd. Chil ... 137 F4
Chilcompton Rd. Mid No ... 137 F4
Chillington Ct. Bris ... 23 F1
Chillyhill La. Ch Mag ... 95 F1
Chillyhill La. Ch St ... 95 F1
Chiltern Cl. Bris ... 80 A2
Chiltern Cl. Kingsw ... 66 B3
Chiltern Park. Thorn ... 15 F4
Chilton Rd. Bath ... 85 D1
Chilton Rd. Bris ... 80 A4
Chilwood Cl. Ir Act ... 26 C2
Chimes The. Nail ... 75 E4
Chine The. Bris ... 50 B3
Chine View. Mang ... 51 F4
Chiphouse Rd. Kingsw ... 51 F2
Chippenham Rd. Marsh ... 70 A4
Chipperfield Dr. Kingsw ... 51 F1
Chipping Cross. Cleve ... 73 E4
Chipping The. Kings ... 11 F2
Chippings The. Bris ... 50 B3
Chisbury St. Bris ... 50 B2
Chittening Rd. Avon ... 33 F4
Chock La. Bris ... 49 D4
Christchurch Ave. Mang ... 51 E3
Christchurch Cl. Nail ... 59 F1
Christchurch La. Mang ... 51 E3
Christchurch Rd. Bris ... 63 D4
Christian Cl. W-S-M ... 89 D2
Christmas St. Bris ... 63 E4
Christmas Steps. Bris ... 63 E4
Christon Rd. Ban ... 107 D1
Christon Rd. Blea ... 123 E3
Christon Terr. W-S-M ... 104 C1
Chubb Cl. Kingsw ... 65 F3
Church Ave. Bris ... 48 C2
Church Ave. Bris ... 50 A1
Church Ave. Falf ... 9 F4
Church Ave. Sist ... 66 B4
Church Cl. Bathf ... 86 A1
Church Cl. Bris ... 34 C1
Church Cl. Cleve ... 57 D1
Church Cl. Fr Cot ... 38 A4
Church Cl. Portis ... 45 E3
Church Cl. Yatt ... 91 E4
Church Cnr. Lymp ... 122 A1
Church Ct. Mid No ... 132 A1
Church Dr. Bris ... 64 C4
Church Dr. Cong ... 91 E2
Church Farm Cl. Marks ... 99 D1
Church Hayes Cl. Nail ... 75 F4
Church Hayes Dr. Nail ... 75 F4
Church Hill. Bris ... 64 C1
Church Hill. Hi Cha ... 120 A3
Church Hill. Kilm ... 133 E2
Church Hill. O-on-S ... 7 D3
Church Hill. Olve ... 14 A2
Church Hill. Tims ... 116 A1
Church La. Axb ... 125 E1
Church La. Back ... 76 B3
Church La. Back ... 76 C4
Church La. Bath ... 102 B2
Church La. Bathe ... 85 F2
Church La. Bi Sut ... 113 E2
Church La. Bitt ... 82 C4
Church La. Blea ... 123 E2
Church La. Bris ... 34 C1
Church La. Bris ... 63 D3
Church La. Bris ... 63 E3
Church La. Bris ... 63 F3
Church La. Ch Sod ... 41 D4
Church La. Ch St ... 112 B4
Church La. Chil ... 137 E3
Church La. Chil ... 137 F1
Church La. Chur ... 108 B3
Church La. Clut ... 114 C2
Church La. Co Bi ... 124 A2
Church La. Co Dan ... 98 B3
Church La. Crom ... 10 A1
Church La. E Harp ... 128 C2
Church La. Farm ... 116 A3
Church La. Fr Cot ... 38 B3
Church La. Li St ... 120 A3
Church La. Lo Ash ... 62 B1
Church La. Lock ... 105 F1
Church La. Lymp ... 122 A1
Church La. Mang ... 37 F1
Church La. Marsh ... 70 A4
Church La. Mid No ... 132 A1
Church La. Nail ... 59 E1
Church La. Nail ... 59 E2
Church La. Paul ... 131 D2
Church La. Paul ... 131 F3
Church La. Portb ... 46 C2
Church La. Tims ... 116 A1
Church La. Wickw ... 16 C1
Church La. Wickw ... 18 A3
Church La. Wins ... 124 C3
Church La. Wint ... 37 E3

Church La. Yatt ... 91 E4
Church Leaze. Bris ... 47 E3
Church Par. Bris ... 64 C1
Church Pl. E in G ... 47 E2
Church Rd N. Portis ... 45 E3
Church Rd S. Portis ... 45 E2
Church Rd. Ab Lei ... 62 A4
Church Rd. Alm ... 23 D1
Church Rd. Alm ... 24 A3
Church Rd. Alve ... 15 D1
Church Rd. Bath ... 84 B1
Church Rd. Bath ... 102 B3
Church Rd. Bitt ... 82 C4
Church Rd. Bris ... 36 A2
Church Rd. Bris ... 48 B2
Church Rd. Bris ... 49 D4
Church Rd. Bris ... 49 E4
Church Rd. Bris ... 49 F1
Church Rd. Bris ... 51 D4
Church Rd. Bris ... 63 E2
Church Rd. Bris ... 64 B4
Church Rd. Bris ... 79 D3
Church Rd. Bris ... 80 A2
Church Rd. Doyn ... 54 A1
Church Rd. Dun ... 78 B1
Church Rd. E in G ... 47 D2
Church Rd. Fr Cot ... 38 B4
Church Rd. Kingsw ... 51 F1
Church Rd. Kingsw ... 51 F2
Church Rd. Lo Ash ... 62 B3
Church Rd. Luck ... 31 F2
Church Rd. Lymp ... 122 A1
Church Rd. O-on-S ... 7 D2
Church Rd. O-on-S ... 7 D3
Church Rd P St J ... 133 D4
Church Rd. Piln ... 22 C3
Church Rd. St Gif ... 36 C2
Church Rd. Thorn ... 8 A1
Church Rd. W-S-M ... 88 C1
Church Rd. Whit ... 80 A2
Church Rd. Whit ... 97 D4
Church Rd. Wick ... 67 D3
Church Rd. Win ... 95 D4
Church Rd. Wins ... 124 C4
Church Rd. Wint ... 37 F2
Church Rd. Yate ... 27 F1
Church Rd. Yatt ... 91 E4
Church Rise. Win ... 95 D4
Church Row. Chil ... 137 F1
Church Sq. Clut ... 114 C1
Church Sq. Mid No ... 132 A1
Church St. Ban ... 107 D2
Church St. Bath ... 84 A1
Church St. Bath ... 102 A2
Church St. Bath ... 102 A3
Church St. Bathf ... 86 A1
Church St. Blag ... 110 C1
Church St. Bris ... 50 A1
Church St. Bris ... 63 F3
Church St. Bris ... 64 A3
Church St. Charl ... 84 C3
Church St. N St P ... 135 F2
Church St. Paul ... 131 E3
Church St. Pens ... 97 E2
Church St. Rad ... 132 C1
Church Town. Back ... 76 B3
Church View. Bris ... 36 A3
Church View. Mang ... 51 E3
Church View. Newp ... 4 B3
Church View. Win ... 95 D3
Church Wlk. E in G ... 47 D2
Church Wlk. Wring ... 92 B1
Churchdown Wlk. Bris ... 47 F3
Churchend La. Char ... 10 C2
Churchfarm Cl. Yate ... 27 F2
Churchhill Rd. Bris ... 64 B2
Churchill Ave. Cleve ... 57 E1
Churchill Cl. Cleve ... 57 E1
Churchill Cl. Kingsw ... 66 A3
Churchill Dr. Bris ... 48 B4
Churchill Gate. Chur ... 108 C2
Churchill Green. Chur ... 108 A3
Churchill Rd. W-S-M ... 105 D4
Churchlands Rd. Bris ... 63 D1
Churchpath Rd. E in G ... 47 E2
Churchside. Bris ... 51 D4
Churchward Cl. Kingsw ... 65 D3
Churchward Rd. W-S-M ... 89 D2
Churchward Rd. Yate ... 27 D2
Churchway. Faulk ... 134 B1
Churchways Ave. Bris ... 49 F3
Churchways Cres. Bris ... 49 F3
Churchways. Whit ... 80 B2
Churston Cl. Bris ... 80 A2
Circle The. Bath ... 101 D2
Circular Rd. Bris ... 48 C1
Circus Mews. Bath ... 101 F4
Circus Pl. Bath ... 101 F4
Circus The. Bath ... 101 F4
City Bsns Pk. Bris ... 64 A4
City Rd. Bris ... 49 F1
Clamp The. Kingsw ... 66 B2
Clanage Rd. Bris ... 62 C2
Clanders Batch. Blag ... 110 B2
Clandown Rd. Paul ... 131 F2
Clapton Dro. W in G ... 45 E1
Clapton La. W in G ... 45 E1
Clapton Rd. Mid No ... 131 E1
Clapton Rd. Ston E ... 131 E1

Clare Ave. Bris ... 49 E2
Clare Gdns. Bath ... 101 E1
Clare Rd. Bris ... 49 E1
Clare Rd. Bris ... 50 A1
Clare Rd. Bris ... 51 E1
Clare St. Bris ... 63 E3
Clare St. Bris ... 64 B4
Clare Wlk. Thorn ... 8 A1
Claremont Ave. Bris ... 49 E2
Claremont Bldgs. Bath ... 85 D1
Claremont Cres. W-S-M ... 87 D1
Claremont Gdns. Cleve ... 57 F1
Claremont Gdns. Nail ... 59 E1
Claremont Gdns. Paul ... 131 D2
Claremont Rd. Bath ... 85 D1
Claremont Rd. Bris ... 49 E2
Claremont St. Bris ... 50 A1
Claremont Terr. Bris ... 64 B4
Claremont Wlk. Bath ... 85 D1
Clarence Ave. Mang ... 51 F3
Clarence Gdns. Mang ... 51 F3
Clarence Grove Rd. W-S-M ... 104 C3
Clarence Pl. Bath ... 101 D3
Clarence Pl. Bris ... 63 E4
Clarence Rd E. W-S-M ... 104 C3
Clarence Rd N. W-S-M ... 104 B3
Clarence Rd S. W-S-M ... 104 B3
Clarence Rd. Bris ... 51 D1
Clarence Rd. Bris ... 63 F3
Clarence Rd. Bris ... 64 A4
Clarence Rd. Mang ... 51 F3
Clarence St. Bath ... 102 A4
Clarendon Rd. Bath ... 102 A3
Clarendon Rd. Bris ... 49 E1
Clarendon Rd. W-S-M ... 104 C4
Clark Dr. Bris ... 50 C4
Clark St. Bris ... 64 A4
Clarke St. Bris ... 63 E2
Clarken Cl. Nail ... 59 F1
Clarken Coombe. Lo Ash ... 62 A2
Clarkson Ave. W-S-M ... 88 B1
Clatworthy Dr. Bris ... 80 A4
Claude Ave. Bath ... 101 E3
Clavell Rd. Bris ... 34 C1
Claverham Cl. Yatt ... 91 E4
Claverham Dro. Yatt ... 74 B3
Claverham Park. Yatt ... 91 F4
Claverham Rd. Bris ... 51 D3
Claverham Rd. Yatt ... 91 F4
Claverton Ct. Bath ... 102 C2
Claverton Down Rd. Bath ... 102 C2
Claverton Rd W. Keyn ... 82 B2
Claverton Rd. Keyn ... 82 B2
Claverton St. Bath ... 102 A3
Clay Bottom. Bris ... 50 C1
Clay Hill. Bris ... 50 C1
Clay La. Bitt ... 66 B1
Clay La. St Gif ... 36 B4
Clay La. Thorn ... 8 C1
Clay Pit Rd. Bris ... 49 D2
Claydon Green. Bris ... 79 F2
Clayfield Rd. Bris ... 64 C2
Clayfield. Yate ... 27 F3
Claymore Cres. Bris ... 51 D1
Claypiece Rd. Bris ... 79 D2
Claypit Hill. Ch Sod ... 40 A4
Claypool Rd. Kingsw ... 65 F4
Clayton Cl. Portis ... 45 F2
Clayton St. Avon ... 33 D1
Clayton St. Bris ... 64 A4
Cleave St. Bris ... 50 A1
Cleeve Ave. Mang ... 51 F4
Cleeve Dr. Brock ... 92 A4
Cleeve Gdns. Mang ... 51 E4
Cleeve Gr. Keyn ... 81 E3
Cleeve Green. Bath ... 100 C3
Cleeve Hill Extension. Mang ... 51 F3
Cleeve Hill Rd. Brock ... 92 B4
Cleeve Hill. Co Mar ... 127 F4
Cleeve Hill. Mang ... 51 E4
Cleeve La. Wick ... 53 E1
Cleeve Lawns. Mang ... 51 F4
Cleeve Lodge Cl. Mang ... 51 F3
Cleeve Lodge Rd. Mang ... 51 F3
Cleeve Park Rd. Mang ... 51 F4
Cleeve Pl. Nail ... 60 A1
Cleeve Rd. Bris ... 51 E4
Cleeve Rd. Bris ... 64 A2
Cleeve Rd. Mang ... 51 F3
Cleeve Rd. Yate ... 27 F1
Cleeve Wood Rd. Mang ... 51 E4
Cleevedale Rd. Bath ... 102 A1
Clement St. Bris ... 63 F4
Cleve Rd. Bris ... 36 A2
Clevedale. Mang ... 51 E4
Clevedon La. W in G ... 59 E4
Clevedon Rd. Bris ... 49 E2
Clevedon Rd. Lo Ash ... 61 E2
Clevedon Rd. Lo Ash ... 77 D4
Clevedon Rd. Mid No ... 132 A1
Clevedon Rd. Nail ... 59 E2
Clevedon Rd. Portis ... 45 E2
Clevedon Rd. W-S-M ... 104 C3
Clevedon Rd. Wrax ... 60 B2
Clevedon Rd. Wrax ... 60 B3
Clevedon Terr. Bris ... 63 E4
Cleveland Cl. Thorn ... 15 F4
Cleveland Pl. Bath ... 102 A4

Cleveland Wlk. Bath

Cleveland Wlk. Bath 102 B3
Cliff Court Dr. Bris 51 D4
Cliff Rd. Priddy 126 A1
Cliff Rd. W-S-M 88 A1
Cliffe Dr. Li St 120 A3
Clifford Gdns. Bris 47 F3
Clifford Rd. Bris 51 E2
Clift House Rd. Bris 63 D2
Clift House Spur. Bris 62 C2
Clift Pl. Bris 63 E3
Clift Rd. Bris 63 D2
Clifton Ave. W-S-M 104 C3
Clifton Cl. Bris 62 C4
Clifton Down Rd. Bris 63 D4
Clifton Down. Bris 62 C4
Clifton Hill. Bris 63 D3
Clifton Park Rd. Bris 62 C4
Clifton Park. Bris 63 D4
Clifton Pl. Bris 64 A4
Clifton Rd. Bris 63 D4
Clifton Rd. W-S-M 104 C3
Clifton St. Bris 63 E2
Clifton St. Bris 64 A4
Clifton St. Portis 45 E1
Clifton Vale Cl. Bris 63 D3
Clifton Vale. Bris 63 D3
Clifton View. Bris 63 F2
Clifton Wood Rd. Bris 63 D3
Cliftonwood Cres. Bris 63 D3
Cliftonwood Terr. Bris 63 D3
Clinton Rd. Bris 63 E1
Clive Rd. Bris 80 B4
Cloisters Rd. Wint 37 F3
Clonmel Rd. Bris 63 E1
Close The. Bris 35 D3
Close The. Fr Cot 38 B3
Close The. Kingsw 51 E2
Close The. St Gif 24 B1
Close The. St Gif 36 B3
Close The. W in G 44 C1
Closemead. Cleve 57 E1
Clothier Rd. Bris 64 C1
Clouds Hill Ave. Bris 64 C4
Clouds Hill Rd. Bris 64 C4
Clovelly Cl. Bris 64 C4
Clovelly Rd. Bris 64 C4
Clovelly Rd. W-S-M 89 D1
Clover Cl. Cleve 57 F2
Clover Ground. Bris 49 D4
Clover Leaze. St Gif 36 B3
Cloverdale Dr. Kingsw 66 A2
Cloverlea Rd. Kingsw 66 B3
Clutton Hill. Clut 115 D2
Clyde Cl. Keyn 81 F2
Clyde Gdns. Bath 101 D3
Clyde Gdns. Bris 65 D3
Clyde Gr. Bris 35 F1
Clyde La. Bris 49 E1
Clyde Park. Bris 49 D1
Clyde Rd. Bris 49 D1
Clyde Rd. Bris 64 A2
Clyde Rd. Fr Cot 38 A4
Clyde Terr. Bris 63 E2
Clyde Terr. Bris 64 A2
Clydesdale Cl. Bris 80 A3
Clynder Gr. Cleve 57 F3
Co-operation Rd. Bris 50 B1
Coalbridge Cl. W-S-M 88 C1
Coaley Rd. Bris 47 E3
Coalpit La. Chil 137 D1
Coalpit Rd. Bathe 86 A2
Coalsack La. West 38 A2
Coalville Rd. Fr Cot 38 B4
Coape Rd. Bris 80 C3
Coates Gr. Nail 60 A1
Coates Wlk. Bris 79 E3
Cobblestone Mews. Bris 63 D4
Cobhorn Dr. Bris 78 C2
Cobley Croft. Cleve 73 E4
Cobourg Rd. Bris 49 F1
Cobthorn Way. Cong 91 F3
Cock And Yew Tree Hill. Win 95 D2
Cock La. Dyrh 54 B3
Cock Rd. Kingsw 65 F3
Cockers Hill. Co Dan 98 B3
Codben St. Bris 64 B4
Codrington Rd. Bris 49 E2
Cody Ct. Kingsw 65 D3
Cogan Rd. Kingsw 51 F2
Cogsall Rd. Bris 80 C3
Coker Rd. W-S-M 89 D1
Colbourne Rd. Bath 101 E1
Colchester Cres. Bris 79 E4
Coldharbour La. Bris 36 C1
Coldharbour La. W-S-M 104 B2
Coldharbour Rd. Bris 49 D2
Coldpark Gdns. Bris 78 C3
Coldpark Rd. Bris 78 C3
Coldrick Cl. Bris 79 F2
Cole Rd. Bris 64 A3
Colebrook Rd. Bris 65 E4
Coleford Rd. Bris 35 E1
Colehouse La. Cleve 73 E4
Coleridge Rd. Bris 50 B2
Coleridge Rd. Cleve 57 E2
Coleridge Rd. W-S-M 105 D2
Coleridge Vale Rd E. Cleve 57 E1
Coleridge Vale Rd N. Cleve 57 E1

Coleridge Vale Rd S. Cleve 57 E1
Coleridge Vale Rd W. Cleve 57 E1
Coles Gdns. Kilm 139 D3
Colesborne Cl. Yate 39 E4
Coleshill Dr. Bris 79 D3
Coley Rd. E Harp 129 D2
Colin Rd. Thorn 8 B1
College Ave. Bris 51 D3
College Ct. Bris 51 D3
College Fields. Bris 62 C4
College Green. Bris 63 E3
College Park Dr. Bris 34 C1
College Rd. Bath 84 C1
College Rd. Bris 49 D4
College Rd. Bris 51 D3
College Rd. Bris 62 C4
College Sq. Bris 63 E3
College St. Bris 63 E3
Collett Cl. Lock 89 E2
Collett Cl. Kingsw 65 D3
Collier Cl. Tims 132 B4
Colliers La. Charl 84 C2
Collin Rd. Bris 64 B2
Collingwood Ave. Kingsw 51 F1
Collingwood Cl. Keyn 82 C1
Collingwood Cl. W-S-M 88 C2
Collingwood Rd. Bris 49 D1
Collins Ave. St Gif 36 B3
Collins St. Avon 47 D4
Collinson Rd. Bris 79 D3
Colliter Cres. Bris 63 D1
Collum La. W St L 88 C1
Collum La. W-S-M 88 C3
Coln Sq. Thorn 15 E4
Colne Green. Keyn 82 A2
Colombo Cres. W-S-M 104 C2
Colston Ave. Bris 63 E4
Colston Cl. Kingsw 51 E2
Colston Cl. Wint 37 F2
Colston Ct. Bris 49 E2
Colston Dale. Bris 50 C2
Colston Hill. Bris 50 B3
Colston Par. Bris 63 F3
Colston Rd. Bris 50 B1
Colston St. Bris 63 E4
Colston St. Kingsw 51 E2
Colthurst Dr. Kingsw 65 F3
Colts Green. Ch Sod 40 C4
Colwyn Rd. Bris 50 B1
Comb Paddock. Bris 49 D4
Combe Ave. Portis 45 E3
Combe End. Mid No 132 C2
Combe Fields. Portis 45 E3
Combe Hay La. Bath 118 A3
Combe Hay La. Sosto 118 A3
Combe La. Paul 131 D3
Combe Rd. Bath 101 D4
Combe Rd. Portis 45 E3
Combe Road Cl. Bath 102 A1
Combe Side. Back 76 A4
Combe The. Blag 109 F1
Combermere. Thorn 15 E4
Combeside. Bath 102 A2
Combfactory La. Bris 64 A4
Commercial Rd. Bris 63 E3
Common (E) The. St Gif 24 B1
Common La. Chur 108 A3
Common La. E in G 47 D1
Common Mead La. Bris 37 D1
Common Rd. Kingsw 65 D2
Common Rd. Wint 37 F4
Common The. Bris 51 D4
Common The. St Gif 24 B1
Commonfield Rd. Bris 34 A1
Commonmead La. Ch Sod 29 D1
Compton Dr. Bris 48 B4
Compton Green. Keyn 81 F2
Compton St. Bris 64 B4
Comrade Ave. Ship 125 F4
Comyn Wlk. Bris 51 D3
Concorde Dr. Bris 35 D1
Concorde Rd. Bris 35 D1
Condor Cl. W-S-M 105 E4
Condover Rd. Bris 65 D2
Conduit Pl. Bris 50 A1
Conduit Rd. Bris 50 A1
Congleton Rd. Bris 64 B4
Conham Hill. Kingsw 65 D3
Conham Rd. Bris 64 C3
Conham Vale. Bris 65 D3
Conham Vale. Kingsw 65 D3
Conifer Cl. Bris 51 E3
Conifer Cl. Fr Cot 26 A1
Conifer Way. Lock 105 F3
Coniston Ave. Bris 48 C3
Coniston Cl. Kingsw 66 B3
Coniston Cres. W-S-M 104 C2
Coniston Rd. Bris 23 F1
Conkwell. Winsl 103 E1
Connaught Rd. Bris 79 F4
Connection Rd. Bath 101 D3
Constable Dr. W-S-M 88 C2
Constable Rd. Bris 50 A3
Constantine Ave. St Gif 36 C3
Constitution Hill. Bris 63 D3

Convent Cl. Bris 34 B2
Convocation Ave. Bath 102 C3
Conway Green. Keyn 82 A2
Conway Rd. Bris 64 B2
Conygar Cl. Cleve 57 F3
Conygre Gr. Bris 36 B2
Conygre Green. Tims 116 A1
Conygre Rd. Bris 36 A2
Conygre Rise. Farm 115 F3
Cook Cl. Kingsw 66 B2
Cook's Folly Rd. Bris 48 B2
Cook's La. Ban 107 D2
Cook's La. Cleve 58 A1
Cook's La. Cleve 58 B1
Cooke's Dr. Alm 23 D1
Cooks Bridle Path. Wring 93 E4
Cooks Cl. St Gif 24 B2
Cooks La. West 38 B2
Cooksley Rd. Bris 64 B4
Cookworthy Cl. Bris 64 A3
Coombe Ave. Thorn 8 A1
Coombe Bridge Ave. Bris 48 B3
Coombe Cl. Bris 34 B2
Coombe Dale. Bris 48 B3
Coombe Dale. Wring 94 A4
Coombe Gdns. Bris 48 C3
Coombe La. Bris 48 C3
Coombe La. Co Bi 124 A2
Coombe La. E Harp 128 C2
Coombe La. E n G 47 D1
Coombe Park. Bath 101 E4
Coombe Rd. Nail 59 F1
Coombe Rd. W-S-M 104 C4
Coombe The. Blag 110 B2
Coombe The. Co Mar 128 A3
Coombe The. Bris 34 C1
Coombes Way. Kingsw 66 B2
Cooper Rd. Thorn 15 D4
Cooper Rd. Bris 48 C4
Cooperage La. Bris 63 D3
Cooperage Rd. Bris 64 B4
Coots The. Bris 80 C3
Cope Park. Alm 24 B3
Copeland Dr. Bris 80 A3
Copford La. Lo Ash 62 A1
Copley Ct. Kingsw 65 F3
Copley Gdns. Bris 50 A3
Copley Gdns. W-S-M 88 C1
Copperfield Dr. W-S-M 88 C2
Coppice End Cnr. Lymp 122 B1
Coppice The. Bris 78 C2
Coppice The. St Gif 36 C4
Copse Cl. W-S-M 105 D1
Copse End. Winsc 107 F1
Copse Rd. Cleve 57 E2
Copse Rd. Keyn 82 B2
Copseland. Bath 102 B3
Copythorne Rd. Bris 50 C2
Coralberry Dr. W-S-M 88 C1
Corbet Cl. Bris 34 B1
Cordington Pl. Bris 63 D4
Cordwell Wlk. Bris 49 E4
Corey Cl. Bris 49 F1
Corfe Cl. Nail 59 E1
Corfe Cres. Keyn 81 F2
Corfe Pl. Kingsw 66 A1
Corfe Rd. Bris 79 E4
Coriander Wlk. Bris 50 B1
Corinthian Ct. Bris 63 F3
Cork St. Bath 101 E4
Corker's Hill. Bris 64 C3
Cormorant Cl. W-S-M 88 C1
Corn St. Bath 101 F3
Corn St. Bris 63 E3
Corner Croft. Cleve 57 E1
Cornhill Dr. Bris 80 A4
Cornish Gr. Bris 80 C3
Cornish Rd. Bris 80 C3
Cornish's Grave. Kilm 139 F2
Cornleaze. Bris 79 D3
Cornwall Cres. Yate 27 F2
Cornwall Rd. Bris 49 E2
Cornwallis Ave. Bris 63 D3
Cornwallis Ave. W-S-M 88 C2
Cornwallis Cres. Bris 63 D3
Cornwallis Gr. Bris 63 D3
Coronation Ave. Bath 101 E2
Coronation Ave. Bris 50 D2
Coronation Ave. Keyn 81 E2
Coronation Cl. Kingsw 66 A3
Coronation Pl. Bris 63 E3
Coronation Rd. Ban 107 D2
Coronation Rd. Bath 101 E4
Coronation Rd. Blea 122 B3
Coronation Rd. Bris 63 D2
Coronation Rd. Kingsw 66 A3
Coronation Rd. Kingsw 66 A4
Coronation Rd. Mang 51 F2
Coronation Rd. W-S-M 88 C1
Corondale Rd. W-S-M 105 D4
Corridor The. Bath 102 A3
Corsley Wlk. Bris 79 E4
Corston View. Bath 101 E1
Corston Wlk. Bris 47 E4

Corston. W-S-M 105 D1
Cossham Cl. Thorn 8 B1
Cossham Rd. Bris 64 B4
Cossham Rd. Puck 53 E2
Cossham St. Mang 52 A3
Cossham Wlk. Bris 51 D1
Cossington Rd. Bris 79 F4
Cossins Rd. Bris 49 D2
Costers Cl. Alve 15 D3
Costiland Dr. Bris 78 C3
Cote Dr. Bris 49 D2
Cote House La. Bris 49 D3
Cote La. Bris 49 D3
Cote Lea Park. Bris 49 D4
Cote Paddock. Bris 48 C2
Cote Rd. Bris 49 D2
Cotham Brow. Bris 49 E1
Cotham Gdns. Bris 49 D1
Cotham Gr. Bris 49 E1
Cotham Hill. Bris 63 E4
Cotham Lawn Rd. Bris 49 E1
Cotham Park N. Bris 49 E1
Cotham Park. Bris 49 E1
Cotham Rd S. Bris 63 E4
Cotham Rd. Bris 63 E4
Cotham Side. Bris 49 E1
Cotham Vale. Bris 49 E1
Cotman Wlk. Bris 50 A3
Cotman Wlk. W-S-M 88 C1
Cotrith Gr. Bris 34 C2
Cotswold Cl. Portis 45 F2
Cotswold La. Ch Sod 41 D4
Cotswold Rd. Bath 101 E2
Cotswold Rd. Bris 63 E2
Cotswold Rd. Ch Sod 40 A4
Cotswold View. Bris 36 A2
Cotswold View. Char 11 D3
Cotswold View. Kingsw 51 E1
Cotswold View. Wickww 18 A3
Cottage Pl. Bris 63 E4
Cottington Ct. Kingsw 65 F3
Cottisford Rd. Bris 50 A2
Cottle Gdns. Bris 80 C3
Cottle Rd. Bris 80 C3
Cottles La. Winsl 120 C3
Cotton Mead. Cor 100 A4
Cottonwood Dr. Kingsw 66 A2
Cottrell Ave. Bris 51 E1
Cottrell Rd. Bris 50 B2
Cotts The. Wring 92 B1
Coulson Dr. W-S-M 89 D2
Coulson Wlk. Bris 51 E1
Coulson's Cl. Bris 80 A2
Coulson's Rd. Bris 80 A2
Counterpool Rd. Kingsw 65 E4
Counterslip Gdns. Bris 80 B3
Counterslip. Bris 63 F3
Countess Wlk. Bris 50 B3
County St. Bris 64 A2
Court Ave. St Gif 36 C3
Court Ave. Yatt 91 E4
Court Cl. Back 76 B3
Court Cl. Bris 49 E4
Court Cl. Portis 45 E2
Court Dr. Wins 108 A2
Court Farm Rd. Bris 79 F2
Court Farm Rd. Kingsw 65 F1
Court Gdns. Bathe 86 A2
Court Hay. E in G 47 D2
Court Hill. Co Dan 98 B3
Court La. Bathf 86 A1
Court La. Cleve 58 A2
Court La. Wick 67 D3
Court La. Wins 125 F4
Court Mead. Stone 3 F2
Court Meadow. Stone 3 F2
Court Pl. W-S-M 88 C1
Court Rd. Bris 49 F3
Court Rd. Fr Cot 37 F4
Court Rd. Kingsw 65 E4
Court Rd. Kingsw 66 B2
Court Rd. W St L 88 A3
Court View. Alm 24 A3
Court View. Wick 67 E4
Courtenay Rd. Keyn 82 A1
Courtenay Wlk. W-S-M 89 D2
Courteney Cres. Bris 79 E4
Courtfield Gr. Bris 51 D2
Courtlands La. Bris 62 C2
Courtlands. Keyn 81 F3
Courtlands. St Gif 24 B1
Courtmead. Sosto 118 C4
Courtney Rd. Kingsw 65 F4
Courtney Way. Kingsw 66 A4
Courtside Mews. Bris 49 E1
Courtville Cl. Alve 15 D2
Courtyard The. Nail 59 F1
Cousins Cl. Bris 34 B2
Cousins La. Bris 64 C4
Couzens Cl. Yate 28 A1
Couzens Pl. St Gif 36 C3
Coventry Wlk. Bris 64 C3
Cowdray Rd. Bris 79 E4
Cowleaze La. E Harp 128 B3
Cowler Wlk. Bris 78 C2
Cowling Dr. Bris 80 B3
Cowling Rd. Bris 80 B3
Cowper Rd. Bris 49 E1

Cropthorne Rd. Bris

Cowper St. Bris 64 B4
Cowship La. Crom 17 E3
Cowship La. Wickw 17 E3
Cowslip La. Blea 123 E2
Cox Ct. Kingsw 65 F2
Cox's Green. Wring 92 C1
Coxley Dr. Bath 85 D1
Coxway. Cleve 57 F1
Crabtree Cl. Dun 78 B1
Crabtree La. Dun 78 B1
Crabtree Wlk. Bris 50 B1
Craddock Cl. Kingsw 66 A2
Cranberry Wlk. Bris 48 B4
Cranbourne Chase. W-S-M 88 A1
Cranbourne Rd. Bris 35 F4
Cranbrook Rd. Bris 49 E2
Crandale Rd. Bath 101 D3
Crandell Cl. Bris 34 C2
Crane Cl. Kingsw 66 A4
Cranford Cl. W-S-M 88 B1
Cranham Cl. Kingsw 51 F1
Cranham Dr. St Gif 24 B1
Cranham Rd. Bris 49 E4
Cranham. Yate 39 E4
Cranhill Rd. Bath 101 E4
Cranleigh Court Rd. Yate 27 E1
Cranleigh Gdns. Bris 48 C2
Cranleigh Rd. Bris 80 A3
Cranleigh. Sosto 118 C4
Cranmore Ave. Keyn 81 F3
Cranmore Cres. Bris 35 E1
Cranmore Pl. Bath 118 C4
Cranmore. W-S-M 105 D1
Cranside Ave. Bris 49 E2
Cransley Cres. Bris 49 E4
Crantock Ave. Bris 79 D4
Crantock Dr. Alm 24 B3
Crantock Rd. Yate 27 E1
Cranwell Gr. Bris 80 A3
Cranwells Park. Bath 101 E4
Crates Cl. Kingsw 65 F4
Craven Way. Kingsw 65 F3
Crawford Cl. Cleve 57 D1
Crawl La. Mid No 132 B2
Craydon Gr. Bris 80 B2
Craydon Rd. Bris 80 B3
Craydon Wlk. Bris 80 B3
Crediton Cres. Bris 63 F1
Crediton. W-S-M 89 D1
Crescent La. Bath 101 F4
Crescent Rd. Bris 51 E3
Crescent The. Back 76 A3
Crescent The. Bris 48 B3
Crescent The. Bris 49 E3
Crescent The. Kingsw 51 E2
Crescent The. Lymp 122 B3
Crescent The. Olve 14 B2
Crescent The. Paul 131 D2
Crescent The. Pens 96 C1
Crescent The. W-S-M 88 A1
Crescent The. Wick 67 E4
Crescent View. Bath 101 F3
Cresswell Cl. W-S-M 89 D1
Crest The. Bris 64 B1
Creswicke Ave. Kingsw 65 E3
Creswicke Rd. Bris 79 F4
Crew's Hole Rd. Bris 64 C4
Crewkerne Cl. Nail 60 A1
Cribbs Causeway Centre.
  Bris 35 D3
Cribbs Causeway. Bris 35 D3
Crickback La. Ch Mag 96 A2
Cricket Field Green. Nail 59 E1
Cricklade Cl. Nail 60 A1
Cricklade Rd. Bris 49 F2
Cripps Rd. Bris 63 E2
Crispin La. Thorn 8 A1
Crispin Way. Kingsw 51 F1
Crockerne Dr. E in G 47 E2
Crocombe La. Tims 116 B2
Crocombe. Tims 116 B2
Croft Ave. Bris 50 B2
Croft Cl. Bitt 82 B4
Croft Rd. Bath 85 D1
Croft The. Back 76 A4
Croft The. Bath 102 C1
Croft The. Cleve 57 F2
Croft The. Kingsw 66 B2
Croft The. Lock 105 F2
Croft The. Mang 51 F3
Croft The. Westw 120 C2
Croft View. Bris 49 E3
Crofton Ave. Bris 49 F3
Crofts End Rd. Bris 50 C1
Crokeswood Wlk. Bris 34 A1
Crome Rd. Bris 50 A4
Cromer Rd. Bris 50 B1
Cromer Rd. W-S-M 104 C3
Cromhall La. Crom 9 F1
Cromwell Ct. Kingsw 65 F3
Cromwell Dr. W-S-M 89 D2
Cromwell Rd. Bris 49 F1
Cromwell Rd. Bris 65 D4
Cromwell St. Bris 63 E2
Cromwells Hide. Bris 50 C3
Crook's La. W-S-M 88 A2
Croomes Hill. Mang 51 E3
Cropthorne Rd. Bris 36 A1

Name	Page	Grid
Crosby Row. Bris	63	D3
Cross Combe Dr. Bris	79	E2
Cross Combez Wlk. Bris	79	E2
Cross Elms La. Bris	48	C3
Cross Hands Rd. Piln	22	B4
Cross La. Co Bi	125	D1
Cross Lanes. E in G	47	E2
Cross Manor Rd. Axb	125	D1
Cross Moor Dr. Axb	125	D1
Cross Moor Dro. Co Bi	124	C2
Cross St. Bris	51	E1
Cross St. Keyn	81	F4
Cross St. W-S-M	104	C4
Cross The. E Harp	128	C2
Cross Tree Gr. St Gif	36	B4
Cross Wlk. Bris	80	A3
Crossfield Rd. Kingsw	51	F2
Crossleaze Rd. Kingsw	65	E2
Crossley Cl. Wint	37	F4
Crossman Ave. Wint	37	F3
Crossman Wlk. Cleve	57	F1
Crosspost La. Co Dan	99	D2
Crossway La. Ston E	137	D4
Crossways Rd. Bris	64	A1
Crossways Rd. Thorn	8	A1
Crossways. Newp	4	C4
Crow La. Bris	34	C1
Crow La. Bris	63	E3
Crow Meadow. Kings	11	F2
Crowe Hill. Li St	120	A3
Crowe La. Hi Cha	120	A3
Crown Gdns. Kingsw	66	A4
Crown Glass Pl. Nail	59	F1
Crown Hill Wlk. Bris	50	C1
Crown Hill. Bath	84	B1
Crown Hill. Bris	64	C4
Crown Hill. Kingsw	66	B2
Crown Hill. Win	95	D2
Crown House. Nail	59	E1
Crown La. Kingsw	66	B2
Crown Rd. Bath	84	A1
Crown Rd. Kingsw	51	E1
Crown Rd. Kingsw	66	B3
Crowndale Rd. Bris	64	A2
Crownleaze. Kingsw	51	E2
Crows Gr. St Gif	24	B2
Crowther Park. Bris	50	A2
Crowther Rd. Bris	50	A2
Crowther St. Bris	63	D2
Crowthers Ave. Yate	27	F2
Croydon St. Bris	64	A4
Crunnis The. St Gif	36	C3
Cuck Hill. Ship	125	F4
Cuckoo La. Clut	115	D2
Cuckoo La. Wint	37	F2
Cuckoo La. Wrax	60	A3
Cuffington Ave. Bris	64	B2
Culleysgate La. Wick	67	F3
Culver La. E Harp	128	C2
Culver St. Bris	63	E3
Culverhay. Co Dan	98	B3
Culverhill Rd. Ch Sod	28	A1
Culvers Rd. Keyn	81	F3
Culverwell Rd. Bris	79	D2
Cumberland Basin Rd. Bris	62	C3
Cumberland Cl. Bris	62	C3
Cumberland Gr. Bris	49	F1
Cumberland Pl. Bris	62	C3
Cumberland Rd. Bris	63	D3
Cumberland Row. Bath	101	F3
Cumberland St. Bris	63	F4
Cumbria Cl. Thorn	8	C1
Cunningham Gdns. Bris	51	D3
Curland Gr. Bris	80	A3
Curlew Cl. Bris	50	C3
Curlew Gdns. W-S-M	88	C1
Currells La. Win	77	D1
Curtis La. St Gif	37	D2
Custom Cl. Bris	80	A4
Cutler Rd. Bris	78	C3
Cutsheath Rd. Tyth	16	B4
Cuttsheath Rd. Thorn	16	B4
Cygnet Cres. W-S-M	88	C1
Cynthia Rd. Bath	101	E3
Cypress Ct. Bris	48	B2
Cypress Gdns. Lo Ash	62	C3
Cypress Gr. Bris	49	E3
Cypress Terr. Rad	132	B1
Cypress Wlk. Col	70	C3
Dafford St. Bath	85	E1
Dafford's Bldgs. Bath	85	E1
Daglands The. Tims	132	C4
Dairy Hill. Well	134	A3
Daisy Green La. N Nib	5	E1
Daisy Rd. Bris	50	B1
Dakota Dr. Bris	80	A2
Dalby Ave. Bris	63	E2
Daldry Gdns. Olve	14	A2
Dale St. Bris	63	F4
Dale St. Bris	64	C4
Daley Cl. W-S-M	89	D2
Dalkeith Ave. Bris	51	E1
Dalrymple Rd. Bris	49	F1
Dalston Rd. Bris	63	D2
Dalton Sq. Bris	63	F4
Dalwood. W-S-M	89	D1
Dame Court Cl. W-S-M	88	C2
Damery La. N Nib	4	A1
Damery La. Stone	4	A1
Dampier Rd. Bris	63	D2
Danbury Cres. Bris	35	E1
Danbury Wlk. Bris	35	E1
Dancey Mead. Bris	78	C4
Dane Cl. Winsl	120	C4
Dane Rise. Winsl	120	C4
Daneacre Rd. Mid No	133	D2
Dangerfield Ave. Bris	78	C3
Daniel Cl. Cleve	57	F2
Daniel Mews. Bath	102	A4
Daniel St. Bath	102	A4
Dapps Hill. Keyn	81	F3
Dapwell La. Co Dan	81	D1
Dark La. Back	76	A3
Dark La. Ban	107	E1
Dark La. Blag	110	C2
Dark La. Ch Mag	95	F2
Dark La. Hi Cha	120	A3
Dark La. Hol	138	B1
Dark La. Hol	139	D1
Darley Cl. Bris	34	B2
Darlington Mews. Bath	102	A4
Darlington Pl. Bath	102	A3
Darlington Rd. Bath	102	A4
Darlington St. Bath	102	A4
Darmead. W-S-M	89	D1
Darnley Ave. Bris	49	F3
Dart Cl. Thorn	15	D4
Dart Rd. Cleve	57	E1
Dartmoor St. Bris	63	D2
Dartmouth Ave. Bath	101	E3
Dartmouth Cl. W-S-M	89	D1
Dartmouth Wlk. Keyn	81	E2
Daubeny Cl. Bris	51	D3
Daventry Rd. Bris	63	F1
Davey St. Bris	49	F1
David St. Bris	63	F4
David's La. Alve	15	D2
David's Rd. Bris	80	B3
David's Rd. Thorn	8	B1
Davids Cl. Alve	15	D2
Davin Cres. E in G	47	E2
Davis Cl. Kingsw	65	F3
Davis Ct. Thorn	8	B1
Davis La. Yatt	73	F4
Davis St. Avon	47	D4
Dawes Cl. Cleve	57	E1
Dawley Cl. Wint	37	F4
Dawlish Rd. Bris	63	E1
Dawn Rise. Kingsw	52	A1
Day Cres. Bath	100	C3
Day House La. Hill	19	E4
Day's Rd. Bris	64	A3
De Clifford Rd. Bris	34	B1
De Verose Ct. Kingsw	65	F2
Deacon Cl. Wint	37	F3
Deacons Cl. W-S-M	88	C1
Deadmill La. Bath	85	E2
Dean Ave. Thorn	8	A1
Dean Cl. Kingsw	65	D2
Dean Cl. W-S-M	89	D2
Dean Cres. Bris	63	E4
Dean Cres. Yate	27	E2
Dean La. Bris	63	E4
Dean Rd. Avon	33	E3
Dean Rd. Yate	27	E2
Dean St. Bris	63	E2
Dean St. Bris	63	F4
Dean's Dr. Bris	51	D1
Deanery Cl. Kingsw	66	A4
Deanery Rd. Bris	63	E3
Deanery Rd. Kingsw	66	A4
Deanhill La. Charl	44	A4
Deans Mead. Bris	48	A4
Deans The. Portis	45	D2
Debecca's La. E in G	47	F2
Deep Coombe Rd. Bris	63	D1
Deep Pit Rd. Bris	50	C1
Deer Mead. Cleve	57	D1
Deerhurst. Kingsw	51	F2
Deerhurst. Yate	39	E4
Deering Cl. Bris	34	A1
Deerleap. Ship	125	F4
Deerswood. Kingsw	52	A1
Delabere Ave. Bris	51	D3
Delapre Rd. W-S-M	104	B2
Delius Gr. Bris	79	E4
Dell The. Bris	48	C3
Dell The. Kingsw	66	B3
Dell The. Nail	59	E1
Dell The. St Gif	36	C4
Dell The. W-S-M	88	C2
Delvin Rd. Bris	49	E4
Denbigh St. Bris	63	F4
Dene Cl. Keyn	81	F2
Dene Rd. Whit	80	B2
Denham House. Bris	79	E2
Denleigh Cl. Bris	80	A2
Denmark Ave. Bris	63	E3
Denmark Pl. Bris	49	F2
Denmark Rd. Bath	101	E4
Denmark St. Bris	63	E3
Denning Ct. W-S-M	89	D2
Dennisworth. Puck	53	F4
Dennor Park. Bris	80	A4
Denny Cl. Portis	45	D3
Denny Isle Dr. Piln	22	A3
Denny La. Ch Mag	96	A1
Denny View. Portis	45	D3
Dennyview Rd. Ab Lei	61	F4
Denston Dr. Portis	45	F2
Denston Wlk. Bris	79	D4
Dentwood Gr. Bris	48	A4
Denys Ct. Olve	14	A2
Derby Rd. Bris	49	F2
Derby St. Bris	64	B4
Derham Cl. Yatt	91	D4
Derham Park. Yatt	91	D4
Derham Rd. Bris	79	D3
Dermot St. Bris	50	A1
Derrick Rd. Kingsw	65	E4
Derricke Rd. Bris	80	C3
Derry Rd. Bris	63	D1
Derwent Cl. Bris	36	A4
Derwent Ct. Thorn	15	E4
Derwent Gr. Keyn	82	A3
Derwent Rd. Bris	50	C1
Derwent Rd. W-S-M	105	D2
Desmond Rd. Lock	89	E2
Deveron Gr. Keyn	82	A2
Devil's La. Char	11	D1
Devon Gr. Bris	64	B4
Devon Rd. Bris	50	B1
Devonshire Bldgs. Bath	101	F2
Devonshire Ct. W-S-M	104	C2
Devonshire Dr. Portis	44	C3
Devonshire Pl. Bath	101	F2
Devonshire Rd. Bath	85	F1
Devonshire Rd. Bris	49	D2
Devonshire Rd. W-S-M	104	C2
Dial Hill Rd. Cleve	57	E2
Dial La. Ba Gu	77	E1
Dial La. Mang	51	E3
Dial La. Win	77	E1
Diamond St. Bris	63	E2
Dibden Cl. Mang	52	A4
Dibden La. Mang	52	A4
Dibden Rd. Mang	52	A4
Dickens Cl. Bris	50	A4
Dickenson Rd. W-S-M	104	C3
Dickenson's Gr. Cong	91	F2
Didsbury Cl. Bris	34	C1
Dighton Gate. St Gif	36	C3
Dighton St. Bris	63	E4
Dillon Ct. Bris	64	B4
Dimond Rd. Bris	64	C4
Dinder Cl. Nail	75	F4
Dinghurst Rd. Chur	108	C2
Dingle Cl. Bris	48	B3
Dingle Rd. Bris	48	B4
Dingle The. Bris	48	B4
Dingle The. Wint	37	F2
Dingle View. Bris	48	B4
Dinglewood Cl. Bris	48	B4
Dings Wlk. Bris	64	A3
Dipland Gr. Blag	110	C1
Dixon Gdns. Bath	84	C1
Dixon Rd. Bris	64	C1
Dock Gate La. Bris	63	D3
Dodington La. Dod	40	B3
Dodington Rd. Ch Sod	40	A4
Dodisham Wlk. Bris	51	D3
Doleberrow. Chur	108	C2
Dolemoor La. Cong	91	D2
Dolemoor La. Cong	91	E2
Dolman Cl. Bris	34	C2
Dolphin Sq. W-S-M	104	B4
Dominion Rd. Bath	101	D3
Dominion Rd. Bris	50	C2
Donald Rd. Bris	78	C4
Doncaster Rd. Bris	49	E4
Doncombe Hill. Col	70	C4
Doncombe La. Col	70	C4
Donegal Rd. Bris	63	E1
Dongola Ave. Bris	49	F2
Dongola Rd. Bris	49	F2
Donnington Wlk. Keyn	81	E2
Doone Rd. Bris	49	F4
Dorcas Ave. St Gif	36	C3
Dorchester Cl. Nail	59	E1
Dorchester Rd. Bris	50	A4
Dorchester St. Bath	102	A3
Dorester Cl. Bris	35	E2
Dorian Cl. Bris	49	F4
Dorian Rd. Bris	49	F4
Dormer Cl. Fr Cot	38	B3
Dormer Rd. Bris	50	A2
Dorset Cl. Bath	101	E3
Dorset Gr. Bris	50	A1
Dorset Rd. Bris	49	D3
Dorset Rd. Kingsw	51	E1
Dorset St. Bath	101	E3
Dorset St. Bris	63	D2
Dorset Way. Yate	28	A2
Douglas Ct. W-S-M	104	C4
Douglas Rd. Bris	49	F4
Douglas Rd. Kingsw	65	E4
Douglas Rd. W-S-M	104	C3
Doulton Way. Bris	80	A3
Dove La. Bris	63	F4
Dove La. Bris	64	B4
Dove St S. Bris	63	E4
Dove St. Bris	63	E4
Dovecote. Yate	39	F4
Dovedale. Thorn	15	E4
Dover Pl. Bath	85	D1
Dovercourt Rd. Bris	50	A3
Dovers La. Bathf	86	B1
Dovers Park. Bathf	86	B1
Dovey Ct. Kingsw	66	B3
Dowdeswell Cl. Bris	34	C2
Dowding Rd. Bath	85	D1
Dowland. W-S-M	89	D1
Dowling Rd. Bris	79	E2
Down Ave. Bath	102	A1
Down Cl. Portis	44	C3
Down Hill. Olve	14	B2
Down La. Bath	85	F1
Down Leaze. Alve	15	D3
Down Rd. Alve	15	D3
Down Rd. Marsh	56	B1
Down Rd. Portis	45	D2
Down Rd. Wint	37	F2
Down The. Alve	14	C3
Down The. Olve	14	B2
Down View. Bris	49	F2
Downend Park Rd. Mang	51	E3
Downend Park. Bris	49	F3
Downend Rd. Bris	49	F3
Downend Rd. Bris	51	E3
Downend Rd. Kingsw	51	E1
Downend Rd. Mang	51	E3
Downfield Cl. Alve	15	D3
Downfield Dr. Fr Cot	38	A4
Downfield Rd. Bris	49	D1
Downland Cl. Bris	79	E3
Downleaze Dr. Ch Sod	40	A4
Downleaze. Bris	48	C2
Downleaze. Mang	51	E4
Downleaze. Portis	45	D3
Downman Rd. Bris	50	A3
Downs Cl. Alve	15	D3
Downs Cl. W-S-M	88	C1
Downs Cote Ave. Bris	48	C3
Downs Cote Dr. Bris	49	D3
Downs Cote Gdns. Bris	49	D3
Downs Cote View. Bris	49	D3
Downs Park E. Bris	49	D2
Downs Park W. Bris	49	D2
Downs Rd. Bris	49	D3
Downs The. Bris	78	B1
Downs The. Portis	45	D2
Downs The. Wickw	17	F4
Downside Cl. Bath	85	F1
Downside Cl. Chil	137	E2
Downside Cl. Kingsw	65	F3
Downside Rd. Bris	49	D1
Downside Rd. W-S-M	104	C2
Downside Rd. Wring	93	F4
Downside. Portis	45	E3
Downsway. Paul	131	E3
Downton Rd. Bris	79	E4
Dowry Rd. Bris	63	D3
Dowry Sq. Bris	63	D3
Doynton La. Doyn	54	A2
Doynton La. Dyrh	54	A2
Dr White's Cl. Bris	63	F3
Dragon Rd. Wint	37	E3
Dragon Wlk. Bris	50	C1
Dragons Hill Cl. Keyn	81	F3
Dragons Hill Ct. Keyn	81	F3
Dragons Hill Gdns. Keyn	81	F3
Dragonswell Rd. Bris	35	D1
Drake Ave. Bath	101	F1
Drake Cl. Keyn	82	B1
Drake Cl. W-S-M	88	C2
Drake Rd. Bris	63	D2
Drakes Way. Portis	45	D3
Draycot Pl. Bris	63	E3
Draycott Rd. Bris	49	F3
Draydon Rd. Bris	79	E4
Drayton Cl. Bris	80	A4
Drayton Rd. Bris	48	B4
Drayton. W-S-M	105	D1
Dring The. Rad	132	C1
Drive The. Bris	49	D3
Drive The. Bris	80	B3
Drive The. Chur	108	C2
Drive The. Pens	96	C1
Drive The. Ship	125	F4
Drive The. W-S-M	104	C4
Drove Ct. Nail	59	F2
Drove Rd. W-S-M	104	C3
Drove The. Portb	46	B3
Drove Way. Winsc	107	F4
Druett's Cl. Bris	49	F3
Druid Hill. Bris	48	C3
Druid Rd. Bris	48	C2
Druid Stoke Ave. Bris	48	B3
Druid Woods. Bris	48	B3
Drumhead Way The. Ship	125	F4
Drummond Ct. Kingsw	65	F2
Drummond Rd. Bris	50	C2
Drummond Rd. Bris	49	F1
Dryleaze Rd. Bris	50	C2
Dryleaze. Keyn	81	F4
Drysdale Cl. W-S-M	88	B1
Dubbers La. Bris	50	C1
Dublin Cres. Bris	49	D3
Duchess Rd. Bris	49	D1
Duchess Way. Bris	50	B3
Duchy Cl. Mid No	132	C3
Duchy Rd. Mid No	132	C3
Ducie Rd. Bris	64	A4
Ducie Rd. Mang	51	F3
Duck La. Chur	109	D4
Duck La. Yatt	74	A3
Duck St. Chur	108	B3
Duck St. Tyth	16	B3
Duckmoor Rd. Bris	63	D2
Dudley Cl. Keyn	81	F2
Dudley Ct. Kingsw	65	F2
Dudley Gr. Bris	50	A4
Dugar Wlk. Bris	49	E2
Duke St. Bath	102	A3
Dulverton Rd. Bris	49	E2
Dumaine Ave. St Gif	36	C3
Dumfries Pl. W-S-M	104	C3
Dumpers La. Ch Mag	96	A1
Duncan Gdns. Bath	84	A2
Duncombe La. Bris	51	D1
Duncombe Rd. Bris	51	D1
Dundas Cl. Bris	34	C1
Dundonald Rd. Bris	49	D2
Dundridge Gdns. Bris	65	D3
Dundridge La. Bris	65	D3
Dundry Cl. Kingsw	65	E3
Dundry La. Dun	78	B2
Dundry La. Win	95	D4
Dundry View. Bris	64	A1
Dunkeld Ave. Bris	35	F1
Dunkerry Rd. Bris	63	E2
Dunkerton Hill. P St J	117	F1
Dunkerton Hill. Pris	117	F1
Dunkery Cl. Nail	59	F1
Dunkery Rd. W-S-M	87	F1
Dunkirk Rd. Bris	50	C2
Dunkite La. W-S-M	88	C2
Dunmail Rd. Bris	35	E1
Dunmore St. Bris	63	F2
Dunsdown La. Tor	55	D3
Dunster Cres. W-S-M	105	D1
Dunster Ct. Wins	125	D3
Dunster Gdns. Kingsw	66	A1
Dunster Gdns. Nail	59	F1
Dunster Rd. Bris	79	F4
Dunster Rd. Keyn	81	F2
Dunsters Rd. Yatt	74	C1
Durban Rd. Bris	35	F4
Durban Way. Yatt	74	A1
Durbin Park Rd. Cleve	57	E3
Durbin Wlk. Bris	64	A4
Durcott Rd. Tims	132	B4
Durham Gr. Keyn	81	E2
Durham Park. Bris	49	D2
Durham Rd. Bris	50	A1
Durham Rd. Char	11	D3
Durleigh Cl. Bris	79	D4
Durley Hill. Keyn	81	E4
Durley Park. Bath	101	F2
Durnford Ave. Bris	63	D2
Durnford Rd. Bris	63	E2
Durnford St. Bris	63	E2
Durnhill. Co Mar	127	F4
Dursley Cl. Yate	27	F1
Dursley Rd. Bris	47	F3
Durston. W-S-M	105	D1
Durville Rd. Bris	79	D3
Durweston Wlk. Bris	80	B4
Dutton Cl. Bris	80	B3
Dutton Rd. Bris	80	B3
Dutton Wlk. Bris	80	B3
Dyer's La. Yate	27	D2
Dyers Cl. Bris	79	E2
Dylan Thomas Ct. Kingsw	66	A3
Dymboro Ave. Mid No	131	F1
Dymboro Cl. Mid No	131	F1
Dymboro Gdns. Mid No	131	F1
Dymboro The. Mid No	131	F1
Dyrham Cl. Bris	49	E3
Dyrham Cl. Kingsw	65	F4
Dyrham Cl. Thorn	8	B2
Dyrham Par. St Gif	36	B4
Dyrham Rd. Kingsw	65	F4
Dyrham. Bris	37	E1
Dyson Cl. Yatt	91	D4
Eagle Cl. W-S-M	105	E4
Eagle Cres. Puck	53	E2
Eagle Dr. Bris	35	F4
Eagle Park. Bathe	85	F3
Eagle Rd. Bathe	85	F3
Eagle Rd. Bris	64	B1
Eagles The. Yatt	91	D4
Eagles Wood Bsns Pk. St Gif	24	B2
Earl Russell Way. Bris	64	A4
Earl St. Bris	63	E4
Earlesfield. Nail	59	E1
Earlham Gr. W-S-M	105	D4
Earlsmead. Bris	50	C2
Earlstone Cl. Kingsw	66	A2
Earlstone Cres. Kingsw	66	A2
Easedale Cl. Bris	35	E1
East Cl. Bath	101	D3
East Clevedon Triangle. Cleve	57	F2
East Croft. Bris	49	E4
East Dundry La. Dun	79	D1

149

East Dundry Rd. Bris — Firgrove Cres. Yate

East Dundry Rd. Bris 79 F1
East Dundry Rd. Whit 79 F1
East Gr. Bris 49 F1
East Hill. Bris 49 D4
East Lea Rd. Bath 101 D4
East Mead. Mid No 132 A1
East Par. Bris 48 B3
East Park Dr. Bris 50 B1
East Park. Bris 50 B1
East Priory Cl. Bris 49 D4
East Ridge Dr. Bris 78 C3
East Shrubbery. Bris 49 D1
East St. Avon 33 D1
East St. Ban 107 E2
East St. Bris 63 E2
East St. Bris 63 F4
East View. Mang 51 F3
East Way. Bath 101 D3
East Wlk. Yate 27 F1
East Wood Pl. Portis 45 F4
Eastbury Cl. Thorn 8 B1
Eastbury Rd. Bris 51 D2
Eastbury Rd. Thorn 8 B1
Eastcombe Gdns. W-S-M 87 F1
Eastcombe Rd. W-S-M 87 F1
Eastcote Pk. Bris 80 A3
Eastcourt Gdns. Bris 50 B3
Eastcourt Rd. Clut 130 C4
Eastcroft Cl. Blag 110 C1
Eastcroft. Blag 110 C1
Eastdown Rd. Mid No 132 C3
Eastertown. Lymp 122 B1
Eastfield Ave. Bath 84 A1
Eastfield Gdns. W-S-M 87 F1
Eastfield Park. Bath 84 A1
Eastfield Park. W-S-M 87 F1
Eastfield Rd. Bris 49 D4
Eastfield Rd. Bris 49 E1
Eastfield Rd. Lock 105 F1
Eastfield Terr. Bris 49 D3
Eastfield. Bris 49 D4
Eastgate Office Centre. Bris 50 A2
Eastlake Cl. Bris 50 A4
Eastland Ave. Thorn 8 B1
Eastland Rd. Thorn 8 B1
Eastlea. Cleve 57 D1
Eastleigh Cl. Kingsw 51 F2
Eastleigh Rd. Bris 35 E1
Eastleigh Rd. Kingsw 51 F2
Eastley Cl. Falf 9 F4
Eastlyn Rd. Bris 79 D4
Eastmead La. Ban 107 E2
Eastmead La. Bris 48 C2
Eastnor Rd. Bris 80 A2
Easton Hill Rd. Thorn 8 B1
Easton Rd. Bris 64 A4
Easton Rd. E in G 47 E2
Easton Way. Bris 64 A4
Eastover Cl. Bris 49 D4
Eastover Gr. Bath 101 E1
Eastover Rd. Paul 115 E1
Eastville. Bath 85 D1
Eastway Cl. Nail 59 E1
Eastway Sq. Nail 59 F2
Eastway. Nail 59 F2
Eastwood Cl. Paul 115 E1
Eastwood Cres. Bris 64 C2
Eastwood Rd. Bris 64 C2
Eastwoods. Bathe 86 A2
Eaton Cl. Bris 51 D2
Eaton Cl. Bris 80 C3
Eaton Cres. Bris 63 D4
Eaton St. Bris 63 E2
Ebdon Rd. W ST L 89 D3
Ebdon Rd. W-S-M 88 C2
Ebenezer La. Bris 48 C3
Ebenezer St. Bris 64 B4
Eckweek Gdns. P St J 133 E4
Eckweek La. P St J 133 F4
Eckweek Rd. P St J 133 E4
Eclipse Office Pk. Kingsw 51 E2
Eden Gr. Bris 36 A1
Eden Park Cl. Bathe 86 A2
Eden Park Dr. Bathe 86 A2
Edgarley Ct. Cleve 57 E3
Edgecombe Ave. W-S-M 88 B1
Edgecombe Cl. Kingsw 51 F1
Edgecorner La. Burt 43 D2
Edgecumbe Rd. Bris 49 E1
Edgefield Cl. Bris 79 F2
Edgefield Rd. Bris 79 F2
Edgehill Rd. Cleve 57 E3
Edgeware Rd. Bris 63 E2
Edgeware Rd. Kingsw 51 E2
Edgewood Cl. Bris 80 A4
Edgewood Cl. Kingsw 66 A2
Edgeworth Rd. Bath 101 E1
Edgeworth. Yate 39 E3
Edinburgh Pl. W-S-M 104 C4
Edinburgh Rd. Keyn 81 F2
Edington Gr. Bris 35 D1
Edmund Cl. Mang 51 E3
Edmund Ct. Puck 53 D3
Edna Ave. Bris 64 C2
Edward Rd S. Cleve 57 F3
Edward Rd W. Cleve 57 F3
Edward Rd. Bris 64 A2
Edward Rd. Cleve 57 F3
Edward Rd. Kingsw 65 F4
Edward St. Bath 101 E4
Edward St. Bath 102 A4
Edward St. Bris 50 B1
Edward St. Bris 64 B4
Edwin Short Cl. Bitt 82 C4
Effingham Rd. Bris 49 F2
Egerton Brow. Bris 49 E2
Egerton Rd. Bath 101 F2
Egerton Rd. Bris 49 E2
Eggshill La. Yate 27 E1
Eighth Ave. Bris 36 A1
Eirene Terr. E in G 47 E2
Elberton Rd. Aust 14 A2
Elberton Rd. Bris 48 A4
Elberton Rd. Olve 14 A2
Elberton. Kingsw 66 A4
Elborough Ave. Yatt 91 D4
Elbury Ave. Bris 51 E1
Elderberry Wlk. W-S-M 89 D1
Elderbury Wlk. Bris 35 E2
Elderwood Dr. Kingsw 66 A2
Elderwood Rd. Bris 80 A4
Eldon Pl. Bath 85 D1
Eldon Terr. Bris 63 E2
Eldon Way. Bris 64 B3
Eleanor Cl. Bath 101 D3
Eleventh Ave. Bris 36 A1
Elfin Rd. Bris 51 D3
Elgar Cl. Bris 79 E3
Elgar Cl. Cleve 57 F1
Elgin Ave. Bris 35 F1
Elgin Croft. Bris 79 D2
Elgin Park. Bris 49 D1
Elgin Rd. Bris 51 D1
Eliot Cl. W-S-M 105 D2
Elizabeth Cl. Lock 105 E2
Elizabeth Cl. Thorn 15 E4
Elizabeth Cres. St Gif 36 C2
Elizabeth House. E in G 47 E2
Elkstone Wlk. Kingsw 66 B1
Ellacombe Rd. Kingsw 65 F1
Ellan Hay Rd. St Gif 37 D3
Ellbridge Cl. Bris 48 B3
Ellenborough Park N. W-S-M 104 B3
Ellenborough Park Rd. W-S-M 104 C3
Ellenborough Park S. W-S-M 104 B3
Ellencroft Rd. W-u-E 11 F4
Ellesmere Rd. Bris 64 B1
Ellesmere Rd. Kingsw 65 E4
Ellesmere Rd. W-S-M 104 B1
Ellesmere. Thorn 15 E4
Ellfield Cl. Bris 78 C3
Ellick Rd. Blag 126 B4
Ellicks Cl. St Gif 24 C1
Ellinghurst Cl. Bris 35 D1
Elliot Rd. Bris 49 F3
Elliott Ave. Bris 37 E1
Ellis Ave. Bris 79 D4
Elliston Dr. Bath 101 D2
Elliston La. Bris 49 E1
Elliston Rd. Bris 49 E1
Ellsbridge Cl. Keyn 82 A3
Ellsworth Rd. Bris 34 C2
Elm Cl. Ch Sod 28 A1
Elm Cl. Nail 59 E1
Elm Cl. Ship 108 B1
Elm Cl. St Gif 36 B4
Elm Cl. Yatt 91 D4
Elm Ct. Keyn 81 E2
Elm Gr. Bath 85 E1
Elm Gr. Bath 101 E2
Elm Gr. Lock 105 F2
Elm La. Bris 49 D1
Elm Park. Bris 36 A1
Elm Rd. Bris 49 F3
Elm Rd. Kingsw 65 F3
Elm Rd. Paul 131 F3
Elm Terr. Rad 132 B1
Elm Terr. Rod 138 B4
Elm Tree Ave. Mang 52 A4
Elm Tree Ave. Rad 132 B1
Elm Tree Rd. Cleve 57 E1
Elm Tree Rd. Lock 106 A2
Elm View. Mid No 132 A1
Elm Wlk. Portis 45 E2
Elm Wlk. Yatt 91 D4
Elm Wood. Yate 39 F4
Elmcroft Cres. Bris 50 A2
Elmdale Cres. Thorn 8 B2
Elmdale Gdns. Bris 51 D2
Elmdale Rd. Bris 63 D1
Elmdale Rd. Bris 63 D4
Elmfield Cl. Kingsw 65 F3
Elmfield Rd. Bris 49 D4
Elmfield. Kingsw 65 F3
Elmgrove Ave. Bris 64 A4
Elmgrove Dr. Yate 27 F1
Elmgrove Park. Bris 49 E1
Elmgrove Rd. Bris 49 E1
Elmgrove Rd. Bris 50 C2
Elmhurst Ave. Bris 50 B2
Elmhurst Est. Bathe 86 A2
Elmhurst Gdns. Lo Ash 77 F4
Elmhurst Rd. Lock 105 F1
Elmhyrst Rd. W-S-M 104 C4
Elming Down Cl. St Gif 36 B3
Elmlea Ave. Bris 48 C3
Elmleigh Ave. Mang 52 A3
Elmleigh Cl. Mang 52 A3
Elmleigh Rd. Mang 52 A3
Elmore Rd. Bris 23 F1
Elmore Rd. Bris 50 A3
Elmore. Kingsw 51 F1
Elmore. Yate 39 E4
Elms Gr. St Gif 24 A1
Elms The. Bris 37 E1
Elmsleigh Rd. W-S-M 104 B2
Elmsley La. W St L 88 B3
Elmtree Cl. Kingsw 51 E1
Elmtree Dr. Bris 78 C3
Elmtree Way. Kingsw 51 E1
Elmvale Dr. Lock 105 F2
Elsbert Dr. Bris 78 C3
Elstree Rd. Bris 50 C1
Elton La. Bris 49 E1
Elton Rd. Bris 49 E1
Elton Rd. Bris 51 E1
Elton Rd. Bris 63 E4
Elton Rd. Cleve 57 E2
Elton Rd. W-S-M 89 D2
Elton St. Bris 63 F4
Elvard Cl. Bris 79 D2
Elvard Rd. Bris 79 D2
Elvaston Rd. Bris 63 F2
Elwell La. Dun 77 F1
Elwell La. Win 77 F1
Ely Gr. Bris 48 A4
Embassy Rd. Bris 50 C1
Embassy Wlk. Bris 50 C1
Embercourt Dr. Back 76 A3
Embleton Rd. Bris 35 E1
Emerson Sq. Bris 50 A4
Emery Gate. Ban 107 D2
Emery Rd. Bris 64 C1
Emlyn Cl. W-S-M 89 D2
Emlyn Rd. Bris 50 B1
Emmett Wood. Bris 80 A2
Emra Cl. Bris 50 C1
Enderleigh Gdns. Chur 108 C2
Enfield Rd. Bris 51 D2
Engine Common La. Yate 27 E3
Engine La. Nail 75 D4
England's Cres. Wint 37 F4
Englishcombe La. Bath 101 E2
Englishcombe Rd. Bris 79 E2
Englishcombe Way. Bath 101 F2
Enmore. W-S-M 105 D1
Ennerdale Cl. W-S-M 105 D3
Ennerdale Rd. Bris 35 E1
Entry Hill Dr. Bath 101 F2
Entry Hill Gdns. Bath 101 F2
Entry Hill Park. Bath 101 F1
Entry Hill. Bath 101 F1
Entry Rise. Bath 101 F1
Epney Cl. Bris 23 F1
Epsom Cl. Mang 37 F1
Epworth Rd. Bris 35 D2
Equinox. St Gif 24 B2
Erin Wlk. Bris 79 E4
Ermine Way. Bris 47 E4
Ermleet Rd. Bris 49 E1
Ernestville Rd. Bris 50 C2
Ernist Barker Cl. Bris 64 A4
Ervine Terr. Bris 63 F4
Esgar Rise. W-S-M 88 C2
Eskdale Cl. W-S-M 105 E4
Eskdale. Thorn 15 E4
Esmond Gr. Cleve 57 E2
Esplanade Rd. Portis 45 D4
Essery Rd. Bris 50 B1
Essex St. Bris 63 E2
Esson Rd. Bris 51 D1
Estoril. Yate 27 F1
Estune Wlk. Lo Ash 62 A1
Etloe Rd. Bris 49 D2
Eton La. Ban 106 C4
Eton Rd. Bris 64 B2
Ettlingen Way. Cleve 57 F1
Ettricke Dr. Bris 51 D3
Eugene St. Bris 63 E4
Eugene St. Bris 63 F4
Evans Rd. Bris 49 D1
Eve Rd. Bris 50 A1
Evelyn Rd. Bath 101 D4
Evelyn Rd. Bris 49 E4
Evelyn Terr. Bath 85 D1
Evenlode Gdns. Bris 47 F3
Evenlode Way. Keyn 82 A2
Evercreech Rd. Bris 80 A2
Everest Ave. Bris 50 C2
Everest Rd. Bris 50 C2
Evergreen Cl. Winsc 107 F1
Ewart Rd. W-S-M 105 E4
Exbourne. W-S-M 89 D1
Excelsior St. Bath 102 A3
Excelsior Terr. Mid No 132 A1
Exchange Ave. Bris 63 E3
Exeter Bldgs. Bris 49 D1
Exeter Rd. Bris 63 D2
Exeter Rd. Portis 45 F2
Exeter Rd. W-S-M 104 C3
Exford Cl. W-S-M 104 C1
Exley Cl. Kingsw 66 B3
Exmoor Rd. Bath 101 F1
Exmoor St. Bris 63 D2
Exmouth Rd. Bris 63 F1
Exton Cl. Bris 80 A3
Exton. W-S-M 105 D1
Eyer's La. Bris 63 F4

Faber Gr. Bris 79 E2
Fabian Dr. St Gif 36 C3
Factory Rd. Wint 37 F4
Failand Cres. Bris 48 B3
Failand La. Portb 46 C1
Failand La. Wrax 61 D4
Failand Wlk. Bris 48 B3
Fair Cl. N St P 135 F2
Fair Furlong. Bris 79 D2
Fair Hill. Ship 125 F4
Fair Lawn. Kingsw 66 A2
Fair View Dr. Bris 49 E1
Fairacre Cl. Bris 50 A3
Fairacre Cl. Lock 106 A2
Fairacres Cl. Keyn 81 F3
Fairfax St. Bris 63 E4
Fairfield Ave. Bath 85 D1
Fairfield Cl. Back 76 B4
Fairfield Cl. Marsh 69 F4
Fairfield Cl. W-S-M 88 A1
Fairfield Mead. Back 76 B4
Fairfield Park Rd. Bath 85 D1
Fairfield Pl. Bris 63 D2
Fairfield Rd. Bath 85 D1
Fairfield Rd. Bris 49 F1
Fairfield Rd. Bris 63 E2
Fairfield St. Bris 64 A2
Fairfield Terr. P St J 133 E4
Fairfield Way. Back 76 B3
Fairfield. Rode 136 C1
Fairfoot Rd. Bris 64 A2
Fairford Cl. Kingsw 51 F1
Fairford Cres. St Gif 36 B4
Fairford Rd. Bris 47 E4
Fairhaven Rd. Bris 49 E2
Fairhaven. Yate 27 F1
Fairlawn Ave. Bris 36 A2
Fairlawn Rd. Bris 49 F1
Fairlyn Dr. Kingsw 51 F2
Fairoaks. Kingsw 66 A2
Fairseat Workshops. Ch St 112 C4
Fairview Rd. Kingsw 65 F4
Fairview. W-S-M 88 C2
Fairway Cl. Kingsw 66 A2
Fairway Cl. W-S-M 88 A1
Fairway Ind Centre. Bris 35 F2
Fairway. Bris 64 B1
Fairways. Keyn 82 C1
Fairy Hill. Co Dan 98 B3
Falcon Cl. Bris 35 F4
Falcon Cl. Bris 48 C4
Falcon Cl. Portis 45 E2
Falcon Cres. W-S-M 105 E4
Falcon Dr. Bris 35 F4
Falcon Way. Thorn 8 B1
Falcon Wlk. Bris 23 F1
Falcondale Rd. Bris 48 C4
Falcondale Wlk. Bris 49 D4
Falconer Rd. Bath 84 A2
Falfield Rd. Bris 64 B2
Falfield Wlk. Bris 49 E4
Falkland Rd. Bris 49 F1
Fallodon Ct. Bris 49 D3
Fallodon Way. Bris 49 D3
Fallowfield. Kingsw 66 B3
Fallowfield. W-S-M 88 C2
Falmouth Cl. Nail 60 A1
Falmouth Rd. Bris 49 F2
Fane Cl. Bris 35 D2
Fanshawe Rd. Bris 80 A4
Far Handstones. Kingsw 66 A2
Faraday Rd. Bris 62 C3
Farington Rd. Bris 49 E4
Farleigh Hospital Cotts. Back 77 D4
Farleigh La. Crom 10 B1
Farleigh Rd. Back 76 B4
Farleigh Rd. Cleve 57 D1
Farleigh Rd. Keyn 81 E2
Farleigh Rd. N St P 136 A3
Farleigh Rise. Mon Far 86 C1
Farleigh View. Westw 120 C2
Farleigh Wick. Mon Far 103 F3
Farleigh Wlk. Bris 79 D4
Farler's End. Nail 75 F4
Farley Cl. St Gif 36 B4
Farm Ct. Mang 51 F4
Farm La. Alm 22 C1
Farm La. Piln 22 C1
Farm La. Well 118 C1
Farm Lees. Char 11 D3
Farm Rd. Lock 105 F1
Farm Rd. Mang 51 F4
Farmer Rd. Bris 78 C2
Farmhouse Cl. Nail 59 F1
Farmhouse Ct. Nail 59 F1
Farmwell Cl. Bris 79 D3
Farndale Rd. W-S-M 105 E4
Farndale. Bris 65 D3
Farne Cl. Bris 49 D3
Farr St. Avon 47 D4
Farr's La. Bris 63 E3
Farrant Cl. Bris 79 E3
Farrington Fields. Paul 131 E2
Farrington Rd. Paul 131 E3
Farrington Way. Paul 131 D2
Farrs La. Bath 102 A1
Farthing Row. Rode 136 C1
Faukland View. P St J 133 F4
Faulkland La. Well 134 B2
Faulkland Rd. Bath 101 E3
Faversham Dr. W-S-M 105 D1
Fawkes Cl. Kingsw 66 A4
Fearnville Est. Cleve 57 E1
Featherbed La. Clut 114 B3
Featherbed La. O-on-S 7 D3
Featherbed La. Pens 114 B3
Featherbed La. Win 95 D2
Featherstone Rd. Bris 50 C2
Fedden Village. Portis 44 C3
Feeder Rd. Bris 64 A3
Felix Rd. Bris 64 A4
Felstead Rd. Bris 35 F1
Feltham Rd. Puck 53 E3
Felton Gr. Bris 79 D4
Felton La. Win 94 C4
Felton St. Win 94 B4
Fenbrook Cl. Bris 37 D1
Feniton. W-S-M 89 D1
Fennel La. Axb 125 D1
Fennell Gr. Bris 35 D1
Fenners. W-S-M 89 D2
Fenshurst Gdns. Lo Ash 77 F4
Fenswood Mead. Lo Ash 61 F1
Fenswood Rd. Lo Ash 61 F1
Fenton Cl. Keyn 82 B2
Fenton Rd. Bris 49 E2
Ferenberge Cl. Farm 116 A3
Fermaine Ave. Bris 64 C2
Fern Cl. Bris 35 D2
Fern Gr. Nail 75 E4
Fern Lea. Blea 122 A3
Fern Rd. Mang 51 E3
Fernbank Rd. Bris 49 E1
Ferndale Ave. Bris 65 D1
Ferndale Ave. Kingsw 66 A2
Ferndale Rd. Bath 85 E2
Ferndale Rd. Bris 36 A1
Ferndale Rd. Portis 45 E3
Ferndean. St Gif 24 B1
Ferndown Cl. Bris 48 A4
Ferndown. Yate 27 F1
Fernhill La. Bris 34 A1
Fernhill. Alve 24 B4
Fernhill. Olve 24 B4
Fernhurst Rd. Bris 50 C1
Fernlea Gdns. E in G 47 D2
Fernlea Rd. W-S-M 105 E4
Fernleaze. Fr Cot 38 B3
Fernside. Back 76 A4
Fernsteed Rd. Bris 78 C3
Ferry La. Bath 102 A3
Ferry Rd. Kingsw 65 E1
Ferry St. Bris 63 F3
Ferry Steps Ind Est. Bris 64 A2
Fiddes Rd. Bris 49 E2
Field La. Aust 14 A4
Field La. Dyrh 54 C3
Field La. Kingsw 65 F2
Field La. Ston E 130 A1
Field La. Tyth 15 F2
Field Rd. Bris 51 E1
Field View Dr. Bris 51 E3
Fielders The. W-S-M 89 D2
Fieldgardens Rd. Clut 114 C1
Fielding's Rd. Bath 101 E3
Fieldings. Winsl 120 C4
Fieldway. Wins 108 A2
Fiennes Cl. Kingsw 51 F2
Fifth Ave. Bris 36 A1
Fifth Way. Avon 33 F1
Filby Dr. St Gif 36 B4
Filer Cl. P St J 133 E4
Filton Ave. Bris 36 A1
Filton Ave. Bris 36 A2
Filton Gr. Bris 49 F3
Filton La. Bris 36 B1
Filton Rd. Bris 36 B1
Filton Rd. Bris 37 D1
Filwood Broadway. Bris 79 F4
Filwood Dr. Kingsw 65 F4
Filwood Rd. Bris 51 D2
Finch Cl. Thorn 8 B1
Finch Cl. W-S-M 105 F4
Finch Rd. Ch Sod 40 A4
Finmere Gdns. W-S-M 89 D2
Fir La. Priddy 126 A3
Fir Leaze. Nail 59 D1
Fir Rd. Col 70 C3
Fir Tree Ave. Lock 105 F2
Fir Tree Ave. Paul 131 F2
Fir Tree Cl. Bris 35 F4
Fir Tree La. Bris 65 D4
Fircliff Park. Portis 45 D4
Fire Engine La. Fr Cot 38 B4
Fireclay Rd. Bris 64 B3
Firework Cl. Kingsw 66 A4
Firgrove Cres. Yate 28 A1

Firgrove La. P St J ... 117 D1
Firs Ct. Keyn ... 81 E2
Firs The. Bath ... 102 A1
Firs The. Li St ... 120 A3
Firs The. Mang ... 51 F3
First Ave. Bris ... 101 E2
First Ave. Bris ... 64 C3
First Ave. Portb ... 46 C3
First Ave. Rod ... 138 B4
First Way. Avon ... 33 E1
Fisher Ave. Kingsw ... 52 A1
Fisher Rd. Kingsw ... 52 A1
Fishponds Rd. Bris ... 50 C2
Fishpool Hill. Bris ... 35 D2
Fitchett Wlk. Bris ... 34 C2
Fitzgerald Rd. Bris ... 63 F2
Fitzroy Rd. Bris ... 51 D1
Fitzroy St. Bris ... 64 A2
Fitzroy Terr. Bris ... 49 D1
Five Acre Dr. Bris ... 50 C4
Five Arches Cl. Mid No ... 132 B1
Flagstaff Rd. Blea ... 123 E4
Flamingo Cres. W-S-M ... 105 F4
Flat The. Clut ... 114 B3
Flatwoods Cres. Bath ... 102 C2
Flatwoods Rd. Bath ... 102 C2
Flax Bourton Rd. Wrax ... 61 D2
Flaxman Cl. Bris ... 50 A3
Flaxpits La. Wint ... 37 F3
Florence Gr. W-S-M ... 105 D4
Florence Park. Alm ... 24 B3
Florence Park. Bris ... 49 D2
Florence Rd. Kingsw ... 51 F2
Florida Terr. Mid No ... 132 B1
Flowers Hill Cl. Bris ... 64 C1
Flowers Hill. Bris ... 64 C1
Flowerwell Rd. Bris ... 79 D3
Folleigh Cl. Lo Ash ... 62 A1
Folleigh Dr. Lo Ash ... 62 A1
Folleigh La. Lo Ash ... 62 A1
Folliot Cl. Bris ... 51 D4
Folly Bridge Cl. Yate ... 27 E1
Folly La. Bris ... 64 A3
Folly La. Ship ... 125 F4
Folly La. W-S-M ... 104 C1
Folly Rd. Ir Act ... 25 F2
Folly The. Keyn ... 82 C1
Folly The. Mang ... 51 F4
Fontana Cl. Kingsw ... 66 A2
Fonthill Rd. Bath ... 84 C1
Fonthill Rd. Bris ... 35 E1
Fonthill Way. Kingsw ... 66 B3
Fontmell Ct. Bris ... 80 B4
Fontwell Dr. Mang ... 37 F1
Footes La. Fr Cot ... 38 A4
Footshill Cl. Kingsw ... 65 E3
Footshill Dr. Kingsw ... 65 E4
Footshill Rd. Kingsw ... 65 E3
Ford La. P St J ... 133 E4
Ford La. Litt ... 129 E1
Ford Rd. Well ... 118 C1
Ford St. Bris ... 64 B3
Forde Cl. Kingsw ... 65 F3
Fordell Pl. Bris ... 64 A2
Forefield Pl. Bath ... 102 A3
Forefield Rise. Bath ... 102 A3
Forest Ave. Bris ... 51 D2
Forest Dr. Bris ... 35 E2
Forest Edge. Kingsw ... 65 E2
Forest Hills. Alm ... 24 A3
Forest Rd. Bris ... 51 D2
Forest Rd. Kingsw ... 65 E4
Forest Wlk. Bris ... 51 D1
Forest Wlk. Kingsw ... 65 E4
Forester Ave. Bath ... 102 A4
Forester La. Bath ... 102 A4
Forester Rd. Bath ... 102 A4
Forester Rd. Portis ... 45 E2
Forge End. Portb ... 46 C2
Fortescue Rd. Rad ... 132 C1
Fortfield Rd. Bris ... 80 A3
Forty Acre La. Alve ... 15 D2
Foss La. O-on-S ... 7 F3
Fosse Barton. Nail ... 59 E1
Fosse Cl. Nail ... 59 E1
Fosse Gdns. Bath ... 118 B4
Fosse Green. Mid No ... 132 C2
Fosse La. Bathe ... 86 A2
Fosse La. Mid No ... 132 B2
Fosse La. Nail ... 59 E1
Fosse Way Cotts. Rad ... 132 B1
Fosse Way. Nail ... 59 E1
Fossedale Ave. Bris ... 80 B3
Fossefield Rd. Kilm ... 138 A4
Fosseway Gdns. Rad ... 132 B1
Fosseway S. Kilm ... 138 A4
Fosseway The. Bris ... 63 D4
Fosseway. Chil ... 137 F1
Fosseway. Chil ... 138 A2
Fosseway. Cleve ... 57 E1
Fosseway. Mid No ... 132 C2
Fosseway. Rod ... 138 B4
Foster St. Bris ... 50 A1
Foundry La. Bris ... 50 C1
Fountain Ct. St Gif ... 24 B2
Fountain La. Wins ... 125 D2
Fountaine Ct. Bris ... 50 B1
Fountains Dr. Kingsw ... 65 F3

Four Acre Ave. Mang ... 51 F4
Four Acre Cres. Mang ... 37 F1
Four Acre Rd. Mang ... 51 F4
Four Acres Cl. Bris ... 78 C2
Four Acres Cl. Nail ... 75 F4
Four Acres. Bris ... 78 C2
Fourth Ave. Bris ... 36 A1
Fourth Ave. Rod ... 138 B4
Fourth Way. Avon ... 33 F1
Fowey Cl. Nail ... 76 A4
Fowey Rd. W-S-M ... 89 D2
Fox And Hounds La. Keyn ... 81 F3
Fox Ave. Yate ... 27 E1
Fox Ct. Kingsw ... 65 F2
Fox Den Rd. St Gif ... 36 B2
Fox Hill. Bath ... 102 A1
Fox House. Bris ... 64 C2
Fox Rd. Bris ... 50 A1
Foxborough Gdns. St Gif ... 24 B1
Foxcombe Rd. Bath ... 101 D4
Foxcombe Rd. Bris ... 80 A2
Foxcote Rd. Bris ... 63 D2
Foxcote. Kingsw ... 65 F4
Foxcroft Cl. St Gif ... 36 C3
Foxcroft Rd. Bris ... 64 B4
Foxe Rd. Fr Cot ... 38 A4
Foxfield Ave. St Gif ... 24 B2
Foxglove Cl. Bris ... 50 C2
Foxglove Cl. Thorn ... 8 B1
Foxholes La. Olve ... 14 B2
Foye House. Lo Ash ... 62 B3
Fraley Rd. Bris ... 49 D4
Frampton Cres. Bris ... 51 E2
Frampton Ct. Kingsw ... 65 F2
Frampton End Rd. Fr Cot ... 38 B4
Frampton End Rd. Ir Act ... 26 B2
France La. H Up ... 20 A1
Francis Fox Rd. W-S-M ... 104 C4
Francis Pl. Kingsw ... 65 F2
Francis Rd. Bris ... 49 E4
Francis Rd. Bris ... 63 E1
Francombe Gr. Bris ... 49 F3
Frankland Cl. Bath ... 84 A1
Frankley Bldgs. Bath ... 85 D1
Franklin Ct. Bris ... 63 F3
Franklin's Way. Yatt ... 74 C1
Franklyn La. Bris ... 49 F1
Franklyn St. Bris ... 49 F1
Fraser Cl. W-S-M ... 88 C2
Fraser St. Bris ... 63 E2
Frayne Rd. Bris ... 63 D2
Frederick Ave. P St J ... 133 E4
Frederick Pl. Bris ... 63 D4
Fredrick St. Bris ... 64 A2
Free Tank. Bris ... 63 F3
Freeland Bldgs. Bris ... 50 B1
Freeland Pl. Bris ... 62 C3
Freelands. Cleve ... 73 E4
Freemans La. Ba Gu ... 77 D1
Freemantle Gdns. Bris ... 50 B2
Freemantle La. Bris ... 49 E1
Freemantle Rd. Bris ... 49 E1
Freemantle Rd. Bris ... 50 B2
Freemantle Sq. Bris ... 49 E1
Freestone Rd. Bris ... 64 A3
Freeview Rd. Bath ... 101 D3
Freezinghill La. Co Ash ... 68 A2
French Cl. Nail ... 59 F2
French Cl. P St J ... 133 E4
Frenchay Hill. Bris ... 51 E4
Frenchay Park Rd. Bris ... 50 C3
Frenchay Rd. Bris ... 51 D1
Frenchay Rd. W-S-M ... 104 C2
Frenchfield Rd. P St J ... 133 E4
Freshford La. Hi Cha ... 120 A3
Freshland Way. Bris ... 65 D4
Freshmoor. Cleve ... 57 F2
Friar Ave. W-S-M ... 88 C2
Friary Cl. Cleve ... 57 E3
Friary Cl. Westw ... 120 C2
Friary Grange Park. Wint ... 37 F3
Friary Rd. Bris ... 49 E2
Friary Rd. Portis ... 45 D3
Friendly Row. E in G ... 47 E3
Friendship Gr. Nail ... 59 F1
Friendship Rd. Bris ... 64 A1
Friendship Rd. Nail ... 59 F2
Friezewood Rd. Bris ... 63 D2
Fripp Cl. Bris ... 64 A3
Frith La. Yate ... 17 F2
Frobisher Ave. Portis ... 45 D3
Frobisher Cl. W-S-M ... 88 C2
Frobisher Rd. Bris ... 63 D2
Frog La. Bris ... 63 E3
Frog La. Co Mar ... 111 D4
Frog La. N Nib ... 5 E3
Frog La. Win ... 94 B4
Frog La. Win ... 94 C3
Frog La. Yate ... 38 C4
Frogmore St. Bris ... 63 E3
Frome Ct. Thorn ... 15 E4
Frome Glen. Wint ... 37 F2
Frome Old Rd. Rad ... 133 D1
Frome Pl. Bris ... 50 C3
Frome Rd. Bath ... 101 E1
Frome Rd. Ch Sod ... 28 A1
Frome Rd. Kilm ... 139 E4

Frome Rd. N St P ... 135 F2
Frome Rd. Rad ... 133 D1
Frome St. Bris ... 63 F4
Frome Terr. Bris ... 50 C3
Frome Valley Rd. Bris ... 50 C3
Frome View. Fr Cot ... 38 A4
Frome Way. Wint ... 37 F3
Fromeside Park. Bris ... 51 D4
Froomshaw Rd. Bris ... 51 D4
Frost Hill. Yatt ... 91 E4
Fry's Cl. Bris ... 50 B2
Fry's La. Blag ... 109 F2
Fry's Well. Chil ... 137 E2
Fryth House. Wrax ... 60 B2
Fryth Way. Nail ... 59 E1
Fulford Rd. Bris ... 79 E3
Fulford Wlk. Bris ... 79 D3
Fullens Cl. W-S-M ... 105 E4
Fuller Rd. Bath ... 85 E1
Fullers La. Wins ... 125 D3
Fullers Way. Bath ... 118 B4
Fulmar Cl. Thorn ... 8 B1
Fulmar Rd. W-S-M ... 88 C1
Fulwell Cl. Faulk ... 134 B1
Fulwell La. Faulk ... 134 B1
Furber Ct. Bris ... 65 D3
Furber Rd. Bris ... 65 D3
Furber Ridge. Bris ... 65 D3
Furber Vale. Bris ... 65 D3
Furland Rd. W-S-M ... 88 B1
Furlong Cl. Mid No ... 137 F4
Furnleaze. Clut ... 114 C2
Furnwood. Bris ... 65 D3
Furze Cl. W-S-M ... 88 A1
Furze Rd. Bris ... 51 E2
Furze Rd. W-S-M ... 88 A2
Furzewood Rd. Kingsw ... 65 F4
Fussell Ct. Kingsw ... 65 F4
Fylton Croft. Bris ... 80 A2

Gable Cl. Alm ... 23 D1
Gable Rd. Bris ... 50 A1
Gables Cl. Ban ... 107 D2
Gadshill Dr. St Gif ... 36 C3
Gadshill Rd. Bris ... 50 B1
Gages Cl. Kingsw ... 65 F4
Gages Rd. Kingsw ... 65 F4
Gainsborough Dr. W-S-M ... 88 C2
Gainsborough Gdns. Bath ... 101 E4
Gainsborough Rd. Keyn ... 81 F3
Gainsborough Sq. Bris ... 50 A4
Gallivan Cl. St Gif ... 36 A4
Galway Rd. Bris ... 63 F1
Gambril La. Crom ... 9 F3
Gander Cl. Bris ... 79 D3
Garden Cl. Bris ... 48 B3
Gardeners Wlk. Lo Ash ... 62 A1
Gardens Rd. Cleve ... 57 E2
Gardens The. Kingsw ... 51 E2
Gardner Ave. Bris ... 78 C4
Gardner Rd. Portis ... 45 E3
Garfield Rd. Bris ... 65 D4
Garner Ct. W-S-M ... 89 D2
Garnet St. Bris ... 63 D2
Garnett Pl. Mang ... 51 F4
Garonor Way. E in G ... 46 C3
Garrett Dr. St Gif ... 36 B4
Garrick Rd. Bath ... 100 C3
Garsdale Rd. W-S-M ... 105 E4
Garston La. Blag ... 110 C2
Garstons Cl. Wring ... 92 C1
Garstons Orch. Wring ... 92 B1
Garstons The. Portis ... 45 E2
Garstons. Bathf ... 86 B1
Garstons. Cleve ... 73 D4
Garstons. Wring ... 92 C1
Garth Rd. Bris ... 79 D4
Gas La. Bris ... 64 A3
Gasferry Rd. Bris ... 63 D3
Gaskins The. Bris ... 50 A3
Gaston Ave. Keyn ... 81 F3
Gastons The. Bris ... 48 A4
Gatcombe Dr. St Gif ... 36 C2
Gatcombe Rd. Bris ... 79 D3
Gatehouse Ave. Bris ... 79 D3
Gatehouse Cl. Bris ... 79 D3
Gatesby Mead. St Gif ... 36 C3
Gathorne Rd. Bris ... 63 D2
Gatton Rd. Bris ... 50 A1
Gaunt's Earthcott La. Alve ... 25 D3
Gaunt's La. Bris ... 63 E3
Gaunts Ct. Portis ... 44 C2
Gaunts Rd. Ch Sod ... 40 A4
Gay Elms Rd. Bris ... 79 D2
Gay St. Bath ... 101 F4
Gay's Hill. Bath ... 102 A4
Gayner Rd. Bris ... 36 A1
Gays Rd. Kingsw ... 65 D2
Gaythorne Cres. Yate ... 27 E1
Gazelle Rd. W-S-M ... 105 D2
Gazzard Cl. Wint ... 37 F4
Gazzard Rd. Wint ... 37 F4
Gee Moors. Kingsw ... 65 F4
Geldof Dr. Mid No ... 132 A1
Gelfe Rd. Bris ... 63 D3
Geoffrey Cl. Bris ... 78 C3

George & Dragon La. Bris ... 64 B4
George La. Marsh ... 55 F1
George St. Bath ... 101 F4
George St. Bris ... 64 B4
George St. Portis ... 45 E1
George St. W-S-M ... 104 C4
George Whitefield Ct. Bris ... 63 F4
George's Bldgs. Bath ... 102 A4
George's Rd. Bath ... 85 D1
Georgian View. Bath ... 101 E1
Gerald Rd. Bris ... 63 D2
Gerard Rd. W-S-M ... 104 C4
Gerrish Ave. Bris ... 64 B4
Gerrish Ave. Mang ... 51 F3
Gibbet La. Whit ... 80 B1
Gibbets Brow. Priddy ... 128 A2
Gibbsfold Rd. Bris ... 79 E2
Gibson Rd. Bris ... 49 E1
Gifford Cl. Wickw ... 27 D4
Gifford Cres. St Gif ... 36 B3
Gifford Rd. Bris ... 34 C2
Gilbeck Rd. Nail ... 59 E1
Gilbert Rd. Bris ... 64 B4
Gilbert Rd. Kingsw ... 51 E1
Gilberyn Dr. W-S-M ... 89 D2
Gilda Cl. Bris ... 80 B3
Gilda Cres. Bris ... 80 A3
Gilda Par. Bris ... 80 B3
Gilda Sq W. Bris ... 80 A3
Gill Ave. Bris ... 51 D3
Gill Mews. W-S-M ... 89 D2
Gillard Rd. Bris ... 65 D4
Gillard Rd. Bris ... 65 D4
Gillebank Cl. Bris ... 80 B2
Gillingham Hill. Bris ... 65 D3
Gillingham Terr. Bath ... 85 D1
Gillingstool. Thorn ... 15 E4
Gillmore Cl. W-S-M ... 88 B1
Gillmore Rd. W-S-M ... 88 B1
Gillray Cl. Bris ... 50 A3
Gillson Cl. Lock ... 105 E1
Gilpin Cl. Kingsw ... 51 F1
Gilroy Cl. Kingsw ... 66 A2
Gilslake Ave. Bris ... 35 D2
Gimblet Rd. W-S-M ... 89 D2
Gingell's Green. Bris ... 65 D4
Gipsy Patch La. St Gif ... 36 B3
Glades The. Bris ... 50 C1
Gladstone Dr. Kingsw ... 51 F2
Gladstone La. Fr Cot ... 38 B4
Gladstone Rd. Bath ... 102 B1
Gladstone Rd. Bris ... 80 A3
Gladstone Rd. Kingsw ... 51 E1
Gladstone St. Bris ... 63 D2
Gladstone St. Bris ... 64 B4
Gladstone St. Kingsw ... 51 E2
Gladstone St. Mid No ... 132 A4
Glaisdale Rd. Bris ... 51 D3
Glanville Dr. Hin Ble ... 129 F3
Glanville Gdns. Kingsw ... 65 F4
Glass House La. Bris ... 64 A3
Glastonbury Cl. Nail ... 60 A1
Glastonbury Cl. Kingsw ... 65 F3
Glastonbury Way. W-S-M ... 89 D1
Glebe Ave. Portis ... 45 F2
Glebe Field. Alm ... 24 A3
Glebe Rd. Bath ... 101 D2
Glebe Rd. Bris ... 64 C4
Glebe Rd. Cleve ... 57 E1
Glebe Rd. Lo Ash ... 62 B1
Glebe Rd. Portis ... 45 F2
Glebe Rd. W-S-M ... 104 C4
Glebe The. Hi Cha ... 120 A2
Glebe The. Hin Cha ... 119 E1
Glebe The. Piln ... 22 B4
Glebe The. Tims ... 116 A2
Glebe The. Wring ... 92 B1
Glebe Wlk. Keyn ... 81 E2
Glebelands Rd. Bris ... 36 A2
Glebelands. Rad ... 132 B1
Gledemoor Dr. Fr Cot ... 38 B4
Glen Av. Ab Lei ... 61 F4
Glen Dr. Bris ... 48 B3
Glen La. Bris ... 64 B1
Glen Park Gdns. Bris ... 65 D4
Glen Park. Bris ... 50 B1
Glen Park. Bris ... 65 D4
Glen The. Bris ... 49 D2
Glen The. Keyn ... 82 C1
Glen The. Kingsw ... 65 D2
Glen The. W-S-M ... 88 A1
Glen The. Yate ... 27 F1
Glen Yeo Terr. Cong ... 91 E2
Glena Ave. Bris ... 64 A1
Glenarm Rd. Bris ... 64 C1
Glenarm Wlk. Bris ... 64 C1
Glenavon Park. Bris ... 48 B2
Glenburn Rd. Bris ... 51 D1
Glencoyne Sq. Bris ... 35 E1
Glendale. Bris ... 62 C3
Glendale. Bris ... 64 B1
Glendale. Mang ... 51 F4
Glendare St. Bris ... 64 B3
Glendevon Rd. Bris ... 80 A2
Gleneagles Cl. Nail ... 60 A1
Gleneagles Cl. W-S-M ... 88 C2
Gleneagles Dr. Bris ... 34 B2
Gleneagles Rd. Kingsw ... 66 A3

Gleneagles. Yate ... 27 E1
Glenfall. Yate ... 39 E4
Glenfrome Rd. Bris ... 50 A2
Glenroy Ave. Bris ... 51 D1
Glenside Cl. Bris ... 51 E4
Glenside Park. Bris ... 50 C3
Glentworth Rd. Bris ... 49 E1
Glentworth Rd. Bris ... 63 D3
Glenview Rd. Bris ... 64 B1
Glenwood Dr. Kingsw ... 66 A2
Glenwood Rd. Bris ... 49 E4
Glenwood Rise. Portis ... 44 C3
Glenwood. Bris ... 51 E2
Gloster Ave. Bris ... 50 B2
Gloucester Cl. St Gif ... 36 B3
Gloucester La. Bris ... 63 F4
Gloucester Rd N. Bris ... 36 A2
Gloucester Rd. Alm ... 24 C2
Gloucester Rd. Alve ... 14 C1
Gloucester Rd. Avon ... 33 D1
Gloucester Rd. Bath ... 85 E3
Gloucester Rd. Bathe ... 85 E3
Gloucester Rd. Bris ... 36 A4
Gloucester Rd. Bris ... 49 F2
Gloucester Rd. Kingsw ... 51 F2
Gloucester Rd. St Gif ... 24 A2
Gloucester Rd. Thorn ... 8 B1
Gloucester Row. W-u-E ... 11 F4
Gloucester St. Bath ... 101 F4
Gloucester St. Bris ... 50 B2
Gloucester St. Bris ... 62 C4
Gloucester St. Bris ... 63 F4
Gloucester St. W-S-M ... 104 B4
Glovers Field. Ship ... 125 F4
Glyn Vale. Bris ... 63 F1
Goddard Dr. W-S-M ... 89 D2
Godfrey Ct. Kingsw ... 65 F2
Goffenton Dr. Bris ... 51 D3
Goldcrest Rd. Ch Sod ... 39 F4
Golden La. Kings ... 11 F2
Golden Valley La. Bitt ... 66 C3
Goldfinch Way. Puck ... 53 E2
Goldney Ave. Bris ... 63 D3
Goldney Ave. Sist ... 66 C3
Goldney Cl. Clut ... 114 C1
Goldney Rd. Bris ... 63 D3
Goldney Way. Clut ... 114 C1
Goldsbury Wlk. Bris ... 34 A1
Golf Club La. Keyn ... 82 C1
Golf Course La. Bris ... 35 F2
Golf Course Rd. Bath ... 102 B3
Golledge Cl. Chil ... 137 E2
Gooch Way. W-S-M ... 89 D2
Good Shepherd Cl. Bris ... 49 E2
Goodeve Park. Bris ... 48 B2
Goodeve Rd. Bris ... 48 B2
Goodhind St. Bris ... 64 A4
Goodneston Rd. Bris ... 51 D2
Goodring Hill. Bris ... 34 A1
Goodwin Dr. Bris ... 79 F2
Goodwin Dr. Nail ... 59 E2
Goodwood Gdns. Mang ... 37 F3
Goold Cl. Cor ... 100 A4
Goolden St. Bris ... 64 A2
Goosard La. Paul ... 131 E4
Goose Acre. St Gif ... 36 C3
Goose Green Way. Yate ... 27 E2
Goose Green. Fr Cot ... 38 B4
Goose Green. Yate ... 27 E2
Gooseland Cl. Bris ... 79 E2
Goosy La. Lock ... 89 E1
Gordano Gdns. E in G ... 47 D2
Gordano Rd. E in G ... 46 B4
Gordano View. Portis ... 45 E3
Gordano Way. E in G ... 46 C3
Gordon Ave. Bris ... 50 C1
Gordon Cl. Bris ... 50 C1
Gordon Rd. Bath ... 102 A3
Gordon Rd. Bris ... 49 F1
Gordon Rd. Bris ... 50 B1
Gordon Rd. Bris ... 63 D3
Gordon Rd. P St J ... 133 E4
Gordon Rd. W-S-M ... 104 C4
Gore Rd. Bris ... 63 D2
Gore's Marsh Rd. Bris ... 63 D1
Gorham Cl. Bris ... 34 B1
Gorlands Rd. Ch Sod ... 28 A1
Gorlangton Cl. Bris ... 80 A4
Gorse Cover Rd. Piln ... 22 A4
Gorse Hill. Bris ... 51 E2
Gorse La. Bris ... 63 D3
Gorse La. Co Ash ... 68 B4
Gorse La. Marsh ... 54 C1
Gosforth Rd. Bris ... 35 D1
Goslet Rd. Bris ... 80 C3
Goss Barton. Nail ... 59 E1
Goss Cl. Nail ... 59 E1
Goss La. Nail ... 59 E1
Goss View. Nail ... 59 E1
Gotley Rd. Bris ... 64 B1
Gott Dr. Bris ... 64 B3
Goulston Rd. Bris ... 79 D3
Goulston Wlk. Bris ... 79 D3
Goulter St. Bris ... 64 A3
Gournay Ct. Paul ... 131 D2
Gournay Cl. Bris ... 50 A1
Grace Cl. Ch Sod ... 28 A1
Grace Cl. Yatt ... 91 D4

Grace Ct. Mang 51 E3
Grace Dr. Kingsw 66 A4
Grace Dr. Mid No 132 A1
Grace Park Rd. Bris 64 B1
Grace Rd. Mang 51 E3
Grace Rd. W-S-M 89 D2
Gradwell Cl. W-S-M 89 D2
Graeme Cl. Bris 51 D2
Graham Rd. Bris 50 A1
Graham Rd. Bris 63 E2
Graham Rd. Mang 51 F3
Graham Rd. W-S-M 104 C4
Grainger Ct. Bris 47 F4
Graitney Cl. Brock 92 A4
Grampian Cl. Kingsw 66 B2
Granby Hill. Bris 62 C3
Grand Par. Bath 102 A3
Grandmother's Rock La.
      Bitt 67 E1
Grange Ave. Kingsw 65 E3
Grange Ave. St Gif 36 B3
Grange Cl. N Bris 49 D3
Grange Cl. St Gif 24 B1
Grange Cl. W-S-M 104 C1
Grange Court Rd. Bris 49 D3
Grange Ct. Kingsw 65 E3
Grange Dr. Bris 51 E3
Grange End. Rod 138 A4
Grange Park. Bris 49 D3
Grange Park. Bris 51 E4
Grange Rd. Bris 63 D4
Grange Rd. Bris 79 D3
Grange Rd. Keyn 82 B2
Grange Rd. W-S-M 104 C1
Grange The. Bris 48 B4
Grangeville Cl. Kingsw 66 A2
Grangewood Cl. Bris 51 E3
Granny's La. Kingsw 65 F3
Grantham La. Bris 65 E4
Grantham Rd. Bris 51 E1
Grantson Cl. Bris 64 C1
Granville Cl. Kingsw 65 D2
Granville Rd. Bath 84 C2
Granville St. Bris 64 B3
Grasmere Cl. Bris 49 D4
Grasmere Dr. W-S-M 104 C2
Grass Meers Dr. Bris 80 A2
Grassington Dr. Ch Sod ... 40 A4
Grassmere Gdns. Kingsw . 66 B3
Grassmere Rd. Yatt 91 D4
Gratitude Rd. Bris 50 B1
Gravel Hill Rd. Yate 28 A3
Gravel Hill. Ch St 112 A4
Gravel Hill. Win 112 A4
Graveney Cl. Bris 64 B1
Gray's Cl. Bris 34 C1
Grayle Rd. Bris 35 D1
Grays Hill. Well 134 A3
Great Ann St. Bris 63 F4
Great Bedford St. Bath .. 101 F4
Great Brockeridge. Bris 48 C3
Great Dowles. Kingsw 66 A2
Great George St. Bris 63 E3
Great George St. Bris 63 F4
Great Hayles Rd. Bris 80 A4
Great Leaze. Kingsw 66 A2
Great Meadow Rd. St Gif .. 36 C3
Great Meadow. St Gif 37 D3
Great Park Rd. St Gif 24 B2
Great Pulteney St. Bath ... 102 A4
Great Stanhope St. Bath .. 101 F3
Great Stoke Way. St Gif ... 36 B2
Great Stoke. St Gif 37 D3
Great Western Bridge.
      W-S-M 104 C4
Great Western La. Bris 64 A3
Great Western Rd. Cleve .. 57 E1
Great Western Way. Bris .. 63 F3
Greatstone La. Win 94 C3
Green Cl. Bris 50 A4
Green Croft. Bris 51 D1
Green Dell Cl. Bris 34 B2
Green Ditch La. Chil 137 D3
Green Ditch La. Ston E ... 137 D3
Green Dragon Rd. Wint 37 E3
Green Hayes. Ch Sod 40 B4
Green La. Avon 33 D1
Green La. But 94 B2
Green La. But 111 D4
Green La. Chil 137 F1
Green La. Hin Cha 119 F1
Green La. Marsh 69 F4
Green La. Paul 130 C3
Green La. Thorn 16 A4
Green La. Win 94 B2
Green La. Wrax 61 E2
Green Park Rd. Bath 101 F3
Green Park. Bath 101 F3
Green Parlour Rd. Kilm .. 133 E1
Green Side. Mang 52 A3
Green St. Bath 102 A4
Green St. Bris 63 F2
Green St. Well 133 F3
Green The. Back 75 F3
Green The. Bath 101 E1
Green The. E in G 47 E2
Green The. Hin Cha 119 F1

Green The. Kingsw 51 F1
Green The. Lock 106 A2
Green The. Olve 14 A1
Green The. St Gif 36 C2
Green The. Wins 125 D4
Green Tree Rd. Mid No ... 132 A2
Green Wlk. Bris 64 A1
Greenacre Rd. Bris 80 A2
Greenacre. W-S-M 88 A1
Greenacres. Bath 84 A2
Greenacres. Bris 48 C4
Greenacres. Mid No 131 F1
Greenbank Ave W. Bris ... 50 B1
Greenbank Ave. Bris 50 B1
Greenbank Gdns. Bath 84 A1
Greenbank Rd. Bris 50 B1
Greenbank Rd. Bris 63 D2
Greenbank Rd. Kingsw 65 E3
Greenbank View. Bris 50 B1
Greendale Rd. Bris 49 D2
Greendale Rd. Bris 63 F1
Greenditch Ave. Bris 79 E3
Greenditch Cl. Chil 137 E2
Greenditch St. Piln 13 E1
Greendown Pl. Bath 102 A1
Greendown. Bris 65 D4
Greenfield Ave. Bris 49 E4
Greenfield Cres. Nail 59 F2
Greenfield Park. Portis 45 E2
Greenfield Pl. W-S-M 104 B4
Greenfield Rd. Bris 35 E1
Greenfields Ave. Ban 107 D2
Greenfinch Lodge. Bris 50 C3
Greenhaven. Bris 50 B1
Greenhill Cl. Nail 59 E1
Greenhill Cl. W-S-M 89 D2
Greenhill Down. Alve 15 D2
Greenhill Gdns. Alve 15 D2
Greenhill Gr. Bris 63 D1
Greenhill La. Alve 14 C2
Greenhill La. Bris 34 B1
Greenhill La. Wins 108 A2
Greenhill Par. Alve 15 D3
Greenhill Pl. Mid No 132 A2
Greenhill Rd. Alve 15 D3
Greenhill Rd. Mid No 132 A2
Greenhill Rd. Wins 108 A2
Greenhill. Alve 15 D2
Greenland Rd. W-S-M 88 B1
Greenlands Rd. P St J 133 E4
Greenlands Way. Bris 34 C2
Greenleaze Ave. Mang 37 F1
Greenleaze Cl. Mang 37 F1
Greenleaze. Bris 64 A1
Greenmore Rd. Bris 64 A1
Greenore. Kingsw 65 E4
Greenpark Rd. Bris 35 F1
Greenridge Cl. Bris 78 C2
Greenridge. Clut 114 C2
Greenside Cl. Bris 34 B2
Greenslade Gdns. Nail 59 E2
Greensplott Rd. Avon 33 F4
Greenvale Cl. Tims 116 A1
Greenvale Dr. Tims 116 A1
Greenvale Rd. Paul 131 E3
Greenvale. Tims 116 A1
Greenview. Kingsw 66 A1
Greenway Bush La. Bris ... 63 D2
Greenway Ct. Bath 101 F2
Greenway Dr. Bris 49 E4
Greenway La. Bath 102 A2
Greenway Park. Bris 49 E4
Greenway Park. Cleve 57 F2
Greenway Rd. Bris 49 D1
Greenway The. Bris 51 E2
Greenways Rd. Yate 27 F2
Greenways. Chil 137 E1
Greenways. Kingsw 52 A1
Greenwell La. Chur 109 E4
Greenwood Cl. Bris 49 F4
Greenwood Dr. Alve 14 C2
Greenwood Rd. Bris 64 A1
Greenwood Rd. W-S-M 88 C1
Gregory Ct. Kingsw 66 A3
Gregorys Tyning. Paul 131 F3
Greinton. W-S-M 105 D1
Grenville Ave. Lock 106 A2
Grenville Cl. Bris 64 C4
Grenville Pl. Bris 62 C3
Grenville Rd. Bris 49 F2
Greve Ct. Kingsw 65 F2
Greville Rd. Bris 63 D2
Greville St. Bris 63 E2
Grey Hollow. E Harp 128 C2
Greyfield Comm. Paul 115 E1
Greyfield Rd. Paul 115 E1
Greyfield View. Clut 114 C1
Greylands Rd. Bris 78 C4
Greystoke Ave. Bris 35 E1
Greystoke Gdns. Bris 49 D4
Greystones. Mang 37 F1
Grib La. Blag 110 C1
Griffin Cl. W-S-M 89 D1
Griffin Rd. Cleve 57 F2
Griggfield Wlk. Bris 80 A4
Grimsbury Rd. Kingsw 66 A4
Grindell Rd. Bris 64 B4

Grinfield Ave. Bris 79 E2
Grinfield Cl. Bris 79 E2
Grinfield Ct. Bris 79 E2
Grittleton Rd. Bris 49 F4
Grosvenor Bridge Rd. Bath . 85 E1
Grosvenor Park. Bath 85 E1
Grosvenor Pl. Bath 85 E1
Grosvenor Rd. Bris 49 F1
Grove Ave. Bris 48 B4
Grove Ave. Bris 50 C2
Grove Ave. Bris 63 E3
Grove Bank. Bris 37 E1
Grove La. Dyrh 54 B3
Grove La. Faulk 134 B1
Grove La. W-S-M 104 B4
Grove Leaze. Bris 47 E3
Grove Park Ave. Bris 64 B1
Grove Park Rd. Bris 64 B1
Grove Park Rd. W-S-M 87 E1
Grove Park Terr. Bris 50 C2
Grove Park. Bris 49 E1
Grove Pk. Bris 64 B1
Grove Rd. Bris 48 B4
Grove Rd. Bris 49 D1
Grove Rd. Bris 50 C2
Grove Rd. W-S-M 88 B1
Grove Rd. W-S-M 104 B4
Grove St. Bath 102 A4
Grove The. Bris 63 E3
Grove The. Kingsw 66 A2
Grove The. Wickw 27 D4
Grove The. Winsc 107 F1
Grove The. Wrax 60 B2
Grove View. Bris 50 C3
Grove Wood Rd. Rod 138 C4
Grovesend Rd. Thorn 15 E4
Guernsey Ave. Bris 64 C2
Gug The. Paul 115 E1
Guildford Rd. Bris 64 C3
Guinea La. Bath 101 F4
Guinea La. Bris 51 D2
Guinea St. Bris 63 E3
Gullen. Well 134 A3
Gulliford's Bank. Cleve 57 F1
Gullimores Gdns. Bris 79 D2
Gulliver Pl. Ch Sod 40 A4
Gullon Wlk. Bris 78 C3
Gullons Cl. Bris 79 D3
Gully La. Rock 8 C4
Gully The. Wint 37 F4
Gullybrook La. Bris 64 A3
Gunter's Hill. Bris 65 D3
Guthrie Rd. Bris 63 D4
Gwilliam St. Bris 63 E2
Gwyn St. Bris 49 F1
Gypsy La. Keyn 99 D4

Haberfield Hill. Ab Lei 47 F1
Hacket Hill. Thorn 15 F4
Hacket La. Thorn 15 F4
Hadley Cl. W-S-M 66 A3
Hadley Rd. Bath 102 A1
Hadrian Cl. Bris 48 B2
Hagg Hill. Tims 116 A1
Haggs La. Bris 50 C1
Haig Cl. Bris 48 A4
Halbrow Cres. Bris 51 E3
Haldon Cl. Bris 63 E1
Hales Horn Cl. St Gif 36 B3
Half Yd. Wring 109 E4
Halfacre Cl. Bris 80 A2
Halfacre La. Bris 80 A2
Halfpenny Row. Rode 136 C1
Halifax Rd. Yate 27 E2
Hall End La. Yate 17 E1
Hall La. Co Ash 68 A2
Hall La. Co Ash 68 C2
Hall La. Hort 29 F3
Hall St. Bris 63 D1
Hallam Rd. Cleve 57 E2
Hallards Cl. Bris 47 F4
Hallatrow Rd. Paul 131 E3
Hallen Cl. Bris 34 B2
Hallen Dr. Bris 48 B4
Hallen Rd. Bris 34 B2
Halletts Way. Portis 45 E3
Halliwell Rd. Portis 44 B2
Halls Rd. Kingsw 65 E4
Halsbury Rd. Bris 49 D2
Halstock Ave. Bris 50 C2
Halston Dr. Bris 63 F4
Halswell Gdns. Bris 79 D2
Halswell Rd. Cleve 57 E1
Halt End. Whit 80 B2
Ham Cl. Clut 114 C1
Ham Gr. Paul 131 F4
Ham Green. E in G 47 E2
Ham La. Bi Sut 113 A3
Ham La. Bris 50 C3
Ham La. Dun 78 B2
Ham La. K Sey 72 C1
Ham La. O-on-S 7 E3
Ham La. Paul 130 C3
Ham La. Paul 131 F3
Ham La. Wick 53 F1
Ham La. Wrax 60 A2
Ham La. Yatt 74 A2

Ham Link. Blag 109 F2
Ham Rd. Berr 121 D2
Ham Wood Cl. W-S-M ... 105 D1
Hamble Cl. Thorn 15 E4
Hambledon Rd. Lock 89 E2
Hambrook La. Bris 37 D2
Hambrook La. St Gif 37 D2
Hamersmith Rd. Bris 64 B4
Hamilton Rd. Bath 84 C1
Hamilton Rd. Bris 63 D2
Hamilton Rd. Bris 64 A4
Hamilton Rd. W-S-M 87 E1
Hamlet The. Nail 60 A2
Hammer La. Faulk 135 E1
Hammond Cl. Bris 64 B1
Hammond Gdns. Bris 48 C4
Hampden Cl. Yate 27 E2
Hampden Rd. Bris 64 A2
Hampden Rd. W-S-M 88 C1
Hampshire Way. Yate 27 F2
Hampstead Rd. Bris 64 B2
Hampton Cl. Kingsw 66 A3
Hampton Cnr. Bris 47 F3
Hampton La. Bris 49 D1
Hampton Park. Bris 49 D1
Hampton Rd. Bris 49 D1
Hampton Row. Bath 102 A4
Hampton St. Kingsw 51 E1
Hampton View. Bath 85 D1
Hams La. Badg 123 E1
Hams Rd. Keyn 81 F4
Hanbury Cl. Kingsw 65 E3
Hanbury Rd. Bris 63 D4
Handel Ave. Bris 64 B4
Handel Rd. Keyn 81 F3
Handford Way. Kingsw 66 A2
Hanford Ct. Bris 80 B4
Hang Hill. Well 134 A3
Hanham Bsns Pk. Kingsw . 65 D3
Hanham La. Paul 131 F4
Hanham Rd. Kingsw 65 E1
Hanham Way. Nail 59 E1
Hannah More Cl. Wring 92 C1
Hannah More Rd. Nail 75 E4
Hanny's La. Ch Mag 96 A2
Hanover Cl. W-S-M 89 D2
Hanover Ct. Bris 63 F4
Hanover Ct. Rad 133 E1
Hanover Pl. Bris 63 D3
Hanover St. Bris 85 D1
Hanover St. Bris 63 E3
Hanover St. Bris 64 B4
Hansford Cl. Bath 101 F1
Hansford Sq. Bath 101 F1
Hanson's Way. Cleve 57 E1
Hantone Hill. Bath 102 C4
Happerton La. E in G 47 E1
Hapsburg Cl. W-S-M 89 D2
Harbour Rd. Portis 45 E3
Harbour Wall. Bris 48 B2
Harbour Way. Bris 63 E3
Harbury Rd. Bris 49 E4
Harbutts. Bath 85 F1
Harcombe Hill. Wint 37 F2
Harcombe Rd. Wint 37 E3
Harcourt Ave. Bris 65 D3
Harcourt Cl. Keyn 82 C1
Harcourt Gdns. Bath 84 A1
Harcourt Hill. Bris 49 E2
Harcourt Rd. Bris 49 D2
Harden Rd. Bris 80 C3
Hardenhuish Rd. Bris 64 B3
Harding Pl. Keyn 82 A3
Hardwick Cl. Bris 64 C2
Hardwick Cl. Kingsw 66 B3
Hardwick Rd. E in G 47 E3
Hardwicke. Yate 39 E4
Hardy Ave. Bris 63 D2
Hardy Ct. Kingsw 65 F3
Hardy La. Olve 14 A1
Hardy La. Piln 23 F4
Hardy Rd. Bris 63 D1
Hareclive Rd. Bris 79 E2
Harefield Cl. Kingsw 65 E1
Harescombe. Yate 39 F4
Harewood Rd. Bris 51 D1
Harford Cl. Bris 48 B4
Harford Dr. Bris 37 E1
Harford Sq. Ch Mag 96 A2
Harington Pl. Bath 101 F3
Harlech Way. Kingsw 66 A1
Harleston St. Bris 64 A4
Harley La. Cleve 58 B3
Harley St. Bath 101 F4
Harmer Cl. Bris 34 C2
Harmony Dr. Portis 44 C2
Harnhill Cl. Bris 79 D2
Harolds Way. Kingsw 65 D2
Harptree Ct. Kingsw 66 A2
Harptree Gr. Bris 63 D1
Harptree Hill. E Harp 128 A3
Harptree. W-S-M 105 D1
Harrier Path. W-S-M 105 F4
Harrington Ave. Bris 80 C3
Harrington Gr. Bris 80 C3
Harrington Rd. Bris 80 C3
Harrington Wlk. Bris 80 C3
Harris Barton. Fr Cot 38 A4

Harris Ct. Kingsw 65 F2
Harris La. Ab Lei 61 F4
Harrow Rd. Bris 64 B2
Harrowdene Rd. Bris 64 A2
Harry Stoke Rd. St Gif 36 C1
Hart's La. Paul 131 D4
Hartcliffe Rd. Bris 79 E4
Hartcliffe Way. Bris 79 E4
Hartcliffe Wlk. Bris 79 F4
Hartcombe Rd. E in G 47 D1
Hartfield Ave. Bris 49 E1
Hartgill Cl. Bris 79 D2
Hartington Park. Bris 49 E1
Hartland. W-S-M 89 D1
Hartley Cl. Ch Sod 28 A1
Harts Paddock. Mid No ... 131 F2
Harvey Cl. W-S-M 89 D2
Harveys La. Bris 64 C4
Harwood Gdns. W-S-M 88 C2
Haselbury Gr. Keyn 82 C1
Haskins Ct. Kingsw 66 A2
Haslands. Nail 75 E4
Haslemere Ind Est. Avon .. 33 E1
Hassage Hill. Well 134 C4
Hassell Dr. Bris 64 A4
Hastings Cl. Bris 63 E1
Hastings Rd. Bris 63 E1
Hatchet Hill. Kilm 139 F2
Hatchet La. St Gif 36 C2
Hatchet Rd. St Gif 36 C3
Hatchmere. Thorn 15 E4
Hatfield Bldgs. Bath 102 A3
Hatfield Rd. Bath 101 F2
Hatfield Rd. W-S-M 105 D1
Hatherley Rd. Bris 49 F2
Hatherley. Yate 39 F4
Hathway Wlk. Bris 64 A1
Hatters' La. Ch Sod 28 A1
Havage Dro. Ban 107 E4
Haven The. Kingsw 51 F1
Haversham Cl. W-S-M 88 B1
Haverstock Rd. Bris 64 A2
Haviland Gr. Bath 84 A2
Haviland Park. Bath 84 A1
Havory. Bath 85 E1
Havyat Rd. Wring 109 F4
Haw La. Olve 14 A2
Hawarden Terr. Bath 85 D1
Hawburn Cl. Bris 64 B1
Haweswater Cl. Kingsw 66 B3
Hawke Rd. W-S-M 88 C2
Hawkesbury Rd. Bris 50 C2
Hawkesbury Rd. Hill 19 E4
Hawkesley Dr. St Gif 36 B3
Hawkfield Cl. Bris 79 E3
Hawkfield Rd. Bris 79 E3
Hawkfield Way. Bris 79 E3
Hawkins Cl. Kingsw 66 A3
Hawkins St. Bris 63 F4
Hawkley Dr. St Gif 24 C3
Hawksmoor Cl. Bris 80 A4
Hawksworth Dr. Kingsw 65 D3
Hawksworth Dr. W-S-M 89 D2
Hawlyn Cl. Bris 48 B3
Hawthorn Ave. Kingsw 65 D3
Hawthorn Cl. Bris 35 F4
Hawthorn Cl. Char 11 D2
Hawthorn Cl. Portis 44 C2
Hawthorn Coombe. W-S-M . 88 C2
Hawthorn Cres. Thorn 8 B1
Hawthorn Cres. Yatt 74 A1
Hawthorn Gdns. W-S-M 88 B1
Hawthorn Gr. Bath 101 F1
Hawthorn Hill. W-S-M 88 C1
Hawthorn Hts. W-S-M 88 B2
Hawthorn Park. W-S-M 88 C2
Hawthorn Rd. Rad 133 D1
Hawthorn Way. Nail 60 A1
Hawthorn Way. St Gif 36 C3
Hawthorne Cl. Puck 53 E3
Hawthorne Gdns. Kingsw .. 51 F2
Hawthorne St. Bris 64 A2
Hawthornes The. Kingsw ... 51 F2
Hawthorns La. Keyn 81 F3
Hay Hill. Bath 101 F4
Hay La. Win 94 B3
Hay Leaze. Yate 27 E2
Hay St. Marsh 70 A4
Hay St. Ston E 137 D4
Haycombe Dr. Bath 101 D2
Haycombe La. Engl 100 C2
Haycombe. Bris 79 F2
Haycroft La. Newp 4 B3
Haycroft Rd. Bris 36 A2
Haydock Cl. Mang 37 F1
Haydon Gate. Rod 138 C4
Haydon Gdns. Bris 50 A3
Haydon Hill. Rod 138 C4
Haydon Ind Est. Rod 138 C4
Hayeley Dr. St Gif 36 C3
Hayes Cl. Bris 64 A4
Hayes La. Gr Bad 30 C1
Hayes Park Rd. Mid No ... 131 F1
Hayes Rd. Mid No 131 F2
Hayesfield Park. Bath 101 F3
Hayeswood Rd. Farm 115 F2

Hayeswood Rd. Tims 116 A1
Hayfield. Marsh 70 A4
Hayleigh House. Bris 79 E2
Haymarket The. Bris 63 E4
Haymarket Wlk. Bris 63 E4
Haynes La. Mang 51 E3
Haythorn Ct. Mang 51 F3
Haytor Park. Bris 48 B3
Hayward Cl. Cleve 57 E1
Hayward Rd. Bris 64 B4
Hayward Rd. Kingsw 51 E2
Haywood Cl. W-S-M 105 D1
Haywood Gdns. W-S-M 105 D1
Hazel Ave. Bris 49 D1
Hazel Cres. Thorn 8 B1
Hazel Gdns. Alve 14 C2
Hazel Gr. Bath 101 E2
Hazel Gr. Bris 50 A4
Hazel La. Olve 14 C2
Hazel Terr. Rod 138 B4
Hazelbury Dr. Kingsw 66 B3
Hazelbury Rd. Nail 59 E1
Hazelcote Rd. Bris 80 A2
Hazeldene Rd. Bris 36 A4
Hazeldene Rd. W-S-M 105 D4
Hazell Cl. Cleve 57 F1
Hazelton Rd. Bris 49 E2
Hazelwood Ct. Bris 48 B2
Hazelwood Rd. Bris 48 B2
Hazleton Gdns. Bath 102 C2
Headford Ave. Bris 65 D4
Headley La. Bris 79 D3
Headley Park Ave. Bris 79 D4
Headley Park Rd. Bris 79 D4
Headley Rd. Bris 79 D3
Headley Wlk. Bris 79 D4
Healey Dr. Dyrh 54 B3
Heart Meers. Bris 80 A3
Heath Cl. Wint 37 F3
Heath Ct. Mang 51 E4
Heath Gdns. Fr Cot 38 B3
Heath Gdns. Mang 51 E4
Heath Rd. Bris 50 A2
Heath Rd. Kingsw 65 D2
Heath Rd. Mang 51 E4
Heath Rd. Nail 59 F2
Heath Ridge. Lo Ash 62 A1
Heath Rise. Kingsw 66 A3
Heath St. Bris 50 B2
Heath Wlk. Mang 51 E4
Heathcote Dr. Fr Cot 38 B4
Heathcote La. Fr Cot 38 B4
Heathcote Rd. Bris 51 D1
Heathcote Rd. Mang 51 F3
Heathcote Wlk. Bris 51 E1
Heather Ave. Fr Cot 38 A3
Heather Cl. Bris 65 D4
Heatherdene. Bris 79 F4
Heathfield Cl. Bath 84 A2
Heathfield Cl. Keyn 81 E3
Heathfield Cres. Bris 80 A4
Heathfield Rd. Nail 59 F2
Heathfield Way. Nail 59 F1
Heathgate. Yatt 91 D4
Hebden Rd. Westw 120 C2
Heber St. Bris 64 B4
Hebron Rd. Bris 63 E2
Hedgemead Cl. Bris 50 B3
Hedgemead View. Bris 50 C3
Hedges Cl. Cleve 57 D1
Hedges The. Lock 89 E1
Hedwick Ave. Bris 64 C4
Hedwick St. Bris 64 C4
Heggard Cl. Bris 79 D3
Helens Rd. Wins 108 A3
Hellier Wlk. Bris 79 E2
Helston Rd. Nail 60 A1
Hemming Way. Lock 105 F2
Hemmings Par. Bris 64 A4
Hemplow Cl. Bris 80 B4
Hempton La. St Gif 24 A1
Hen La. Win 94 C2
Henacre Rd. Bris 47 F4
Henbury Gdns. Bris 34 C1
Henbury Hill. Bris 34 C1
Henbury Rd. Bris 34 C1
Henbury Rd. Kingsw 65 D3
Hencliffe Rd. Bris 80 B4
Hencliffe Way. Kingsw 65 D2
Henderson Rd. Kingsw 65 D3
Hendre Rd. Bris 63 D1
Henfield Cres. Kingsw 66 A2
Henfield Rd. Fr Cot 38 B2
Henfield Rd. West 38 B2
Hengaston St. Bris 63 D1
Hengrove Ave. Bris 80 A4
Hengrove La. Bris 80 A4
Hengrove Rd. Bris 64 A1
Hengrove Way. Bris 79 E3
Henleaze Ave. Bris 49 D3
Henleaze Gdns. Bris 49 D3
Henleaze Park Dr. Bris 49 E3
Henleaze Park. Bris 49 E3
Henleaze Rd. Bris 49 D3
Henleaze Terr. Bris 49 D4
Henley Gr. Bris 49 D3

Henley La. Yatt 91 E4
Henley Lodge. Yatt 91 E4
Henley Park. Yatt 91 E4
Henley View. Well 118 B1
Hennessy Cl. Bris 79 F2
Henrietta Gdns. Bath 102 A4
Henrietta Mews. Bath 102 A4
Henrietta Pl. Bath 102 A4
Henrietta Rd. Bath 102 A4
Henrietta St. Bath 102 A4
Henrietta St. Bris 50 A1
Henrietta St. Bris 63 E4
Henry St. Bath 102 A3
Henry St. Bris 63 F2
Henry Williamson Ct.
    Kingsw 66 A3
Henshaw Cl. Bris 51 E1
Henshaw Rd. Bris 51 E1
Henshaw Wlk. Bris 51 E1
Hensley Gdns. Bath 101 F2
Hensley Rd. Bath 101 F2
Hensman's Hill. Bris 63 D3
Hepburn Rd. Bris 49 F1
Herald Cl. Bris 48 B3
Herapath St. Bris 64 B3
Herbert Cres. Bris 50 B2
Herbert Rd. Bath 101 E3
Herbert Rd. Cleve 57 E2
Herbert St. Bris 63 E2
Herbert St. Bris 64 B4
Hercules Cl. St Gif 36 B3
Hereford Rd. Bris 50 A1
Hereford St. Bris 63 E2
Heritage Cl. P St J 133 E4
Herkomer Cl. Bris 50 A4
Herluin Way. W-S-M 105 D3
Hermitage Cl. Bris 47 F4
Hermitage Rd. Bath 84 C1
Hermitage Rd. Mang 51 F3
Hern La. Ba Gu 77 F3
Heron Cl. W-S-M 105 F4
Heron Rd. Bris 50 A1
Heron Way. Ch Sod 40 A4
Herridge Cl. Bris 79 D2
Herridge Rd. Bris 79 D2
Hersey Gdns. Bris 78 C2
Hesding Cl. Kingsw 65 E2
Hestercombe Rd. Bris 79 D3
Heyford Ave. Bris 50 A2
Heyron Wlk. Bris 79 D2
Heywood Rd. E in G 47 E2
Heywood Terr. E in G 47 E2
Hibbs Cl. Marsh 69 F4
Hicks Cl. Marsh 69 F4
Hicks Common Rd. Wint 37 F3
Hicks Ct. Kingsw 65 F2
High Acre. Paul 131 F2
High Bannerdown. Bathe 86 A2
High Elm. Kingsw 65 F3
High Gr. Bris 48 A4
High Mead Gdns. Bi Sut 113 E4
High Meadows. Mid No 131 F1
High Park. Bris 64 A1
High Park. Paul 131 E3
High St. Axb 125 D1
High St. Ban 107 D1
High St. Bath 84 A1
High St. Bath 85 F1
High St. Bath 101 D3
High St. Bath 102 A3
High St. Bathe 85 F2
High St. Bathf 86 B1
High St. Bitt 82 C4
High St. Blag 110 B2
High St. Bris 47 E4
High St. Bris 49 D1
High St. Bris 49 D4
High St. Bris 50 A1
High St. Bris 63 E3
High St. Ch Mag 96 A2
High St. Ch Sod 28 A1
High St. Charl 84 C3
High St. Cong 91 E2
High St. Doyn 53 F1
High St. Dyrh 54 B2
High St. E Harp 128 C3
High St. Gr Bad 30 C1
High St. H Up 19 F1
High St. Hi Cha 120 A3
High St. Hill 19 E4
High St. Hin Cha 119 D1
High St. Ir Act 26 B2
High St. Keyn 81 F3
High St. Keyn 82 C2
High St. Kings 11 F2
High St. Kingsw 51 E2
High St. Kingsw 65 E3
High St. Kingsw 65 F4
High St. Kingsw 66 A4
High St. Kingsw 66 B2
High St. Mang 51 E2
High St. Marsh 69 F4
High St. Mid No 132 A1
High St. N St P 135 F2
High St. Nail 59 F1
High St. Paul 115 D1
High St. Paul 131 F3
High St. Pens 97 F2

High St. Portb 46 B2
High St. Portis 45 E3
High St. Rode 136 C1
High St. Ston E 130 C1
High St. Thorn 15 D4
High St. Tims 116 A1
High St. W-S-M 88 C1
High St. W-S-M 104 B4
High St. Well 118 B1
High St. Wick 67 E3
High St. Wickw 18 A3
High St. Win 95 D4
High St. Wint 37 E3
High St. Wring 92 B2
High St. Yatt 74 C1
High St. Yatt 91 D4
High View. Portis 45 D2
Higham St. Bris 63 F2
Highbury Pl. Bath 85 D1
Highbury Rd. Bris 49 F4
Highbury Rd. Bris 63 E1
Highbury Rd. Paul 131 D4
Highbury Rd. W-S-M 87 E1
Highbury Terr. Bath 85 D1
Highbury Villas. Bris 63 E4
Highcroft. Kingsw 66 B3
Highdale Ave. Cleve 57 F2
Highdale Cl. Bris 80 A2
Highdale Pl. Cleve 57 E2
Highdale Rd. Cleve 57 F2
Highett Dr. Bris 50 A1
Highfield Ave. Kingsw 65 E3
Highfield Cl. Bath 101 D3
Highfield Cl. St Gif 36 C2
Highfield Cres. Chil 137 E2
Highfield Dr. Portis 44 C2
Highfield Gdns. Kingsw 66 B1
Highfield Gr. Bris 49 E3
Highfield La. Co Mar 128 A3
Highfield La. E Harp 129 D2
Highfield La. H Up 29 F4
Highfield La. Hort 29 F4
Highfield Rd. Ch Sod 28 A1
Highfield Rd. Keyn 81 F1
Highfield Rd. P St J 133 E4
Highfield Rd. W-S-M 105 D1
Highfields. H Up 19 F1
Highfields. Pens 96 C1
Highfields. Rad 132 B1
Highgrove St. Bris 64 A2
Highland Cl. W-S-M 88 A1
Highland Cres. Bris 49 D1
Highland Rd. Bath 101 D3
Highland Sq. Bris 49 D1
Highland Terr. Bath 101 E3
Highlands Dr. N Nib 5 F2
Highlands Rd. Lo Ash 62 A1
Highlands Rd. Portis 45 D3
Highleaze Rd. Kingsw 66 B2
Highmead Gdns. Bris 78 C2
Highmore Ct. Bris 50 A4
Highmore Gdns. Bris 50 B4
Highnam Cl. St Gif 24 A1
Highridge Cres. Bris 78 C3
Highridge Green. Bris 78 C3
Highridge Park. Bris 78 C3
Highridge Rd. Bris 63 D1
Highridge Rd. Bris 78 C2
Highridge Rd. Dun 78 C2
Highridge Wlk. Bris 78 C4
Highview Rd. Kingsw 51 F1
Highwall La. Co Dan 80 C1
Highway. Yate 27 F1
Highwood La. Bris 35 E4
Highwood Rd. Bris 35 F4
Highworth Cres. Yate 39 E4
Highworth Rd. Bris 64 B3
Hill Ave. Bath 101 F1
Hill Ave. Bris 63 F2
Hill Burn. Bris 49 E3
Hill Crest. Bris 64 A1
Hill Dr. Wrax 61 E2
Hill End Dr. Bris 34 B2
Hill Gay Cl. Portis 44 C2
Hill Gr. Bris 49 E3
Hill House Rd. Mang 51 F3
Hill La. Ch Sod 41 D4
Hill La. Nail 58 B2
Hill La. O-On-S 1 C1
Hill La. Rock 2 A2
Hill La. Ship 109 D1
Hill Lawn. Bris 64 B2
Hill Moor. Cleve 57 F1
Hill Park. Cong 91 F3
Hill Rd E. W-S-M 88 C1
Hill Rd. Cleve 57 E2
Hill Rd. Dun 78 B1
Hill Rd. W-S-M 88 C1
Hill Rd. W-S-M 104 C4
Hill Rd. Wins 108 A2
Hill St. Bris 63 E3
Hill St. Bris 63 F2
Hill St. Bris 64 C4
Hill St. Kingsw 65 F4
Hill The. Alm 24 A2
Hill The. Hi Cha 120 B3
Hill Top. Portis 45 D2
Hill View Cl. Kingsw 66 B2

Hill View Ct. W-S-M 105 E4
Hill View Rd. Bath 85 D1
Hill View Rd. Bris 79 D4
Hill View Rd. Puck 53 E3
Hill View Rd. W-S-M 105 D4
Hill View. Bris 36 A2
Hill View. Bris 49 E3
Hill View. Bris 63 D3
Hill View. Kingsw 51 E1
Hill View. Marks 99 D1
Hill View. Paul 131 D2
Hill View. Pris 117 D3
Hillbrook Rd. Thorn 15 E4
Hillburn Rd. Bris 65 D4
Hillcrest Cl. Nail 59 F1
Hillcrest Dr. Bath 101 E2
Hillcrest Rd. Nail 59 F1
Hillcrest Rd. Portis 44 C3
Hillcrest. P St J 133 E4
Hillcrest. Pens 97 F2
Hillcrest. Thorn 8 A1
Hillcroft Cl. W-S-M 88 A1
Hilldale Rd. Back 76 A3
Hillesley Rd. Kings 11 F2
Hillesley Rd. Kings 11 F2
Hillfields Ave. Bris 51 E2
Hillgrove St N. Bris 63 E4
Hillgrove Terr. W-S-M 104 B1
Hillier's La. Chur 108 B2
Hillmead. Chur 109 D3
Hillmer Rise. Ban 106 C2
Hillpath. Ban 107 D1
Hills Cl. Keyn 82 A3
Hillsborough Rd. Bris 64 B2
Hillsborough. Bris 63 D3
Hillsdon Rd. Bris 48 C4
Hillside Ave. Bris 65 E4
Hillside Ave. Mid No 137 F4
Hillside Cl. Fr Cot 38 B4
Hillside Cl. Paul 131 F3
Hillside Cres. Mid No 137 F4
Hillside Gdns. W-S-M 88 A1
Hillside La. Fr Cot 38 B4
Hillside Rd. Back 76 A2
Hillside Rd. Bath 101 E2
Hillside Rd. Blea 122 A4
Hillside Rd. Bris 65 D4
Hillside Rd. Cleve 57 E2
Hillside Rd. Lo Ash 62 A1
Hillside Rd. Mid No 137 F4
Hillside Rd. Portis 44 B2
Hillside St. Bris 64 A2
Hillside View. P St J 133 E4
Hillside W. Lock 105 F1
Hillside. Bris 63 E4
Hillside. Mang 52 A3
Hillside. Portb 46 C2
Hilltop Gdns. Bris 65 D2
Hilltop Gdns. Kingsw 51 E1
Hilltop Rd. Kingsw 51 E1
Hilltop View. Bris 65 D4
Hillview Ave. Cleve 57 E1
Hillview Gdns. Win 94 B4
Hillview Rd. Blea 123 E2
Hillview. Tims 116 A1
Hillyfield Rd. Bris 79 D3
Hillyfields Way. Wins 125 D4
Hillyfields. Wins 125 D4
Hilverton Gdns. Bris 49 F1
Hind Pitts. Wins 125 F4
Hinton Cl. Bath 100 C3
Hinton Cl. Keyn 82 C2
Hinton Dr. Kingsw 66 B3
Hinton Hill. Hin Cha 119 D1
Hinton La. Bris 62 C3
Hinton Rd. Bris 50 B1
Hinton Rd. Bris 51 D2
Hinton Villas. Hin Cha 119 F1
Hinton. W-S-M 104 C1
Hippisley Dr. Axb 125 E1
Hiscocks Dr. Bath 101 F2
Hitchen Cl. Marsh 69 F4
Hither Green. Cleve 57 F1
Hoare's La. Kilm 139 D2
Hobart Rd. W-S-M 104 C2
Hobb's La. Bris 63 E3
Hobbiton Rd. W-S-M 89 D3
Hobbs Ct. Nail 59 F1
Hobbs La. Ba Gu 77 F2
Hobbs La. Sist 52 A1
Hobhouse Cl. Bris 49 E4
Hobwell La. Lo Ash 62 B1
Hockey's La. Bris 51 D2
Hoddon La. Puck 53 E3
Hodshill. Sosto 118 C3
Hoecroft Gdns. Chil 137 E4
Hogarth Mews. W-S-M 89 D2
Hogarth Wlk. Bris 50 B4
Hogarth Wlk. W-S-M 89 D2
Hogues Wlk. Bris 79 D2
Holbeach Way. Bris 80 A4
Holbrook Cres. Bris 79 E2
Holbrook La. Wick 67 D4
Holcombe Cl. Bath 85 F1
Holcombe Gn. Bath 84 A1
Holcombe Gr. Keyn 81 E2
Holcombe La. Bath 85 F1
Holcombe Vale. Bath 85 F1

Holcombe. Bris 80 A3
Holdenhurst Rd. Bris 51 E1
Holders Wlk. Lo Ash 61 F1
Holford Cl. Nail 59 F1
Holford Ct. Bris 80 A3
Holland Rd. Bath 85 D1
Holland Rd. Cleve 57 D1
Holland St. Bris 63 F3
Holland St. W-S-M 105 D4
Hollidge Gdns. Bris 63 E2
Hollies La. Bathe 86 A3
Hollis Ave. Portis 45 E2
Hollis Cl. Lo Ash 78 A4
Hollis Cres. Portis 45 E2
Hollis Gdns. Luck 31 F2
Hollister's Dr. Bris 79 E2
Hollow La. W-S-M 88 C2
Hollow Marsh La. Hin Ble .. 130 A2
Hollow Rd. Alm 24 A2
Hollow Rd. Kingsw 65 F4
Hollow The. Bath 101 D2
Hollow The. Pris 117 E2
Holloway. Bath 101 F3
Hollowbrook La. Ch Mag .. 113 E3
Hollowmead Cl. Yatt 91 F4
Hollows The. West 38 B2
Hollway Cl. Bris 80 C3
Hollway Rd. Bris 80 C3
Holly Cl. Bris 51 D1
Holly Cl. Nail 60 A2
Holly Cl. Puck 53 E3
Holly Cl. W-S-M 89 D1
Holly Cres. Kingsw 51 F1
Holly Dr. Col 70 C3
Holly Gr. Bris 51 E2
Holly Green. Kingsw 52 A1
Holly Hill Rd. Kingsw 51 F1
Holly Hill. Ir Act 26 C2
Holly La. Cleve 57 F3
Holly Lodge Rd. Bris 50 C1
Holly Ridge. Portis 45 D3
Holly Wlk. Keyn 81 E2
Holly Wlk. Rad 132 C1
Hollybush Cl. A Tur 43 D3
Hollybush Cl. Winsl 120 C4
Hollybush La. Bris 48 C2
Hollybush La. Bris 48 C3
Hollyguest Rd. Kingsw 65 F3
Hollyleigh Ave. Bris 35 F1
Hollyman Wlk. Cleve 57 F2
Hollymead La. Bris 48 C2
Hollyridge. Bris 80 B3
Hollywood La. Alm 35 D4
Hollywood Rd. Bris 64 B1
Holm La. Piln 13 D1
Holm Rd. Lock 105 F1
Holmdale Rd. Bris 36 B2
Holmes Gr. Bris 49 D3
Holmes Hill Rd. Bris 64 C4
Holmes St. Bris 64 A3
Holmesdale Rd. Bris 63 F2
Holmoak Rd. Keyn 81 E2
Holms Rd. W-S-M 105 D3
Holmwood Cl. Wint 37 E3
Holmwood. Kingsw 65 E3
Holsom Cl. Bris 80 C3
Holsom Rd. Bris 80 C3
Holst Gdns. Bris 79 E4
Holton Rd. Bris 50 A3
Holy Well Cl. Bris 64 C1
Holyrood Cl. St Gif 36 B2
Home Cl. Bris 35 F1
Home Cl. Wring 92 C2
Home Farm Cl. P St J 133 D4
Home Farm Rd. Ab Lei 44 A4
Home Farm Way. Alm 23 D1
Home Ground. Bris 49 D3
Home Orch. Ch St 112 B4
Home Orch. Yate 27 E1
Homeapple Hill. Sist 66 C3
Homefield Cl. Keyn 82 C2
Homefield Cl. Lock 106 A3
Homefield Cl. Winsc 107 F1
Homefield Dr. Bris 51 D3
Homefield Rd. Keyn 82 C2
Homefield Rd. Puck 53 D3
Homefield. Cong 91 F2
Homefield. Lock 106 A3
Homefield. Thorn 15 E4
Homefield. Yate 27 F2
Homeground. Cleve 57 F1
Homelea Park E. Bath 101 D4
Homelea Park W. Bath 101 D4
Homeleaze Rd. Bris 35 E2
Homemead Dr. Bris 64 B1
Homestead Gdns. Bris 35 E2
Homestead Rd. Bris 35 F1
Homestead The. Cleve 57 E2
Homestead The. Keyn 81 F1
Homestead Way. Wins 125 D4
Homestead. Portis 44 C2
Honey Garston Cl. Bris 79 D2
Honey Garston Rd. Bris 79 D2
Honey Hill Rd. Kingsw 65 F4
Honey Way. Kingsw 65 F4
Honeyborne Way. Wickw 18 A3

Honeyhall La. Cong 108 B4
Honeylands. Portis 45 E2
Honeymead. Bris 80 B3
Honeysuckle Cl. St Gif 24 C1
Honeysuckle La. Bris 50 C2
Honiton Rd. Bris 51 D2
Honiton Rd. Cleve 57 F1
Honiton. W-S-M 89 D1
Hook La. Hin Ble 129 F2
Hooks Batch. Blag 110 B2
Hooper Rd. Bris 80 B3
Hope Ct. Bris 63 D3
Hope Rd. Bris 63 E2
Hope Rd. Ir Act 27 D1
Hope Sq. Bris 62 C3
Hope Terr. Mid No 132 A1
Hopechapel Hill. Bris 62 C3
Hopetoun Rd. Bris 49 F2
Hopewell Gdns. Bris 47 F4
Hopkins Ct. Bris 49 D1
Hopkins St. W-S-M 104 C4
Hopland Cl. Kingsw 66 A2
Hopp's Rd. Kingsw 65 E4
Horesham Gr. Bris 79 E3
Horfield Rd. Bris 63 E4
Horley Rd. Bris 50 A1
Horn's La. Axb 125 D1
Hornbeam Wlk. Keyn 81 E2
Hornbeams The. Bris 37 D1
Horse La. Thorn 8 B3
Horse Race La. Wrax 61 D3
Horse St. Ch Sod 28 A1
Horsecastle Cl. Yatt 74 A1
Horsecastle Farm Rd. Yatt .. 74 A1
Horsecombe Brow. Bath 102 A1
Horsecombe Gr. Bath 102 A1
Horsecombe Vale. Bath 102 A1
Horsecroft Gdns. Kingsw 66 A3
Horsefair The. Bris 63 F4
Horsefield Rd. Char 11 D3
Horseleaze La. Ship 108 B1
Horsepool La. Doyn 67 F4
Horsepool Rd. Bris 78 C2
Horseshoe Dr. Bris 48 B2
Horseshoe La. Ch Sod 28 A1
Horseshoe La. Thorn 15 D4
Horseshoe Wlk. Bath 102 A3
Hortham La. Alve 24 C3
Horton Hill. Hort 29 E3
Horton Rd. Ch Sod 28 B2
Horton St. Bris 63 F4
Horwood Ct. Kingsw 66 A2
Horwood La. Wickw 18 A2
Horwood Rd. Nail 59 F1
Hosey Wlk. Bris 79 D3
Host St. Bris 63 E4
Hot Bath St. Bath 101 F3
Hot Water La. Kingsw 52 A2
Hottom Gdns. Bris 50 A4
Hotwell Rd. Bris 62 C3
Houlgate Way. Axb 125 D1
Houlton St. Bris 63 F4
Hounds Cl. Ch Sod 28 A1
Hounds Rd. Ch Sod 28 A1
Hover's La. Fr Cot 26 A2
How Hill. Bath 101 D3
Howard Ave. Bris 64 C4
Howard Cl. Keyn 82 B2
Howard Rd. Bris 49 D2
Howard Rd. Bris 63 E2
Howard Rd. Kingsw 51 E2
Howard Rd. Thorn 8 B1
Howard St. Bris 50 C1
Howecroft Gdns. Bris 48 C2
Howes Cl. Kingsw 66 A3
Howett Rd. Bris 64 B4
Howsmoor La. Mang 52 B4
Hoylake Dr. Kingsw 66 A3
Hoylake. Yate 39 F4
Huckford La. West 38 A2
Huckford Rd. Wint 37 F3
Huckley Way. St Gif 36 C3
Hudd's Hill Gdns. Bris 64 C4
Hudd's Hill Rd. Bris 64 C4
Hudd's Vale Rd. Bris 64 C4
Hudson Cl. Ch Sod 39 F4
Hughenden Rd. Bris 49 D1
Hughenden Rd. Bris 49 F3
Hughenden Rd. W-S-M 105 D4
Huish Ct. Rad 133 D1
Hulbert Cl. Bris 65 D1
Hulse Rd. Bris 64 B1
Humber Way. Avon 33 E3
Humberstan Wlk. Bris 47 F4
Humphry Davy Way. Bris 62 C3
Hung Rd. Bris 47 F3
Hungerford Cl. Bris 80 C1
Hungerford Cres. Bris 64 C1
Hungerford Gdns. Bris 80 C4
Hungerford Rd. Bath 101 E4
Hungerford Rd. Bris 80 C4
Hungerford Terr. Well 118 B1
Hungerford Wlk. Bris 64 C1
Hunstrete Rd. Farm 115 F3
Hunt's La. Yatt 91 F4
Hunter's La. A Tur 42 C3
Hunter's Way. Bris 36 A2
Hunters Cl. Kingsw 65 E3

Hunters Dr. Kingsw 51 F1
Hunters Mead. H Up 20 A1
Hunters Rd. Kingsw 65 E3
Huntingham Rd. Bris 78 C2
Huntley Gr. Nail 60 A1
Hunts La. Bris 49 F3
Hurle Cres. Bris 48 C1
Hurle Rd. Bris 49 D1
Hurlingham Rd. Bris 49 F1
Hurn La. Keyn 82 A2
Hurn Rd. Cleve 57 F1
Hursley Hill. Pens 97 E4
Hursley La. Pens 80 C1
Hurst Rd. Bris 79 F4
Hurst Rd. W-S-M 105 D3
Hurst Wlk. Bris 79 F4
Hurston Rd. Bris 79 F4
Hurstwood Rd. Mang 51 E3
Hutton Cl. Bris 48 C4
Hutton Cl. Keyn 82 A1
Hutton Hill. Lock 105 F1
Hutton Moor Rd. W-S-M 105 E4
Huyton Rd. Bris 50 C2
Hyde Ave. Thorn 8 A2
Hyde The. Cleve 73 E4
Hyde's La. Co Ash 69 D3
Hyland Gr. Bris 48 C4

I.S.F Rd. Avon 33 E2
Ida Rd. Bris 64 B4
Iddesleigh Rd. Bris 49 D1
Iddstone Rd. Bris 51 D2
Idwal Cl. P St J 133 E4
Iford Cl. Keyn 82 C2
Iford Hill. Westw 120 C1
Iford Rd. Hi Cha 120 B2
Ilchester Cres. Bris 63 D1
Ilchester Rd. Bris 79 D4
Ilex Ave. Cleve 57 F1
Ilex Cl. Bris 78 C3
Ilex La. Winsc 107 F1
Ilminster Ave. Bris 79 F4
Ilminster Cl. Cleve 57 F1
Ilminster Cl. Nail 75 E4
Ilminster. W-S-M 105 D1
Ilsyn Gr. Bris 80 B4
Imber Court Cl. Bris 80 A4
Imperial Rd. Bris 49 D1
Imperial Rd. Bris 64 B1
Imperial Wlk. Bris 64 A1
Ingleside Rd. Bris 51 E1
Inglestone Rd. Wickw 18 A3
Ingleton Dr. W-S-M 89 D2
Ingmire Rd. Bris 50 A2
Ingst Hill. Aust 13 D3
Ingst Rd. Aust 13 F2
Inkerman Cl. Bris 49 F4
Inner Down The. Olve 14 B2
Inner Elm Terr. Rad 132 B1
Innicks Cl. Co Mar 111 E1
Innocks Est. N Nib 5 E2
Innox Gdns. Bris 79 D3
Innox Gr. Engl 100 C1
Innox La. Bathe 85 D3
Innox Rd. Bath 101 D3
Inns Court Ave. Bris 79 E3
Inns Court Dr. Bris 79 E3
Instow Rd. Bris 79 F4
Instow Wlk. Bris 79 F4
Instow. W-S-M 89 D1
Inverness Rd. Bath 101 E3
Ipswich Dr. Bris 64 C3
Irby Rd. Bris 63 D1
Irena Rd. Bris 50 C1
Ireton Rd. Bris 63 D2
Iron Hogg La. Falf 9 E2
Ironchurch Rd. Avon 33 E3
Ironmould La. Bris 65 D1
Irving Cl. Cleve 57 F2
Irving Cl. Kingsw 51 F2
Island Gdns. Bris 50 B2
Island The. Mid No 132 A1
Isleys Ct. Kingsw 65 F2
Islington Rd. Bris 63 D2
Ison Hill Rd. Bris 34 B2
Itchington Rd. Alve 15 F2
Itchington Rd. Tyth 15 F2
Itchington Rd. Tyth 16 A2
Ivo Peters Rd. Bath 101 F3
Ivor Rd. Bris 64 B4
Ivy Ave. Bath 101 E2
Ivy Bank Park. Bath 101 F1
Ivy Ct. Portis 44 C3
Ivy Gr. Bath 101 E2
Ivy La. Bris 51 D2
Ivy Pl. Bath 101 E2
Ivybridge. W-S-M 89 D1
Ivywell Rd. Bris 48 C2
Iwood La. Cong 92 A1

Jackson Cl. Piln 22 B4
Jacob St. Bris 63 F4
Jacob's Wells Rd. Bris 63 D3
Jamaica St. Bris 63 F4
James Cl. Kingsw 51 F2
James Pl. Bris 63 F4
James Rd. Kingsw 51 F2
James St W. Bath 101 F3

James St. Bris 50 A1
James St. Bris 63 F4
Jane St. Bris 64 A4
Jarvis St. Bris 64 A3
Jasmine Cl. W-S-M 89 D1
Jasmine Gr. Bris 34 B1
Jasmine La. Yatt 74 C1
Jasper St. Bris 63 D2
Jays The. Tyth 16 A3
Jean Rd. Bris 64 C1
Jefferies Hill Bottom. Bris ... 65 D3
Jeffery Ct. Kingsw 66 A3
Jellicoe Ct. W-S-M 88 C2
Jena St. Keyn 82 B2
Jenner Cl. Ch Sod 40 B4
Jesmond Rd. Cleve 57 E2
Jesse Hughes Ct. Bath 85 E1
Jessop Underpass. Bris 62 C2
Jews La. Bath 101 E3
Jews La. Chur 108 C2
Jocelin Dr. W-S-M 88 C2
Jocelyn Rd. Bris 49 F4
Jockey La. Bris 65 D4
John Cabot Ct. Bris 63 D3
John Carr's Terr. Bris 63 D3
John James Ct. Bris 50 A4
John St. Bath 101 F4
John St. Bris 50 A1
John St. Bris 63 E4
John St. Bris 65 E4
John Wesley Rd. Bris 65 D3
Johnson Dr. Kingsw 65 F4
Johnsons La. Bris 50 B1
Johnsons Rd. Bris 50 B1
Johnstone St. Bath 102 A3
Jones Cl. Yatt 73 F1
Joy Hill. Bris 62 C3
Jubilee Cres. Mang 52 A3
Jubilee Dr. Thorn 8 B1
Jubilee Dr. Wrax 61 D2
Jubilee La. Chur 109 D3
Jubilee La. Crom 17 D4
Jubilee Pl. Bris 63 E3
Jubilee Pl. Cleve 57 E1
Jubilee Rd. Axb 125 E1
Jubilee Rd. Bris 64 B1
Jubilee Rd. Bris 64 B1
Jubilee Rd. Bris 64 C4
Jubilee Rd. Kingsw 51 F2
Jubilee Rd. Rad 132 B1
Jubilee Rd. W-S-M 104 C4
Jubilee St. Bris 63 F3
Jubilee Terr. Paul 131 F3
Jubilee Way. Avon 33 D1
Julian Cl. Bris 48 C2
Julian Rd. Bath 101 F4
Julian Rd. Bris 48 C2
Julius Rd. Bris 49 E2
Junction Ave. Bath 101 F3
Junction Rd. Bath 101 F3
Junction Rd. Bris 64 B2
Juniper Ct. Bris 50 B1
Jupiter Rd. Bris 35 F4
Justice Ave. Keyn 82 C2
Justice Rd. Bris 51 D2
Jutland Rd. Avon 33 D1

Karen Dr. Back 76 A3
Kathdene Gdns. Bris 49 F2
Kathrine Dr. Char 11 D3
Keats Rd. Rod 138 B4
Keble Ave. Bris 78 C3
Keeds La. Lo Ash 61 F1
Keedwell Hill. Lo Ash 61 F1
Keedwell House. Bris 79 E2
Keel's Hill. P St J 133 E4
Keen's Gr. Piln 22 B4
Keene's Way. Cleve 57 E1
Keep The. Kingsw 66 B3
Keep The. W-S-M 89 D2
Keinton Wlk. Bris 35 D1
Kellaway Ave. Bris 49 E3
Kellaway Cres. Bris 49 E3
Kellways. Back 76 A2
Kelston Cl. Keyn 82 B2
Kelston Cl. Yate 39 E4
Kelston Gdns. Bris 49 E4
Kelston Gdns. W-S-M 89 D3
Kelston Gr. Kingsw 65 F3
Kelston Rd. Bath 101 D4
Kelston Rd. Bris 49 E4
Kelston Rd. Keyn 81 E3
Kelston Rd. W-S-M 89 D3
Kelston View. Bath 101 D3
Kelston Wlk. Bris 51 E2
Kelting Gr. Cleve 57 F1
Kemble Cl. Kingsw 65 F3
Kemble Cl. Nail 60 A1
Kemble Gdns. Bris 47 F3
Kempe's Cl. Lo Ash 62 A1
Kemperleye Way. St Gif 36 B4
Kempton Cl. Mang 37 F1
Kempton Cl. Thorn 8 A2
Kencot Wlk. Bris 79 D2
Kendal Rd. Bris 50 A4
Kendall Gdns. Kingsw 51 E2
Kendall Rd. Kingsw 51 E2

Kendon Dr. Bris 49 E4
Kenilworth Cl. Keyn 81 E2
Kenilworth Dr. Kingsw 66 A1
Kenilworth Rd. Bris 49 E1
Kenilworth. Yate 27 F1
Kenmare Rd. Bris 63 F1
Kenmeade Cl. Ship 125 F4
Kenmore Cres. Bris 35 F1
Kenmore Dr. Bris 35 F1
Kenmore Gr. Bris 35 F1
Kenn Cl. W-S-M 105 D3
Kenn Est. Yatt 73 F3
Kenn Moor Dr. Cleve 57 F1
Kenn Rd. Bris 65 D4
Kenn Rd. Yatt 73 F3
Kenn St. Yatt 73 F4
Kennard Cl. Bris 65 E4
Kennard Rd. Bris 65 E4
Kennard Rise. Bris 65 E4
Kennaway Rd. Cleve 57 E1
Kennedy Way. Ch Sod 40 A4
Kennedy Way. Yate 27 F1
Kennel Dr. Gr Bad 30 C1
Kennel La. Co Bi 123 F2
Kennel Lodge Rd. Bris 62 C2
Kennet Park. Bath 85 F1
Kennet Rd. Keyn 82 A2
Kennet Way. Thorn 15 D4
Kenneth Rd. Bris 64 B1
Kennford. W-S-M 89 D1
Kennington Ave. Bris 49 F2
Kennington Ave. Kingsw 51 E1
Kennington Rd. Bath 101 D4
Kennion Rd. Bris 65 D4
Kennmoor Cl. Kingsw 66 A3
Kennmoor Rd. Yatt 74 A3
Kensal Ave. Bris 63 F2
Kensal Rd. Bris 63 F2
Kensington Cl. Thorn 8 A1
Kensington Ct. Bath 85 D1
Kensington Gdns. Bath 85 D1
Kensington Park Rd. Bris 64 B1
Kensington Park. Bris 50 A1
Kensington Pl. Bris 63 D4
Kensington Rd. Bris 49 E1
Kensington Rd. Bris 65 D4
Kensington Rd. Kingsw 51 E2
Kensington Rd. W-S-M 104 C3
Kent Ave. Yate 27 F2
Kent Cl. St Gif 36 B2
Kent Rd. Bris 49 F2
Kent Rd. Cong 91 E3
Kent St. Bris 63 E2
Kent Way. W-S-M 89 D2
Kenton Mews. Bris 49 E3
Kents Green. Kingsw 51 F1
Kentshare La. Win 95 D3
Keppel Cl. Keyn 82 B1
Kerry Rd. Bris 63 F1
Kersteman Rd. Bris 49 E2
Kestrel Cl. Bris 35 F4
Kestrel Cl. Ch Sod 39 F4
Kestrel Cl. Thorn 8 B1
Kestrel Dr. Puck 53 E2
Kestrel Dr. W-S-M 88 C1
Kestrel Pl. Rod 138 B4
Keswick Wlk. Bris 35 E1
Ketch Rd. Bris 63 F2
Ketley Hill. Mid No 132 B2
Kew Rd. W-S-M 87 F1
Kew Wlk. Bris 80 B4
Kewside. W-S-M 88 A2
Kewstoke Rd. Bath 102 A1
Kewstoke Rd. Bris 48 C2
Kewstoke Rd. W-S-M 88 B2
Keyes Path. W-S-M 88 C2
Keynsham By-pass. Keyn 81 F4
Keynsham Rd. Bitt 82 A4
Keys Ave. Bris 49 F4
Kielder Dr. W-S-M 88 C2
Kilbirnie Rd. Bris 80 A2
Kilburn St. Bris 64 A4
Kildare Rd. Bris 63 E1
Kilkenny La. Engl 118 A4
Kilkenny St. Bris 63 F3
Killcott Rd. Hill 19 F4
Kilmersdon Hill. Kilm 139 D3
Kilmersdon Rd. Bris 79 D2
Kilmersdon Rd. Rod 138 C4
Kilminster Rd. Bris 47 E4
Kiln Cl. Bris 51 D1
Kiln Park. W-S-M 105 D3
Kilnhurst Cl. Kingsw 65 F1
Kilve. W-S-M 104 C1
Kilvert Cl. Bris 64 B3
Kimberley Ave. Bris 51 E3
Kimberley Cl. Mang 51 F4
Kimberley Cres. Bris 51 E3
Kimberley Rd. Bris 51 E3
Kimberley Rd. Cleve 57 E1
Kimberley Rd. Kingsw 51 E1

King George's Rd. Bris 78 C3
King John's Rd. Bris 51 D1
King La. Clut 114 C2
King La. Hort 29 D4
King Rd. Bris 64 B1
King Road Ave. Avon 33 D1
King Sq. Bris 63 E4
King Square Ave. Bris 63 E4
King St. Avon 33 D1
King St. Bris 50 B1
King St. Bris 63 E3
King St. Bris 65 D4
King William Ave. Bris 63 E3
King William St. Bris 63 D2
King's Ave. Bris 49 E2
King's Dr. Bris 49 E2
King's Head La. Bris 78 C4
King's La. W-S-M 104 C4
King's Parade Ave. Bris 49 D1
King's Parade Mews. Bris 49 D1
King's Rd. Bris 63 D4
King's Rd. Bris 64 B2
King's Rd. Cleve 57 E3
King's Rd. Portis 44 C2
Kingfisher Cl. Thorn 8 B1
Kingfisher Dr. Bris 50 C3
Kingfisher Dr. Rod 138 A4
Kingfisher Rd. Ch Sod 40 A4
Kingfisher Rd. W-S-M 105 F4
Kingrove Cres. Ch Sod 40 B4
Kingrove La. Ch Sod 40 B4
Kings Ave. Kingsw 65 D2
Kings Chase. Kingsw 65 E4
Kings Dr. Kingsw 65 D2
Kings Oak Meadow. Clut 114 C1
Kings Park Ave. Bris 64 B3
Kings Rd. Wring 92 B1
Kings Weston Ave. Bris 47 E4
Kings Weston La. Avon 33 F2
Kings Weston La. Bris 48 A4
Kings Weston Rd. Bris 34 B1
Kings Wlk. Bris 78 C4
Kingscote Park. Bris 65 D3
Kingscote. Yate 39 E3
Kingscourt Cl. Bris 80 A2
Kingsdown Gr. Box 86 C2
Kingsdown Par. Bris 63 E4
Kingsdown View. Bath 85 D1
Kingsfield La. Kingsw 65 F2
Kingsfield La. Kingsw 65 F3
Kingsfield. Bath 101 E2
Kingshill Gdns. Nail 59 E1
Kingshill House. Bris 64 A1
Kingshill La. Ch St 112 B3
Kingshill Rd. Bris 64 A1
Kingshill. Nail 59 E1
Kingsholm Rd. Bris 49 E4
Kingsholme Rd. Kingsw 51 E1
Kingsland Cl. Bris 64 A3
Kingsland Rd Br. Bris 64 A3
Kingsland Rd. Bris 64 A3
Kingsland Trading Est. Bris . 64 A4
Kingsleigh Ct. Kingsw 65 F4
Kingsleigh Gdns. Kingsw 65 F4
Kingsleigh Park. Kingsw 65 F4
Kingsley Rd. Bris 49 E1
Kingsley Rd. Bris 50 B1
Kingsley Rd. Cleve 57 E1
Kingsley Rd. Rad 132 B1
Kingsley Rd. W-S-M 104 C2
Kingsmead N. Bath 101 F3
Kingsmead Rd. Bris 51 D1
Kingsmead Sq. Bath 101 F3
Kingsmead St. Bath 101 F3
Kingsmead W. Bath 101 F3
Kingsmead Wlk. Bris 51 D1
Kingsmead. Nail 59 E1
Kingsmill. Bris 48 B3
Kingston Ave. Cleve 57 F2
Kingston Ave. Keyn 82 B2
Kingston Cl. Mang 52 A4
Kingston Dr. Mang 52 A4
Kingston Dr. Nail 75 E4
Kingston La. Win 94 C4
Kingston Mead. Win 94 C4
Kingston Par. Bath 102 A3
Kingston Rd. Bath 102 A3
Kingston Rd. Bris 63 E2
Kingston Rd. Nail 75 E4
Kingston Way. Nail 75 E4
Kingstree St. Bris 64 A2
Kingsway Ave. Bris 65 D4
Kingsway Cres. Bris 65 D4
Kingsway. Bath 101 E2
Kingsway. Bris 65 D4
Kingsway. St Gif 36 B3
Kingswear Rd. Bris 63 E1
Kingswear. W-S-M 89 D1
Kingswood Rd. Hill 19 E4
Kingswood Trading Est.
   Kingsw 51 E1
Kington La. Thorn 7 F1
Kington Rd. O-on-S 7 F2
Kington Rd. Thorn 7 F2
Kingwell View. Paul 115 C1
Kinsale Rd. Bris 80 B4
Kinsale Wlk. Bris 63 F1

Name	Page	Grid
Kinvara Rd. Bris	79	F4
Kipling Rd. Bris	36	A1
Kipling Rd. Rad	132	B1
Kipling Rd. W-S-M	105	D2
Kiplingave. Bath	101	F2
Kirkby Rd. Bris	34	A1
Kirkstone Gdns. Bris	35	E1
Kirtlington Rd. Bris	50	A2
Kite Hay Cl. Bris	50	C3
Kite Wlk. W-S-M	105	F4
Kites Cl. St Gif	24	B1
Kitland La. Chur	109	E4
Knapp La. Crom	10	A2
Knapp Rd. Thorn	8	C1
Knapps Cl. Wins	124	C4
Knapps Dr. Wins	124	C4
Knapps La. Bris	50	C1
Knightcott Gdns. Ban	106	C2
Knightcott Ind Est Ban	106	C2
Knightcott Park. Ban	107	D2
Knightcott Rd. Ab Lei	61	F4
Knightcott Rd. Ban	107	D2
Knighton Rd. Bris	35	F1
Knights Cl. W-S-M	89	D3
Knightstone Cl. Axb	125	E1
Knightstone Cl. P St J	133	D4
Knightstone Cswy. W-S-M	104	B4
Knightstone Cswy. Bris	50	B1
Knightstone Pl. Bath	84	A1
Knightstone Pl. Kingsw	65	D2
Knightstone Rd. W-S-M	104	B4
Knightstone Sq. Bris	80	B3
Knightwood Rd. St Gif	36	C3
Knobsbury Hill. Kilm	139	E3
Knobsbury La. Kilm	139	E4
Knobsbury La. Rad	133	E1
Knole Cl. Alm	23	F2
Knole La. Bris	35	D2
Knole Park. Alm	23	F2
Knoll Hill. Bris	48	B2
Knoll The. Portis	45	D4
Knovill Cl. Bris	34	A1
Knowle Rd. Bris	63	F2
Knowles Rd. Cleve	57	E1
Knowsley Rd. Bris	50	C2
Kylross Ave. Bris	80	A3
Kynges Mill Cl. Bris	51	D4
Kyrle Gdns. Bathe	85	F2
Labbott The. Keyn	81	F3
Laburnham Wlk. Keyn	81	E2
Laburnum Cl. Mid No	137	F4
Laburnum Ct. W-S-M	105	D4
Laburnum Gr. Bris	51	D2
Laburnum Gr. Mid No	137	F4
Laburnum Rd. Kingsw	65	E3
Laburnum Rd. W-S-M	105	D4
Lacey Rd. Bris	80	C3
Lacock Dr. Kingsw	65	F3
Ladd Cl. Kingsw	65	F4
Ladden Ct. Thorn	15	E4
Ladies Mile. Bris	48	C1
Ladman Gr. Bris	80	C3
Ladman Rd. Bris	80	C3
Ladycroft. Cleve	57	D1
Ladye Bay. Cleve	57	E4
Ladye Wake. W-S-M	88	C2
Ladymead La. Chur	108	C3
Ladymeade. Back	76	A4
Ladysmith Rd. Bris	49	D1
Ladywell. Wring	92	B1
Laggan Gdns. Bath	84	C1
Lake Rd. Bris	49	E4
Lake Rd. Portis	45	D4
Lake View Rd. Bris	64	B4
Lakemead Gdns. Bris	78	C2
Lakemead Gr. Bris	78	C3
Lakeside. Bris	50	C2
Lakewood Cres. Bris	49	D4
Lakewood Rd. Bris	49	D4
Lamb St. Bris	63	F4
Lambert Pl. Bris	79	E3
Lambley Rd. Bris	64	C4
Lambourn Cl. Bris	63	E2
Lambourn Rd. Keyn	82	A2
Lambridge Mews. Bath	85	E1
Lambridge Pl. Bath	85	E1
Lambridge St. Bath	85	E1
Lambrook Rd. Bris	51	D2
Lamford Gate. St Gif	36	C3
Lampard's Bldgs. Bath	101	F4
Lampeter Rd. Bris	49	D4
Lampley Rd. K Sey	73	E1
Lampley Rd. Yatt	73	E1
Lampton Ave. Bris	79	F2
Lampton Gr. Bris	79	F2
Lampton Rd. Lo Ash	61	F1
Lanaway Rd. Bris	51	D3
Lancashire Rd. Bris	49	F2
Lancaster Cl. St Gif	36	B2
Lancaster Rd. Bris	50	A1
Lancaster Rd. Yate	27	F2
Lancaster St. Bris	64	B4
Land The. Fr Cot	38	B4
Landemann Cir. W-S-M	87	F1
Landsdown View. Kingsw	65	F4
Landseer Ave. Bris	50	A4
Landseer Cl. W-S-M	88	C2

Name	Page	Grid
Landseer Rd. Bath	101	D3
Lane The. Alm	22	C1
Lanercost Rd. Bris	35	E1
Lanesborough Rise. Bris	80	B4
Laneys Dro. Lock	105	F3
Langdale Rd. Bris	50	C2
Langdale Rd. Bath	101	D2
Langfield Cl. Bris	34	C2
Langford La. Blag	109	F3
Langford Rd. Bris	78	C4
Langford Rd. Chur	109	D3
Langford Way. Kingsw	65	F4
Langford Way. Kingsw	65	F4
Langham Pl. Rode	136	C1
Langhill Ave. Bris	79	E4
Langley Cres. Bris	62	C1
Langley's La. Ston E	131	E1
Langport Gdns. Nail	75	F4
Langport Rd. W-S-M	104	C3
Langridge La. Charl	84	B4
Langthorn Cl. Fr Cot	38	B4
Langton Court Rd. Bris	64	B3
Langton Park. Bris	63	E2
Langton Rd. Bris	64	B3
Langton Way. Bris	64	C3
Lansdown Cl. Kingsw	51	F1
Lansdown Cres. Bath	101	F4
Lansdown Cres. Tims	116	B1
Lansdown Gdns. W-S-M	89	D3
Lansdown Gr. Bath	101	F4
Lansdown La. Bath	84	A2
Lansdown La. Bitt	67	E1
Lansdown La. Charl	84	A2
Lansdown Park. Bath	84	C2
Lansdown Pl. Bris	63	D4
Lansdown Pl. Paul	115	E1
Lansdown Place W. Bath	84	C2
Lansdown Rd. Bath	84	C2
Lansdown Rd. Bris	49	E1
Lansdown Rd. Bris	63	D4
Lansdown Rd. Bris	64	A4
Lansdown Rd. Keyn	82	C2
Lansdown Rd. Kingsw	51	E1
Lansdown Rd. Puck	53	E3
Lansdown Terr. Bath	84	B1
Lansdown Terr. Bris	49	E3
Lansdown View. Bath	84	A1
Lansdown View. Bath	101	E3
Lansdown View. Faulk	134	B1
Lansdown View. Tims	116	B1
Lansdown. Yate	39	F4
Lansdowne. Bris	37	E1
Lapdown La. Tor	41	E1
Laphams Ct. Kingsw	65	F2
Lapwing Cl. St Gif	24	B1
Lapwing Gdns. Bris	50	C3
Lapwing Gdns. W-S-M	88	C1
Larch Cl. Chur	109	D3
Larch Cl. Nail	60	A1
Larch Ct. Rod	138	B4
Larch Rd. Col	70	C3
Larch Rd. Kingsw	51	F2
Larch Way. Bris	35	F4
Larches The. W-S-M	89	D2
Larchgrove Cres. W-S-M	88	C1
Larchgrove Wlk. W-S-M	89	D1
Lark Cl. Rod	138	A4
Lark Rd. W-S-M	88	C1
Lark's Field. Bris	50	C3
Lark's La. Fr Cot	26	A4
Larkfield. Fr Cot	38	B4
Larkhall Pl. Bath	85	E1
Larksleaze Rd. Kingsw	65	F1
Larkspur Cl. Thorn	8	B1
Lasbury Gr. Bris	79	E3
Latchmoor House. Bris	79	D4
Late Broads. Winsl	120	B4
Latimer Cl. Bris	64	C2
Latteridge La. Ir Act	26	A4
Latteridge La. Tyth	26	A4
Latteridge Rd. Ir Act	26	B2
Latton Rd. Bris	49	F4
Launceston Ave. Kingsw	65	D3
Launceston Rd. Bris	51	D1
Laura Pl. Bath	102	A4
Laurel Dr. Col	70	C3
Laurel Dr. Nail	59	F1
Laurel Dr. Paul	131	F3
Laurel Dr. W-S-M	104	C1
Laurel Gdns. Yatt	74	A1
Laurel St. Kingsw	65	E4
Laurel Terr. Yatt	74	A1
Laurels The. Mang	52	A3
Laurels The. W-S-M	104	C1
Laurie Cres. Bris	49	E3
Laurie Lee Ct. Kingsw	66	A3
Lavender Cl. Thorn	8	B1
Lavers Cl. Kingsw	65	F3
Lavington Rd. Cleve	57	D1
Lavington Rd. Bris	65	D3
Lawford Ave. St Gif	36	B3
Lawford St. Bris	63	F4
Lawfords Gate. Bris	63	F4
Lawn Ave. Bris	51	D3
Lawn Rd. Bris	51	D3

Name	Page	Grid
Lawns Rd. Yate	27	F1
Lawns The. Bris	47	F4
Lawns The. W-S-M	89	D2
Lawns The. Yatt	74	A1
Lawnside. Back	76	A3
Lawnwood Rd. Bris	64	A4
Lawrence Ave. Bris	50	A1
Lawrence Cl. W-S-M	88	C1
Lawrence Dr. Yate	27	D1
Lawrence Gr. Bris	49	D2
Lawrence Hill Ind Pk. Bris	64	A4
Lawrence Hill Roundabout. Bris	64	A4
Lawrence Hill. Bris	64	A4
Lawrence Mews. W-S-M	88	C1
Lawrence Rd. W-S-M	88	C1
Lawrence Rd. Wring	92	C1
Lawrence Weston Rd. Avon	33	F3
Lawrence Weston Rd. Bris	34	A1
Lawrence Weston Rd. Bris	34	B1
Lawson Cl. Keyn	82	B1
Laxey Rd. Bris	49	F4
Laxton Cl. Olve	14	A2
Laxton Dr. Kings	11	F2
Laxton Way. P St J	133	E4
Lays Dr. Keyn	81	E3
Lays La. Blag	110	B2
Lea Croft. Bris	79	D2
Lea Grove Rd. Cleve	57	E2
Leach Cl. Cleve	57	E1
Leafy Way. Lock	106	A2
Leaholme Gdns. Bris	80	A2
Leaman Cl. Ch Sod	28	A1
Leap Vale. Mang	52	A4
Leap Valley Cres. Mang	52	A4
Leaze La. Priddy	126	C4
Leaze The. Rod	138	B4
Leaze The. Yate	27	E1
Leda Ave. Bris	80	A4
Ledbury Rd. Bris	51	E2
Lee Cl. Bris	35	F4
Leechpool Way. Yate	27	F3
Leeming Way. Avon	47	E4
Lees Hill. Kingsw	51	F1
Lees La. Kingsw	66	B3
Lees The. Cong	91	E2
Leeside. Portis	45	E3
Leewood Rd. W-S-M	87	F1
Leg La. Blag	110	A2
Leicester Sq. Kingsw	51	E2
Leicester St. Bris	63	E2
Leicester Wlk. Bris	64	C3
Leigh Cl. Bath	85	D1
Leigh La. Co Ash	69	D2
Leigh La. West	39	E1
Leigh Rd. Bris	63	D4
Leigh St. Bris	63	D2
Leigh View Rd. Portis	45	F4
Leighton Cres. W-S-M	122	A4
Leighton Rd. Bath	84	A2
Leighton Rd. Bris	63	D2
Leighton Rd. Bris	64	A1
Leighwood Dr. Nail	59	D1
Leighwood House. Lo Ash	62	B3
Leinster Ave. Bris	79	E4
Lemon La. Bris	63	F4
Lena Ave. Bris	50	B1
Lena St. Bris	50	B1
Lenover Gdns. Bris	79	D2
Leonard La. Bris	63	E4
Leonard Rd. Bris	64	B4
Leonards Ave. Bris	50	B1
Leopold Rd. Bris	49	F1
Lescren Way. Avon	33	E1
Leslie Rise. Westw	120	C2
Lester Dr. W-S-M	89	D2
Lewin St. Bris	64	B4
Lewington Rd. Bris	51	E2
Lewins Mead. Bris	63	E4
Lewis Cl. Kingsw	66	B3
Lewis Rd. Bris	79	D4
Lewis St. Bris	64	A3
Lewisham Gr. W-S-M	105	D4
Lewton La. Wint	37	F4
Ley La. Olve	13	F2
Leyland Wlk. Bris	78	C2
Leys The. Cleve	57	D1
Leyton Villas. Bris	49	D1
Liberty Ind Park. Bris	63	D1
Liberty La. Blag	110	C1
Lichfield Rd. Bris	64	C3
Lilac Cl. Bris	35	E1
Lilac Ct. Keyn	81	E2
Lilac Terr. Mid No	132	B1
Lilian Terr. Paul	131	F3
Lillian St. Bris	64	B4
Lillington Cl. Rad	133	D1
Lillington Rd. Rad	133	D1
Lilliput Ave. Ch Sod	40	A4
Lilliput Ct. Ch Sod	40	A4
Lilstock Ave. Bris	49	F2
Lilton Wlk. Bris	63	D1
Lilymead Ave. Bris	64	A2
Lime Cl. Bris	35	D2
Lime Cl. Col	70	C3
Lime Cl. W-S-M	89	D1
Lime Croft. Yate	27	F2

Name	Page	Grid
Lime Ct. Keyn	81	E2
Lime Gr. Alve	14	C3
Lime Gr. Bath	102	A3
Lime Grove Gdns. Bath	102	A3
Lime Kiln Gdns. St Gif	24	B2
Lime Rd. Bris	63	D2
Lime Rd. Kingsw	65	D3
Lime Terr. Rad	132	B1
Lime Tree Gr. E in G	47	E2
Limeburn Hill. Ch Mag	95	F3
Limekiln La. Bath	102	C2
Limekiln Rd. Yate	27	E4
Limerick Rd. Bris	49	E1
Limes The. Bris	37	D1
Limes The. Gr Bad	30	C1
Limpley Stoke Rd. Winsl	120	B3
Lincoln Cl. Keyn	81	E2
Lincoln St. Bris	64	A4
Lincombe Ave. Mang	51	E3
Lincombe Rd. Mang	51	E3
Lincombe Rd. Rod	138	B4
Lincott View. P St J	133	E4
Linden Ave. W-S-M	105	D4
Linden Cl. Bris	51	D1
Linden Cl. Bris	80	C3
Linden Cl. Col	70	C3
Linden Cl. Rod	138	C4
Linden Cl. Wint	37	F3
Linden Dr. St Gif	36	C4
Linden Gdns. Bath	101	E4
Linden Rd. Bris	49	D2
Linden Rd. Cleve	57	E2
Lindens The. W-S-M	88	C2
Lindrea St. Bris	63	D2
Lindsay Rd. Bris	50	A2
Lindsey Cl. Portis	44	C2
Linemere Cl. Back	76	B3
Lines Way. Whit	80	B2
Lingfield Park. Mang	37	F1
Link La. Blag	109	F2
Link Rd. Bris	35	F2
Link Rd. Bris	36	A1
Link Rd. Nail	59	F1
Link Rd. Portis	45	E3
Link Rd. Yate	27	F1
Links Rd. W-S-M	104	B1
Linkside. Cleve	57	F3
Linley Cl. Bath	101	D3
Linleys The. Bath	101	E4
Linnell Cl. Bris	50	A3
Linnet Cl. Bris	35	F4
Linnet Cl. W-S-M	88	C1
Linnet Way. Rod	138	A4
Lintern Cres. Kingsw	66	A3
Lintham Dr. Kingsw	65	F3
Linton Rd. Bris	63	E1
Lion Cl. Nail	59	E1
Lippiat Hill. Faulk	134	B2
Lippiatt La. Ship	125	F4
Lippiatt La. Tims	116	A2
Lisburn Rd. Bris	63	F1
Lisle Rd. W-S-M	89	D2
Lister Gr. Westw	120	C2
Litfield Rd. Bris	62	C4
Litt Hill. Litt	129	F1
Little Ann St. Bris	63	F4
Little Birch Croft. Bris	80	A2
Little Bishop St. Bris	63	F4
Little Bristol La. Char	11	D2
Little Caroline Pl. Bris	62	C3
Little Dowles. Kingsw	66	A2
Little George St. Bris	63	F4
Little George St. W-S-M	104	C4
Little Green La. Piln	22	A4
Little Halt. Portis	44	C2
Little Ham. Cleve	73	E4
Little Headley Cl. Bris	79	E4
Little King St. Bris	63	E3
Little La. Farm	116	A3
Little Mead Cl. Lock	105	F2
Little Mead. Bris	34	A1
Little Mead. Bris	34	A1
Little Meadow End. Nail	75	F4
Little Meadow. St Gif	37	D3
Little Orch. W-S-M	104	B1
Little Paradise. Bris	63	E2
Little Paul St. Bris	63	E4
Little Solsbury La. Bathe	85	F2
Little Stanhope St. Bath	101	F3
Little Stoke La. St Gif	36	B4
Little Stoke Rd. Bris	48	C2
Little Withey Mead. Bris	48	C3
Littlebrook. Paul	131	F3
Littledean. Yatte	39	F4
Littlefields Ave. Ban	107	D2
Littlefields Rd. Ban	107	D2
Littleton Ct. Bris	23	F1
Littleton La. Ch Mag	95	E2
Littleton La. Dun	95	E4
Littleton La. Well	134	B4
Littleton La. Win	95	E4
Littleton Rd. Bris	63	E1
Littleton St. Bris	50	B1
Littlewood Cl. Bris	80	A2
Littlewood La. Brock	75	E1
Litton. W-S-M	105	D4
Livingstone Rd. Bath	101	E3
Llewellyn Ct. Bris	49	D4

Name	Page	Grid
Llewellyn Way. W-S-M	89	D2
Lock Gdns. Bris	78	C4
Lockemor Rd. Bris	79	F2
Locking Head Dro. Lock	106	A4
Locking Moor Rd. W-S-M	105	E4
Locking Rd. W-S-M	105	D4
Lockingwell Rd. Keyn	81	E3
Lockleaze Rd. Bris	50	A3
Locksbrook Rd. Bath	101	E3
Locksbrook Rd. W-S-M	89	D3
Lodge Causeway. Bris	51	D2
Lodge Cl. Yatt	91	D4
Lodge Dr. Kingsw	66	B1
Lodge Dr. Lo Ash	62	A1
Lodge Dr. W-S-M	88	A1
Lodge Gdns. Bath	101	E1
Lodge Hill. Bris	51	E1
Lodge La. Wrax	60	A1
Lodge Pl. Bris	63	E4
Lodge Rd. Bris	51	E1
Lodge Rd. Wick	53	D1
Lodge Rd. Yate	27	D2
Lodge St. Bris	63	E4
Lodge Wlk. Mang	51	E3
Lodgeside Ave. Bris	51	E1
Lodgeside Gdns. Bris	51	E1
Lodore Rd. Bris	50	C2
Lodway Cl. E in G	47	E3
Lodway Gdns. E in G	47	E2
Lodway Rd. Bris	64	B1
Lodway. E in G	47	E2
Logan Rd. Bris	49	E2
Logus Ct. Kingsw	65	F2
Lombard St. Bris	63	E2
Lomond Rd. Bris	35	F1
London Rd E. Bathe	86	A2
London Rd W. Bath	85	F1
London Rd. Bath	102	A4
London Rd. Bris	49	F1
London Rd. Sist	66	B4
London Rd. Wick	67	F3
London St. Bath	102	A4
London St. Kingsw	65	E4
Long Acres Cl. Bris	48	B4
Long Ashton Rd. Lo Ash	62	B1
Long Ave. Cleve	57	D1
Long Barnaby. Mid No	132	A1
Long Beach Rd. Kingsw	66	A2
Long Cl. Bris	51	E3
Long Cl. St Gif	36	C3
Long Croft. Yate	27	E2
Long Cross. Bris	34	A1
Long Cross. Win	94	B4
Long Eaton Dr. Bris	80	A4
Long Handstones. Kingsw	66	A2
Long Hay Cl. Bath	101	D3
Long La. Back	76	B2
Long La. But	94	A3
Long La. Wring	93	D1
Long Leaze. Burt	43	D1
Long Mead. Yate	27	F3
Long Meadow. Bris	50	B3
Long Rd. Mang	52	A3
Long Row. Bris	63	F3
Long Thorn La. Win	111	F4
Longacre Rd. Bris	80	A2
Longacre. Cleve	73	D4
Longbottom. Ched	125	F3
Longcross. Crom	10	A1
Longden Rd. Mang	51	F3
Longdown Dr. W-S-M	89	D2
Longfellow Ave. Bath	101	F2
Longfellow Rd. Rad	132	B1
Longfellow Rd. Rod	138	B4
Longfield Rd. Bris	49	F2
Longford Ave. Bris	49	E4
Longford. Yate	39	E4
Longleat Cl. Bris	49	E3
Longleaze Gdns. Lock	105	F2
Longmead Ave. Bris	49	E3
Longmead Croft. Bris	78	C2
Longmeadow Rd. Keyn	81	E2
Longmoor Rd. Bris	63	D1
Longney Pl. Bris	23	F1
Longreach Gr. Bris	80	B3
Longs Dr. Yate	27	E1
Longs View. Char	11	D3
Longton Grove Rd. W-S-M	104	C4
Longton Ind Est. W-S-M	104	C3
Longway Ave. Bris	79	F2
Longwell House. Kingsw	65	F2
Longwood La. Lo Ash	61	F2
Longwood. Bris	65	D1
Lonsdale Ave. W-S-M	104	C2
Lorain Wlk. Bris	34	C1
Lorne Rd. Bath	101	E3
Lorton Rd. Bris	35	D1
Lott's Ave. Back	76	A3
Louisa St. Bris	63	F3
Louise Ave. Kingsw	52	A3
Love La. Ch Sod	40	A4
Love La. Yate	28	A2
Love's La. Farm	115	F3
Lovelinch Gdns. Lo Ash	61	F1
Lovell Ave. Kingsw	66	B2
Lovells Mill. Bi Sut	113	E2
Loveringe Cl. Bris	34	C2
Lovers La. Paul	132	A3

155
Lovers' Wlk. W-S-M
Melrose Ave. Yate

Lovers' Wlk. W-S-M 104 B4
Loves Hill. Tims 116 A1
Lowbourne. Bris 79 F3
Lower Ashley Rd. Bris 49 F1
Lower Ashley Rd. Bris 50 A1
Lower Batch. Ch Mag 96 A2
Lower Borough Walls. Bath 101 F3
Lower Bristol Rd. Bath 101 E3
Lower Bristol Rd. Clut 114 C2
Lower Castle St. Bris 63 F4
Lower Chapel La. Fr Cot 38 B4
Lower Chapel Rd. Kingsw 65 E3
Lower Cheltenham Pl. Bris 49 F1
Lower Church La. Bris 63 E4
Lower Church Rd. W-S-M 104 B4
Lower Claverham. Yatt 74 C2
Lower Clifton Hill. Bris 63 D3
Lower Cock Rd. Kingsw 65 F4
Lower College St. Bris 63 E3
Lower Court Rd. Alm 24 A3
Lower Down Rd. Portis 45 D3
Lower Fallow Cl. Bris 79 F2
Lower Gay St. Bris 63 E4
Lower Grove Rd. Bris 50 C2
Lower Hanham Rd. Kingsw 65 E3
Lower High St. Bris 47 E4
Lower House Cres. Bris 36 A2
Lower Kingsdown Rd. Box 86 C2
Lower Knole La. Bris 35 D2
Lower Knowles Rd. Cleve 57 E1
Lower Lamb St. Bris 63 E3
Lower Linden Rd. Cleve 57 E2
Lower Maudlin St. Bris 63 E4
Lower Moor Rd. Yate 27 F2
Lower Northend Est. Bathe 85 F3
Lower Norton La. W St L 88 B2
Lower Norton La. W-S-M 88 C2
Lower Oldfield Park. Bath 101 F3
Lower Park Row. Bris 63 E4
Lower Queen's Rd. Cleve 57 E2
Lower Rd. Hin Ble 129 F3
Lower Redland Rd. Bris 49 D1
Lower Sidney St. Bris 63 D2
Lower St. Rode 136 C1
Lower Station Rd. Bris 51 D2
Lower Station Rd. Kingsw 51 E2
Lower Stoke. Bath 103 D1
Lower Stoke. Li St 120 A4
Lower Stone Cl. Fr Cot 38 B4
Lower Strode Rd. Cleve 73 D4
Lower Strode. Win 112 A4
Lower Thirlmere Rd. Bris 36 A4
Lower Tockington Rd. Olve 14 A1
Lower Whitelands. Mid No 133 D2
Lowlis Cl. Bris 34 C2
Lowther Rd. Bris 35 E1
Loxley Gdns. Bath 101 E2
Loxton Dr. Bath 101 D3
Loxton Rd. W-S-M 104 C1
Loxton Sq. Bris 80 A3
Lucas Cl. Bris 64 B1
Luccombe Hill. Bris 49 D1
Luckington Cross. Hol 139 D1
Luckington Rd. Bris 49 F4
Lucklands Rd. Bath 84 B1
Luckley Ave. Bris 79 E3
Luckwell Rd. Bris 63 D2
Lucky La. Bris 63 E2
Ludlow Cl. Bris 49 F1
Ludlow Cl. Keyn 81 E3
Ludlow Cl. Kingsw 66 A1
Ludlow Rd. Bris 50 A4
Ludwell Cl. Wint 37 E3
Ludwells Orch. Paul 131 F3
Lullington Rd. Bris 64 A1
Lulsgate Rd. Bris 79 D4
Lulworth Cres. Mang 51 F4
Lulworth Rd. Keyn 81 F2
Lurgan Wlk. Bris 63 E1
Luvers La. Blag 110 B1
Lux Furlong. Bris 48 A4
Luxton St. Bris 64 A4
Lychgate Park. Lock 106 A2
Lydbrook Cl. Yate 39 E4
Lyddington Rd. Bris 49 F4
Lyddon Rd. W-S-M 89 D2
Lydford Wlk. Bris 63 E1
Lydiard Croft. Kingsw 65 E2
Lydney Rd. Bris 49 E4
Lydney Rd. Kingsw 51 F2
Lydstep Terr. Bris 63 E2
Lye Cross Rd. Wring 93 E1
Lye Hole La. Wring 93 E1
Lyefield Rd. W-S-M 88 C2
Lyme Gdns. Bath 101 D4
Lyme Rd. Bath 101 D4
Lymore Ave. Bath 101 E3
Lymore Gdns. Bath 101 E3
Lymore Terr. Bath 101 E2
Lympsham Green. Bath 118 B4
Lympsham Rd. Lymp 122 A1
Lynbrook La. Bath 101 F2
Lynbrook. Lo Ash 61 F1
Lynch Cl. W-S-M 88 C2
Lynch Cres. Wins 124 C4
Lynch Ct. Kingsw 65 F2
Lynch Hill. Chil 137 D2
Lynch The. Wins 124 C4
Lynchmead. Wins 124 C4
Lyncombe Hill. Bath 102 A3
Lyncombe Vale Rd. Bath 102 A2
Lyncombe Vale. Bath 102 A2
Lyncombe Wlk. Bris 51 D1
Lyndale Ave. Bris 48 B3
Lyndale Rd. Bris 64 B4
Lyndale Rd. Yate 27 E1
Lynde Cl. Bris 79 D2
Lyndhurst Rd. Bath 101 E3
Lyndhurst Rd. Bris 48 C4
Lyndhurst Rd. Keyn 81 F2
Lyndhurst Rd. Rod 138 A4
Lyndhurst Rd. W-S-M 104 C2
Lynfield Park. Bath 84 B1
Lynmouth Cl. W-S-M 89 D1
Lynmouth Rd. Bris 50 A1
Lynn Rd. Bris 50 B3
Lynton Cl. Portis 45 F2
Lynton Pl. Bris 64 B4
Lynton Rd. Rod 138 A4
Lynton Way. Bris 37 D1
Lynton. Kingsw 66 A4
Lynwood Cl. Rod 138 A4
Lynx Cres. W-S-M 105 D1
Lyons Court Rd. Bris 80 B4
Lyons Ct. W-S-M 104 C4
Lyppiatt Rd. Bris 64 B4
Lyppincourt Rd. Bris 35 D2
Lysander Rd. Bris 35 E3
Lysander Wlk. St Gif 36 C3
Lytchet Dr. Mang 51 F4
Lytes Cary Rd. Keyn 82 A2
Lytton Gdns. Bath 101 D2
Lytton Gr. Bris 50 A4
Lytton Gr. Keyn 82 A3
Lyveden Gdns. Bris 79 D3
Lyvedon Way. Lo Ash 62 A1

Macaulay Bldgs. Bath 102 B2
Macauley Rd. Bris 50 A4
Macey's Rd. Bris 79 E2
Machin Cl. Bris 34 C2
Machin Rd. Bris 34 C2
Machley La. N St P 135 F2
Macies The. Bath 84 A2
Mackie Ave. Bris 36 A1
Mackie Gr. Bris 36 A1
Mackie Rd. Bris 36 A1
Macleod Cl. Cleve 57 D1
Madam La. W-S-M 88 C1
Madam La. W-S-M 89 D2
Madam's Paddock. Ch Mag 96 A2
Maddocke House. Bris 79 E2
Madeira Rd. Cleve 57 E2
Madeira Rd. W-S-M 87 E1
Madeline Rd. Bris 50 C1
Madison Cl. Yate 27 E1
Maesbury Rd. Keyn 82 A1
Maesbury. Kingsw 65 F3
Maesknoll La. Whit 97 D4
Maesknoll Rd. Bris 64 A1
Magdalen Ave. Bath 101 F3
Magdalen Rd. Bath 101 F3
Magdalen Way. W-S-M 89 D2
Magdalene Pl. Bris 49 F1
Magdalene Rd. Rad 133 E1
Magellan Cl. W-S-M 88 C2
Maggs Folly. Paul 115 E1
Maggs La. Whit 80 B2
Magnolia Ave. W-S-M 89 D1
Magnolia Rd. Rad 132 C1
Magpie Bottom La. Bris 65 E3
Magpie Bottom La. Kingsw 65 E3
Magpie Cl. W-S-M 105 F4
Maiden Way. Avon 47 E4
Maidenhead Rd. Bris 79 E2
Maidstone Gr. W-S-M 105 D1
Maidstone St. Bris 63 F2
Main Rd. Back 76 C4
Main Rd. Brock 75 F1
Main Rd. Lock 105 F1
Main Rd. Puck 52 B3
Main St. Paul 131 D2
Main View. Fr Cot 38 B4
Maisemore Ave. St Gif 24 A1
Maisemore. Yate 39 F3
Makin Cl. Kingsw 66 B3
Malago Rd. Bris 63 E2
Malago Vale Est. Bris 63 E2
Malago Wlk. Bris 78 C2
Maldowers La. Bris 65 D4
Mall The. Bath 102 A3
Mall The. Bris 62 C4
Mallard Cl. Bris 50 C1
Mallard Cl. Ch Sod 40 A4
Mallard Cl. St Gif 24 B1
Mallard Wlk. W-S-M 105 F4
Mallow Cl. Cleve 57 F1
Mallow Cl. Thorn 8 B1
Malmains Dr. Bris 37 D1
Malmesbury Cl. Bris 49 E2
Malmesbury Cl. Kingsw 65 F3
Maltings Ind Est The. Bath 101 D4
Maltings The. W-S-M 88 C1
Maltlands. W-S-M 105 E4
Maltravers Cl. St Gif 36 B4
Malvern Bldgs. Bath 85 D1
Malvern Ct. Bris 64 C4
Malvern Dr. Kingsw 66 B3
Malvern Dr. Thorn 15 E4
Malvern Rd. Bris 64 B2
Malvern Rd. Bris 64 C4
Malvern Rd. W-S-M 104 C3
Mancroft Ave. Bris 47 F4
Mandy Meadows. Mid No 131 F1
Mangotsfield Rd. Mang 52 A3
Manilla Pl. W-S-M 87 E1
Manilla Rd. Bris 63 D4
Manmoor La. Cleve 58 A1
Manor Cl The. Ab Lei 62 A4
Manor Cl. E in G 47 D2
Manor Cl. Fr Cot 38 B3
Manor Cl. Olve 14 B1
Manor Cl. Paul 131 D2
Manor Cl. Well 118 B1
Manor Copse Rd. Rad 133 E1
Manor Court Dr. Bris 49 F4
Manor Ct. Back 76 A3
Manor Ct. Bris 50 C2
Manor Dr. Bathf 86 A1
Manor Farm Cl. W-S-M 105 D1
Manor Farm Cres. W-S-M 105 D1
Manor Farm. St Gif 36 B4
Manor Gdns. Farm 115 F3
Manor Gdns. Lock 106 A2
Manor Gdns. Paul 131 D2
Manor Gdns. W-S-M 88 A2
Manor Gr. Kingsw 52 A2
Manor Gr. St Gif 24 A1
Manor Grange. Blea 122 A4
Manor La. Ab Lei 61 F4
Manor La. Char 11 D2
Manor La. Wint 37 F4
Manor Park. Bath 101 D4
Manor Park. Bris 49 D2
Manor Park. Olve 14 A1
Manor Park. Rad 133 E1
Manor Pl. Bris 37 E1
Manor Rd. Ab Lei 61 F4
Manor Rd. Bath 84 B1
Manor Rd. Bris 49 F2
Manor Rd. Bris 50 C3
Manor Rd. Bris 79 D3
Manor Rd. Ir Act 27 D4
Manor Rd. Keyn 82 A1
Manor Rd. Kingsw 52 A2
Manor Rd. Rad 133 E1
Manor Rd. W-S-M 105 D4
Manor Rd. Wick 67 E3
Manor Rd. Wickw 27 D4
Manor Terr. Rad 133 E1
Manor Valley. W-S-M 88 A1
Manor Villas. Bath 84 B1
Manor Way. Ch Sod 28 A1
Manor Way. Wrax 61 E2
Manor Wlk. Thorn 8 A2
Mansel Cl. Keyn 82 B2
Mansfield Ave. W-S-M 105 D4
Mansfield St. Bris 63 D1
Manston Cl. Bris 80 B4
Manvers St. Bath 102 A3
Manworthy Rd. Bris 64 B2
Manx Rd. Bris 49 F4
Maple Ave. Bris 51 E2
Maple Ave. Thorn 8 B1
Maple Cl. Bris 80 B2
Maple Cl. Kingsw 66 A2
Maple Cl. St Gif 36 B4
Maple Cl. W-S-M 105 D4
Maple Dr. Rad 132 C1
Maple Gdns. Bath 101 F2
Maple Gr. Bath 101 F2
Maple Leaf Ct. Bris 63 D4
Maple Rd. Bris 49 E3
Maple Rd. Bris 64 B3
Maple Wlk. Keyn 81 E2
Maple Wlk. Puck 53 E3
Mapleleaze. Bris 64 B2
Maplemeade. Bris 49 E2
Mapleridge La. Hort 28 B4
Mapleridge La. Yate 28 B4
Maples The. Nail 59 E1
Maplestone Rd. Bris 80 A2
Marbeck Rd. Bris 35 D1
Marchfields Way. W-S-M 105 D3
Marconi Rd. Portis 44 C3
Mardale Cl. Bris 35 E1
Marden Rd. Keyn 82 A2
Mardon Rd. Bris 64 B3
Mardyke Ferry Rd. Bris 63 D3
Marfield Wlk. Bris 78 C4
Margaret Rd. Bris 78 C2
Margaret's Bldgs. Bath 101 F4
Margaret's Hill. Bath 102 A4
Margate St. Bris 63 F2
Marguerite Rd. Bris 78 C4
Marigold Wlk. Bris 63 D1
Marina Gdns. Bris 50 C2
Marindrin Dr. W-S-M 89 D2
Marine Hill. Cleve 57 E2
Marine Par. Cleve 57 E2
Marine Par. E in G 47 E3
Marine Par. W-S-M 104 B3
Mariner's Cl. W-S-M 88 B1
Mariner's Way. E in G 47 E3
Mariners Cl. Back 76 A3
Mariners Dr. Back 76 A3
Mariners Dr. Bris 48 B2
Marion Way. Kingsw 65 D2
Marion Wlk. Bris 65 D4
Marissal Cl. Bris 34 C2
Marissal Rd. Bris 34 C2
Mariston Way. Kingsw 66 B3
Mark La. Bris 63 E3
Market Ind Est. Yatt 74 A1
Market La. W-S-M 104 B4
Market Pl. Marsh 70 A4
Market Pl. Win 94 C4
Market Sq. Bris 51 E2
Markham Cl. Bris 47 E4
Marksbury Rd. Bris 63 E1
Marksbury. Marks 99 D1
Marlborough Ave. Bris 50 C2
Marlborough Bldgs. Bath 101 F4
Marlborough Dr. Bris 37 D1
Marlborough Dr. W-S-M 89 D1
Marlborough Hill Pl. Bris 63 E4
Marlborough Hill. Bris 63 E4
Marlborough La. Bath 101 F4
Marlborough St. Bath 101 F4
Marlborough St. Bris 50 C2
Marlborough St. Bris 63 E4
Marlepit Gr. Bris 78 C3
Marling Rd. Bris 64 C4
Marlwood Dr. Bris 35 D2
Marmaduke St. Bris 63 F2
Marmion Cres. Bris 34 C2
Marne Cl. Bris 80 B2
Marsden Rd. Bath 101 E2
Marsh Cl. Wint 37 F3
Marsh Comm. Piln 22 B3
Marsh La. Bris 63 D1
Marsh La. Bris 64 B3
Marsh La. Clut 115 D1
Marsh La. E in G 46 C3
Marsh La. Paul 131 D2
Marsh Rd. Bris 62 C2
Marsh Rd. Rode 136 C1
Marsh Rd. Yatt 91 D4
Marsh St. Avon 47 E4
Marsh St. Bris 63 E3
Marshacre La. Aust 13 F3
Marsham Way. Kingsw 65 F2
Marshfield La. Bitt 67 E1
Marshfield Rd. Bris 51 E2
Marshfield Rd. Mang 51 E4
Marshfield Rd. Tor 41 F1
Marshfield Way. Bath 85 D1
Marshwall La. Alm 23 F3
Marson Rd. Cleve 57 E2
Marston Rd. Bris 64 A2
Martin Cl. Bris 35 F4
Martin St. Bris 63 D2
Martin's Rd. Kingsw 65 E3
Martindale Ct. W-S-M 105 E4
Martindale Rd. W-S-M 105 E4
Martingale Rd. Bris 64 B2
Martins Cl. Kingsw 65 E3
Martins Gr. W-S-M 88 C1
Martock Cres. Bris 63 E1
Martock Rd. Bris 63 E1
Martock Rd. Keyn 82 A2
Martock. W-S-M 104 C1
Martor Ind Est. Marsh 56 A1
Marwood Rd. Bris 79 F4
Mary Carpenter Pl. Bris 49 F1
Mary St. Bris 64 B4
Marybush La. Bris 63 F4
Marygold Leaze. Kingsw 66 A2
Mascot Rd. Bris 63 E2
Masefield Way. Bris 50 A4
Maskelyne Ave. Bris 49 E4
Masons View. Wint 37 F4
Matchells Cl. Bris 64 C3
Materman Rd. Bris 80 C3
Matford Cl. Bris 35 E2
Matford Cl. Wint 37 F3
Matford La. Stone 3 F2
Matthew's Rd. Bris 64 B4
Matthews Cl. Bris 80 C3
Maules La. St Gif 36 C1
Maunsell Rd. Bris 34 A1
Maurice Rd. Bris 49 F1
Max Mill La. Wins 124 B4
Maxse Rd. Bris 64 A2
May St. Bris 51 E1
May Tree Cl. Nail 59 E1
May Tree Rd. Rad 132 C1
May Tree Wlk. Keyn 81 E2
May's La. Pux 90 B2
Maybank Rd. Yate 27 E1
Maybec Gdns. Bris 65 D3
Maybourne. Bris 65 D1
Maybrick Rd. Bath 101 E3
Maycliffe Park. Bris 49 F1
Mayfair Ave. Nail 59 F1
Mayfield Ave. Bris 51 D1
Mayfield Ave. W-S-M 88 C1
Mayfield Pk N. Bris 51 D1
Mayfield Pk S. Bris 51 D1
Mayfield Pk. Bris 51 D1
Mayfield Rd. Bath 101 E3
Mayfields. Keyn 81 F3
Mayflower Gdns. Nail 60 A1
Maynard Cl. Bris 79 E3
Maynard Cl. Cleve 57 F2
Maynard Rd. Bris 79 E3
Maynard Terr. Clut 115 D2
Maypole Cl. Clut 114 C2
Maysfield Cl. Portis 45 E2
Maysgreen Rd. Pux 90 A2
Maysmead La. Chur 109 E3
Maytree Ave. Bris 79 D4
Maytree Cl. Bris 79 D4
Mayville Ave. Bris 36 A2
Maywood Ave. Bris 51 D2
Maywood Cres. Bris 51 D2
Maywood Rd. Bris 51 E2
Maze St. Bris 64 A3
McAdam Way. Bris 62 C3
Mead Cl. Bath 101 F2
Mead Cl. Bris 47 F3
Mead La. Keyn 82 C2
Mead La. Keyn 83 D2
Mead La. Winsc 107 F2
Mead Lands. Cor 100 A4
Mead Rd. Ch Sod 28 A1
Mead Rd. Portis 45 E1
Mead Rd. St Gif 36 C3
Mead Rise. Bris 63 F2
Mead St. Bris 63 F3
Mead The. Alve 15 D3
Mead The. Bris 36 A2
Mead The. Chil 137 F1
Mead The. Clut 114 C2
Mead The. Dun 78 B1
Mead The. Farm 116 A3
Mead The. Ship 125 F4
Mead The. Tims 116 B2
Mead The. Win 95 D3
Mead The. Winsl 120 C4
Mead Vale. W-S-M 105 F4
Mead Way. Thorn 15 D4
Meadow Cl. Back 76 A3
Meadow Cl. Mang 51 F4
Meadow Cl. Nail 59 F2
Meadow Cl. Portis 44 C3
Meadow Court Dr. Kingsw 66 B2
Meadow Croft. W-S-M 105 D1
Meadow Dr. Lock 106 A2
Meadow Dr. W in G 44 C1
Meadow Gdns. Bath 84 A1
Meadow Gr. Bris 47 E4
Meadow La. Bath 85 E1
Meadow Mead. Fr Cot 38 A4
Meadow Park. Bathe 86 A2
Meadow Rd. Ch Sod 28 A1
Meadow Rd. Cleve 57 F2
Meadow Rd. Crom 10 A2
Meadow Rd. Paul 131 F2
Meadow St. Avon 33 D1
Meadow St. Axb 125 E1
Meadow St. Bris 63 F4
Meadow St. W-S-M 104 C4
Meadow Vale. Bris 51 D1
Meadow View. Fr Cot 38 B4
Meadow View. Rad 133 D1
Meadow Villas. W-S-M 104 C4
Meadow Way. St Gif 36 C4
Meadowbank. W-S-M 88 C2
Meadowland Rd. Bris 34 C2
Meadowland. Yatt 74 A1
Meadowlands. Lock 89 E1
Meadows The. Kingsw 65 E2
Meadowside Dr. Bris 80 A2
Meadowside. Thorn 15 E4
Meadowsweet Ave. Bris 36 A2
Meads The. Burt 43 D2
Meads The. Mang 51 F4
Meadway Ave. Nail 59 E1
Meadway. Bris 48 B3
Meadway. Clut 114 C1
Meadway. Farm 116 A3
Mearcombe La. Blea 122 C3
Meardon Rd. Bris 80 C3
Meare Rd. Bath 102 A1
Meare. W-S-M 104 C1
Mede Cl. Bris 63 F3
Medical Ave. Bris 63 E4
Medina Cl. Thorn 15 E4
Medway Cl. Keyn 82 A2
Medway Ct. Thorn 15 E4
Medway Dr. Fr Cot 38 A4
Medway Dr. Keyn 82 A2
Meere Bank. Bris 34 A1
Meetinghouse La. Brock 75 D1
Meetinghouse La. Yatt 75 D1
Meg Thatchers Cl. Bris 65 D4
Meg Thatchers Gdns. Bris 65 D4
Melbourne Dr. Ch Sod 28 A1
Melbourne Rd. Bris 49 E2
Melbourne Terr. Cleve 57 E1
Melbury Rd. Bris 64 A1
Melcombe Rd. Bath 101 E3
Melita Rd. Bris 49 F2
Mellent Ave. Bris 79 E2
Mells Cl. Keyn 82 A1
Mells La. Kilm 133 D1
Mells La. Rad 133 D1
Melrose Ave. Bris 63 D4
Melrose Ave. Yate 28 A1

Melrose Cl. Yate 28 A1
Melrose Gr. Bath 101 D2
Melrose Pl. Bris 63 D4
Melton Cres. Bris 50 A4
Melville Rd. Bris 49 D1
Melville Terr. Bris 63 E2
Memorial Cl. Kingsw 65 D2
Memorial Cotts. Bath 84 B1
Memorial Rd. Kingsw 65 D2
Memorial Rd. Wring 92 C1
Mendip Ave. W-S-M 88 C1
Mendip Cl. Axb 125 E1
Mendip Cl. Keyn 81 E3
Mendip Cl. Nail 59 F1
Mendip Cl. Paul 131 F2
Mendip Cl. Yatt 91 D4
Mendip Cres. Mang 52 A4
Mendip Edge. W-S-M 121 F4
Mendip Gdns. Bath 118 B4
Mendip Gdns. Yatt 91 D4
Mendip Rd. Bris 63 E2
Mendip Rd. Portis 45 D3
Mendip Rd. W-S-M 105 D4
Mendip Rd. Yatt 91 D4
Mendip Rise. Lock 106 A2
Mendip View Ave. Bris 51 D2
Mendip View. Wick 67 E4
Mendip Villas. Co Mar 127 F4
Mendip Way. 132 C2
Menlea. Blag 110 B2
Merchant St. Bris 63 F4
Merchants Ct. Bris 63 D3
Merchants Quay. Bris 63 E3
Merchants Rd. Bris 63 D3
Merchants Rd. Bris 63 D4
Mercia Dr. Bris 50 A1
Mercier Cl. Yate 27 F1
Meredith Ct. Bris 63 D3
Merfield Rd. Bris 64 A1
Meridian Pl. Bris 63 D4
Meridian Rd. Bris 49 E1
Meridian Vale. Bris 63 D4
Meriet Ave. Bris 79 D2
Merioneth St. Bris 63 F2
Meriton St. Bris 64 A3
Merlin Cl. Bris 48 C4
Merlin Cl. W-S-M 105 F4
Merlin Park. Portis 45 D2
Merlin Rd. Bris 35 E3
Merlin Ridge. Puck 53 E2
Merlin Way. Ch Sod 39 F4
Merrimans Rd. Bris 47 E4
Merryweathers. Bris 64 C1
Merrywood Cl. Bris 63 E2
Merrywood Rd. Bris 63 E2
Merstham Rd. Bris 50 A1
Merton Rd. Bris 49 F3
Mervyn Rd. Bris 49 F2
Metford Dr. Bris 49 D2
Metford Pl. Bris 49 E2
Metford Rd. Bris 49 E2
Methwyn Cl. W-S-M 105 E4
Mews The. Bath 101 C1
Michaels Mead. Bath 84 A1
Middle Ave. Bris 63 E3
Middle La. Bath 85 D1
Middle La. K Sey 73 D2
Middle Rd. Kingsw 51 F2
Middle St. E Harp 128 C2
Middle Stoke. Li St 120 A3
Middle Yeo Green. Nail 59 E2
Middledown Rd. Marsh 55 E1
Middleford House. Bris 79 E2
Middlemead. Chil 137 F2
Middlepiece La. Keyn 99 D4
Middleton Rd. Bris 47 F4
Midford Hill. Hin Cha 119 E2
Midford La. Hi Cha 120 A3
Midford La. Li St 119 F4
Midford Rd. Bath 101 F1
Midford Rd. Sosto 119 D4
Midford. W-S-M 104 C1
Midhaven Rise. W-S-M 88 C2
Midland Bridge Rd. Bath ... 101 F3
Midland Rd. Bath 101 E4
Midland Rd. Bris 63 F4
Midland Rd. Kingsw 51 E2
Midland Terr. Bris 50 C2
Midland Way. Thorn 15 D4
Midsomer Enterprise Park.
Mid No 132 B1
Midsummer Bldgs. Bath 85 D1
Milbourn Cl. Winsl 120 B4
Milburn Rd. W-S-M 104 C4
Mildred St. Bris 64 A4
Mile Wlk. Bris 80 A3
Miles Ct. Kingsw 65 F2
Miles Rd. Bris 49 D1
Miles St. Bath 102 A3
Miles's Bldgs. Bath 101 F4
Milestone Ct. Lock 89 E1
Milford Ave. Wick 67 D4
Milford St. Bris 63 E2
Milk St. Bath 101 F3
Mill Ave. Bris 63 E3
Mill Cl. Fr Cot 38 B4
Mill Cl. Portb 46 B1
Mill Cres. West 39 D2

Mill Hill. Well 118 C1
Mill La. Bath 85 F1
Mill La. Bath 101 D3
Mill La. Bath 119 F4
Mill La. Bitt 66 C1
Mill La. Bitt 82 C4
Mill La. Bris 63 E2
Mill La. But 111 D4
Mill La. Ch Sod 28 A1
Mill La. Ch Sod 40 C3
Mill La. Ch St 112 B4
Mill La. Co Mar 128 A4
Mill La. Cong 91 E2
Mill La. Doyn 53 F1
Mill La. Falf 9 F4
Mill La. Fr Cot 26 A1
Mill La. Kingsw 66 B3
Mill La. Olve 14 A1
Mill La. Portb 46 C1
Mill La. Pris 117 D4
Mill La. Tims 116 A1
Mill La. Wring 109 F4
Mill Leg. Cong 91 F2
Mill Pool Ct. Bris 35 D1
Mill rd. Mid No 133 D1
Mill Rd. Wint 37 E2
Mill Stream Cl. Axb 125 D1
Millard Cl. Bris 35 E1
Millard's Hill. Mid No 132 A2
Millbank Cl. Bris 64 C2
Millbrook Ave. Bris 64 C2
Millbrook Pl. Bath 102 A3
Millbrook Rd. Yate 27 D1
Millcross. Cleve 73 E4
Millers Cl. E in G 47 E2
Millers Dr. Kingsw 66 B3
Millers Rise. W-S-M 89 D2
Millfield Dr. Kingsw 66 B3
Millfield. Mid No 137 F4
Millfield. Thorn 8 B1
Millground Rd. Bris 78 C3
Millier Rd. Brock 92 A4
Milliman Dr. Bris 79 E3
Millmead House. Bris 79 E2
Millmead Rd. Bath 101 E3
Millpond St. Bris 50 A1
Millward Gr. Bris 51 E2
Milner Green. Kingsw 66 A3
Milner Rd. Bris 49 F3
Milsom Cl. Bath 101 F4
Milsom St. Bris 64 A4
Milton Ave. Bath 101 F2
Milton Ave. W-S-M 105 D4
Milton Brow. W-S-M 88 A1
Milton Cl. Nail 59 F2
Milton Cl. Yate 27 E1
Milton Green. W-S-M 88 B1
Milton Hill. W-S-M 88 A1
Milton Park Rd. W-S-M 88 B1
Milton Pk. Bris 64 B4
Milton Rd. Bris 49 F3
Milton Rd. Rad 132 B1
Milton Rd. Yate 27 E1
Milton Rise. W-S-M 88 B1
Miltons Cl. Bris 79 E2
Milverton. W-S-M 104 C1
Milward Rd. Keyn 81 F3
Mina Rd. Bris 50 A1
Minehead Rd. Bris 64 A1
Minerva Gdns. Bath 101 E2
Minor's La. Avon 34 A4
Minsmere Rd. Keyn 82 A2
Minster Way. Bath 102 B4
Minto Rd. Bris 50 A1
Minto Road Ind Centre. Bris 49 F1
Mission Rd. Ir Act 27 D2
Mitchell Ct. Bris 63 F3
Mitchell La. Bris 63 F3
Mitford-Slade Ct. Yatt 91 E4
Mivart St. Bris 50 A1
Mizzymead Cl. Nail 59 E1
Mizzymead Rd. Nail 59 F1
Mizzymead Rise. Nail 59 E1
Modecombe Gr. Bris 34 C2
Mogg St. Bris 50 A1
Molesworth Cl. Bris 79 D2
Molesworth Dr. Bris 79 D2
Molesworth Dr. Bris 79 D2
Molly Cl. Clut 130 C4
Monger La. Mid No 132 A2
Monk Rd. Bris 49 E2
Monk's Park Ave. Bris 49 F4
Monks Ave. Bris 65 D4
Monks Hill. W-S-M 88 A2
Monksdale Rd. Bath 101 E2
Monkton Ave. W-S-M 105 D1
Monkton Farleigh. Mon Far 103 F4
Monkton Rd. Kingsw 65 D3
Monmouth Cl. Portis 44 C2
Monmouth Hill. Alm 23 F2
Monmouth Paddock. N St P 135 F2
Monmouth Pl. Bath 101 F3
Monmouth Rd. Bris 49 E2
Monmouth Rd. E in G 47 E3
Monmouth Rd. Keyn 81 E3
Monmouth St. Bath 101 F3
Monmouth St. Bris 63 F2
Monsdale Cl. Bris 35 D2

Monsdale Dr. Bris 35 D1
Montague Cl. St Gif 36 C3
Montague Hill S. Bris 63 E4
Montague Pl. Bris 63 E4
Montague Rd. Keyn 82 B1
Montague Rd. Well 133 F3
Montague St. Bris 63 E4
Montgomery St. Bris 63 F2
Montpelier E. W-S-M 87 F1
Montpelier. W-S-M 104 C4
Montreal Ave. Bris 50 A4
Montrose Ave. Bris 49 E1
Montrose Dr. Kingsw 66 A3
Montrose Pk. Bris 64 B1
Montroy Cl. Bris 49 E3
Moon St. Bris 63 F4
Moor Croft Dr. Kingsw 65 F2
Moor Croft Rd. Lock 105 F2
Moor End Spout. Nail 59 E1
Moor Gr. Bris 48 A4
Moor Green. Axb 125 E1
Moor La. Back 75 F3
Moor La. Cleve 58 A1
Moor La. Lock 105 E2
Moor La. Nail 58 C2
Moor La. Olve 24 A4
Moor La. Piln 23 F4
Moor La. W in G 45 F1
Moor La. W-S-M 105 F4
Moor Park. Cleve 57 F1
Moor Rd. Ban 107 D3
Moor Rd. Yatt 74 A1
Moordell Cl. Yate 27 E1
Moorend Gdns. Bris 47 F4
Moorend Rd. Wint 37 E2
Moorfield Rd. Back 76 A3
Moorfields Cl. Bath 101 E2
Moorfields Ct. Nail 59 E1
Moorfields Rd. Bath 101 E2
Moorfields Rd. Nail 59 E1
Moorham Rd. Wins 108 A1
Moorhill St. Bris 50 A1
Moorhouse La. Avon 34 A2
Moorings The. E in G 47 E2
Moorland Rd. Bath 101 E3
Moorland Rd. W-S-M 104 C2
Moorland Rd. Yate 27 D1
Moorland St. Axb 125 E1
Moorlands Cl. Nail 59 E1
Moorlands Rd. Bris 50 C2
Moorlands Rd. Bris 51 D1
Moorledge La. Ch Mag 96 B1
Moorledge La. Pens 113 F4
Moorledge Rd. Ch Mag 96 A1
Moorpark Ave. Yate 27 E1
Moorsfield. Clut 114 C2
Moorside Ct. Cleve 57 F1
Moorside Villas. Cleve 57 E1
Moorslade La. Falf 3 E1
Moorslade La. Stone 3 E1
Moravian Ct. Kingsw 65 E4
Moravian Rd. Kingsw 65 E4
Morden Wlk. Bris 80 B4
Moreton Cl. Bris 80 A2
Moreton St. Bris 63 F4
Morford St. Bath 101 F4
Morgan Cl. Keyn 82 B1
Morgan St. Bris 49 F1
Morgan's La. E Harp 128 C2
Morgans Hill Cl. Nail 75 E4
Morley Ave. Kingsw 52 A2
Morley Cl. Kingsw 51 E2
Morley Cl. St Gif 36 B4
Morley Rd. Bris 63 E2
Morley Rd. Kingsw 51 E2
Morley Sq. Bris 49 F2
Morley St. Bris 49 F1
Morley St. Bris 64 A4
Morley Terr. Kingsw 51 E1
Morley Terr. Mid No 133 D2
Mornington Rd. Bris 49 D1
Morpeth Rd. Bris 79 E4
Morris La. Bathe 86 A2
Morris Rd. Bris 50 A3
Morse Rd. Bris 64 B4
Mortimer Cl. Bath 84 A1
Mortimer Rd. Bris 36 A1
Mortimer Rd. Bris 63 D4
Morton St. Bris 64 A4
Morton St. Thorn 8 B2
Morton Way. Thorn 8 B1
Moseley Gr. W-S-M 104 C1
Mount Beacon Row. Bath ... 84 C1
Mount Beacon. Bath 85 D1
Mount Cl. Fr Cot 37 F4
Mount Cres. Wint 37 F3
Mount Gdns. Kingsw 65 E3
Mount Gr. Bath 101 D2
Mount Hill Rd. Kingsw 65 E3
Mount Pleasant Terr. Bris ... 63 E2
Mount Pleasant. Bath 102 B1
Mount Pleasant. E in G 47 E2
Mount Pleasant. Rad 133 D1
Mount Rd. Bath 101 D2
Mount Rd. Bath 101 F4
Mount View. Bath 101 D2
Mountain Ash. Bath 84 B1

Mountain Wood. Bathf 86 B1
Mountbatten Cl. W-S-M 88 C2
Mountbatten Cl. Yate 27 E2
Mounteney's La. Kings 18 B4
Mow Barton. Bris 78 C3
Mow Barton. Yate 27 E1
Mowbray Rd. Bris 80 B4
Mowcroft Rd. Bris 79 E2
Moxham Dr. Bris 79 E2
Mud La. Yatt 74 C1
Muddy La. W ST L 89 D4
Muirfield. Kingsw 66 A3
Muirfield. Yate 39 F4
Mulberry Cl. Back 76 A3
Mulberry Cl. Kingsw 65 F4
Mulberry Dr. Kingsw 51 F1
Mulberry La. Blea 122 B3
Mulberry Rd. Cong 91 F2
Mulberry Wlk. Bris 48 B4
Mule St. N Nib 4 A2
Mullberry Cl. W-S-M 89 D1
Muller Ave. Bris 49 F2
Muller Rd. Bris 50 A2
Mulready Cl. Bris 50 B3
Mumbleys Hill. Thorn 14 C4
Mumbleys La. Thorn 14 C4
Murford Ave. Bris 79 D2
Murford Wlk. Bris 79 D2
Murray St. Bris 63 E2
Musgrove Cl. Bris 34 B1
Myrtle Dr. Bris 47 F3
Myrtle Hill. E in G 47 E3
Myrtle Rd. Bris 63 E4
Myrtle St. Bris 63 D2
Myrtles The. Lock 105 E1

Nags Head Hill. Bris 65 D4
Nailsea Cl. Bris 79 D4
Nailsea Park Cl. Nail 59 F1
Nailsea Park. Nail 59 F1
Nailsea Wall. Nail 74 B4
Nailsea Wall. Yatt 74 B4
Nailsworth Dr. Yate 27 F1
Naish Hill. Wrax 59 F4
Naish La. Ba Gu 77 E2
Naish's Cross. Chil 137 E2
Naishcombe Hill. Wick 67 E4
Naishes Ave. P St J 133 E4
Naite The. O-on-S 7 E3
Nanny Hurn's La. Bi Sut ... 114 A1
Nanny Hurn's La. Clut 130 A4
Napier Ct. Bris 63 D3
Napier Miles Rd. Bris 48 A4
Napier Rd. Avon 33 D1
Napier Rd. Bath 84 A2
Napier Rd. Bris 49 D1
Napier Rd. Bris 50 A1
Napier Sq. Avon 33 D1
Napier St. Bris 64 A3
Narrow La. Kingsw 51 F2
Narrow Plain. Bris 63 F3
Narrow Quay. Bris 63 E3
Narroways Rd. Bris 50 A2
Naseby Wlk. Bris 50 C1
Nash Cl. Keyn 82 A3
Nash Dr. Bris 50 B4
Nates La. Wring 92 C1
Naunton Way. W-S-M 88 A1
Neath Rd. Bris 64 B4
Nelson Ct. W-S-M 88 C1
Nelson Pl W. Bath 101 F3
Nelson Pl. Bath 102 A4
Nelson Rd. Mang 51 E2
Nelson St. Bris 63 D1
Nelson St. Bris 63 E4
Nelson Terr. Bath 102 A4
Nelson Villas. Bath 101 F3
Nempnett St. But 111 E3
Neston Wlk. Bris 79 F4
Netham Park Ind Est. Bris .. 64 B3
Netham Rd. Bris 64 B4
Netham View Ind Park. Bris 64 B4
Netherays. Cleve 57 D1
Nettlestone Cl. Bris 34 C1
Nettleton Rd. Burt 43 D2
Neva Rd. W-S-M 104 C1
Nevalan Dr. Bris 65 D3
Nevil Rd. Bris 49 F2
Neville Rd. Kingsw 51 F1
New Bldgs. Bris 65 C2
New Bldgs. P St J 133 D4
New Bond St. Bath 101 A3
New Bond Street Pl. Bath . 102 A3
New Bristol Rd. W-S-M 88 C1
New Brunswick Ave. Bris ... 65 D4
New Charlotte St. Bris 63 E2
New Cheltenham Rd.
   Kingsw 51 F1
New Cut Bow. K Sey 73 D3
New Fosseway Rd. Bris 80 A3
New John St. Bris 63 E2
New King St. Bath 101 F3
New Kingsley Rd. Bris 63 F3
New La. Alve 15 D2
New Leaze. St Gif 24 B2
New Orchard St. Bath 102 A3
New Queen St. Bris 63 F2
New Queen St. Bris 65 D4

New Rd. Bathf 86 B1
New Rd. Bris 36 A2
New Rd. Bris 36 B2
New Rd. Chur 108 C2
New Rd. E in G 47 E2
New Rd. Farm 115 E2
New Rd. Hi Cha 120 A3
New Rd. Kilm 139 F2
New Rd. N Nib 5 F2
New Rd. Olve 14 A1
New Rd. Paul 115 E2
New Rd. Pens 97 E2
New Rd. Ship 108 C2
New Rd. Tyth 16 B3
New Rd. W-u-E 11 F3
New Rd. Wickw 27 D4
New Rd. Wring 93 F2
New Rd. Yate 17 E1
New Rock Ind Est. Chil 137 E1
New St. Bath 101 F3
New St. Bris 63 F4
New St. Char 11 D3
New Station Rd. Bris 51 D2
New Thomas St. Bris 63 F3
New Tyning La. Hort 29 E2
New Walls. Bris 63 F2
New Wlk. Kingsw 65 D4
Newark St. Bath 102 A3
Newbolt Cl. W-S-M 105 D2
Newbourne Rd. W-S-M 105 E4
Newbridge Cl. Bris 64 B3
Newbridge Ct. Bath 101 D4
Newbridge Gdns. Bath 101 D4
Newbridge Hill. Bath 101 D4
Newbridge Rd. Bath 101 D4
Newbridge Rd. Bris 64 C3
Newbury Rd. Bris 50 A4
Newchurch Rd. W-S-M 104 B1
Newclose La. Co Mar 128 B4
Newcombe Dr. Bris 48 B2
Newcombe Rd. Bris 49 E2
Newditch La. Ba Gu 77 E1
Newent Ave. Bris 65 D4
Newfields. Blag 126 A1
Newfoundland Rd. Bris 63 F4
Newfoundland St. Bris 63 F4
Newfoundland Way. Bris 49 F1
Newgate. Bris 63 F4
Newhaven Pl. Portis 44 C2
Newhaven Rd. Portis 44 B2
Newland Dr. Bris 79 D2
Newland Rd. Bris 79 D2
Newland Rd. W-S-M 104 C3
Newland Wlk. Bris 79 D2
Newlands Ave. Fr Cot 38 B4
Newlands Green. Cleve 57 F1
Newlands Hill. Portis 45 E2
Newlands Rd. Keyn 81 E2
Newlands The. Bris 51 D4
Newlyn Ave. Bris 48 B4
Newlyn Way. Yate 27 F1
Newlyn Wlk. Bris 64 A1
Newman Cl. West 39 D2
Newmans La. Tims 116 A1
Newmarket Ave. Bris 63 E4
Newnham Cl. Bris 80 B4
Newnham Pl. Bris 23 F1
Newpit La. Bitt 66 C1
Newport Cl. Cleve 57 E1
Newport Cl. Portis 44 C2
Newport Rd. E in G 47 E3
Newport St. Bris 63 E2
Newquay Rd. Bris 63 F1
Newry Wlk. Bris 63 F1
Newsome Ave. E in G 47 E2
Newton Cl. E Harp 128 C3
Newton Cl. Kingsw 52 A1
Newton Dr. Kingsw 66 A3
Newton Green. Nail 75 E4
Newton Rd. Bath 100 C3
Newton Rd. Kingsw 66 A3
Newton Rd. W-S-M 104 C3
Newton St. Bris 64 A4
Newton's Rd. W-S-M 88 C2
Newtown. Char 11 D3
Niblett Cl. Kingsw 65 F3
Niblett's Hill. Bris 65 D3
Nicholas La. Bris 65 D3
Nicholas Rd. Bris 50 A1
Nicholas St. Bris 63 F2
Nicholettes. Kingsw 66 B3
Nicholls La. Wint 37 F3
Nigel Park. Bris 47 F3
Nightingale Cl. Fr Cot 38 A3
Nightingale Cl. Thorn 8 B1
Nightingale Cl. W-S-M 88 C1
Nightingale Gdns. Nail 59 E1
Nightingale La. Wint 38 A4
Nightingale Rise. Portis 44 C2
Nightingale Way. Rod 138 A4
Nine Tree Hill. Bris 49 F1
Ninth Ave. Bris 36 A1
Nippors Way. Wins 108 A1
Nithsdale Rd. W-S-M 104 C2
Noble Ave. Kingsw 66 B2

Entry	Page	Grid
Nomis Park. Cong	91	F1
Nore Gdns. Portis	45	E3
Nore Park Dr. Portis	44	C3
Nore Rd. Portis	45	D3
Norfolk Ave. Bris	49	F1
Norfolk Ave. Bris	63	F4
Norfolk Bldgs. Bath	101	F3
Norfolk Cres. Bath	101	F3
Norfolk Gr. Keyn	81	E2
Norfolk Pl. Bris	63	E2
Norfolk Rd. Portis	45	F2
Norland Rd. Bris	62	C4
Norley Rd. Bris	49	F4
Norman Gr. Bris	51	E1
Norman Rd. Bris	50	A1
Norman Rd. Keyn	82	C2
Norman Rd. Sist	66	A4
Normanby Rd. Bris	50	A1
Normans The. Bath	85	F1
Normanton Rd. Bris	49	D1
Norrisville Rd. Bris	49	F1
North Croft. Kingsw	66	B2
North Devon Rd. Bris	51	D3
North Down Cl. Ship	125	F4
North Down La. Ship	125	F4
North East Rd. Thorn	8	B1
North End Rd. Yatt	73	F2
North End. Yatt	74	A1
North Gr. E in G	47	E2
North Green St. Bris	62	C3
North Hills Cl. W-S-M	105	D1
North La. Bath	102	B3
North La. Nail	59	D1
North La. W-S-M	104	C4
North Leaze. Lo Ash	62	A1
North Meadows. P St J	133	F4
North Par. Bath	102	A3
North Par. Yate	27	F1
North Parade Bldgs. Bath	102	A3
North Parade Pas. Bath	102	A3
North Parade Rd. Bath	102	A3
North Pk. Kingsw	51	F1
North Rd. Ban	107	D2
North Rd. Bath	102	B1
North Rd. Bath	102	B3
North Rd. Bris	49	F1
North Rd. Bris	62	B4
North Rd. Bris	63	D2
North Rd. Ir Act	27	D2
North Rd. Lymp	122	B1
North Rd. Mid No	132	A1
North Rd. St Gif	36	C2
North Rd. Thorn	8	B1
North Rd. Tims	116	A1
North Rd. Wint	37	F4
North Rd. Yate	27	D2
North Side Rd. Wring	94	A4
North St. Bris	63	D2
North St. Bris	63	F4
North St. Kingsw	66	B2
North St. Mang	51	F3
North St. N St P	135	F2
North St. Nail	59	D1
North St. W-S-M	104	C4
North St. Wickw	18	A3
North Stoke La. Bitt	83	D4
North View Cl. Bath	101	D3
North View Dr. Ban	107	D1
North View. Bris	49	D2
North View. Kingsw	51	E2
North View. Mang	51	F3
North View. Rad	133	D1
North Way. Bath	101	D3
North Way. Mid No	132	A1
North Wlk. Yate	27	F1
Northampton Bldgs. Bath	101	F4
Northampton House. Wrax	60	B2
Northampton St. Bath	101	F4
Northavon Bsns Centre. Yate	27	E2
Northcote Rd. Bris	48	C1
Northcote Rd. Bris	64	C4
Northcote Rd. Mang	51	F3
Northcote St. Bris	50	A1
Northdown Rd. Paul	132	C3
Northend Ave. Kingsw	51	E1
Northend Gdns. Kingsw	51	E1
Northend Rd. Kingsw	51	E1
Northern Way. Cleve	57	F2
Northfield Ave. Kingsw	65	E3
Northfield Rd. Bris	65	D4
Northfield Rd. Portis	44	C2
Northfield. Mid No	133	D2
Northfield. Tims	116	B2
Northfield. Winsl	120	C4
Northfield. Yate	39	E4
Northfields Cl. Bath	84	C1
Northfields. Bath	84	C1
Northgate St. Bath	102	A3
Northleach Wlk. Bris	47	F3
Northleigh Ave. W-S-M	88	B1
Northmead Ave. Mid No	131	F1
Northmead Cl. Mid No	131	F1
Northmead La. Ir Act	26	B3
Northmead Rd. Mid No	131	F1
Northover Rd. Bris	35	D1
Northridge Bsns Centre. Yate	27	E1
Northumberland Pl. Bath	102	A3
Northumberland Rd. Bris	49	E1
Northumbria Dr. Bris	49	D3
Northville Rd. Bris	36	A1
Northway. Bris	36	A2
Northwick Gdns. Bi Sut	113	E2
Northwick Rd. Bris	49	F4
Northwick Rd. Ch Mag	96	B4
Northwick Rd. Piln	22	B4
Northwick Rd. Whit	96	B4
Northwoods Wlk. Bris	35	E2
Norton Cl. Ch Mag	96	A2
Norton Cl. Kingsw	65	F4
Norton La. Ch Mag	96	B3
Norton La. Hin Cha	135	C4
Norton La. W St L	88	B2
Norton La. Well	135	E4
Norton La. Whit	80	B1
Norton La. Whit	96	B3
Norton Rd. Bris	64	C2
Nortons Wood La. Cleve	58	A3
Norwich Dr. Bris	64	C3
Norwood Ave. Bath	102	C3
Norwood Gr. Portis	44	C3
Notgrove Cl. W-S-M	88	A1
Nottingham Rd. Bris	49	F2
Nottingham St. Bris	63	F2
Nova Scotia Pl. Bris	63	D3
Novers Cres. Bris	79	E4
Novers Hill Trading Est. Bris	63	E1
Novers Hill. Bris	79	E4
Novers La. Bris	79	E4
Novers Park Dr. Bris	79	E4
Novers Park Rd. Bris	79	E4
Novers Rd. Bris	79	E4
Nugent Hill. Bris	49	E1
Nunney Cl. Keyn	82	A1
Nupdown Rd. O-On-S	1	C3
Nupdown Rd. Rock	2	A2
Nursery Gdns. Bris	35	D2
Nursery The. Bris	63	D2
Nutfield Gr. Bris	36	A1
Nutgrove Ave. Bris	63	F2
Nutgrove La. Ch Mag	96	A2
Nuthatch Dr. Bris	50	C3
Nutwell Rd. W-S-M	88	C1
Nutwell Sq. W-S-M	88	C1
Nye Rd. Winsc	107	F3
Nympsfield. Kingsw	51	F1
Oak Ave. Bath	101	E2
Oak Cl. St Gif	36	B4
Oak Cl. Yate	27	E2
Oak Dr. Portis	45	D2
Oak Gr. E in G	47	E3
Oak La. Bris	50	C1
Oak Rd. Bris	49	F3
Oak Rd. Col	70	C3
Oak Rd. Wins	125	D4
Oak St. Bath	101	F3
Oak Terr. Rad	132	B1
Oak Tree Ave. Puck	53	D2
Oak Tree Cl. Kingsw	65	E2
Oak Tree Wlk. Keyn	81	E2
Oakdale Ave. Mang	51	E4
Oakdale Cl. Mang	51	F4
Oakdale Gdns. W-S-M	88	C2
Oakdale Rd. Bris	80	A4
Oakdale Rd. Mang	51	F4
Oakdene Ave. Bris	50	B2
Oakenhill Wlk. Bris	64	C1
Oakes La. Tor	42	A3
Oakfield Gr. Bris	63	D4
Oakfield Pl. Bris	63	D4
Oakfield Rd. Bath	101	E4
Oakfield Rd. Bris	63	D4
Oakfield Rd. Keyn	81	F1
Oakfield Rd. Kingsw	65	E4
Oakford La. Marsh	70	A1
Oakhanger Dr. Bris	34	A1
Oakhill Ave. Kingsw	66	B1
Oakhill Cl. Nail	60	A1
Oakhill Rd. Bath	101	F1
Oakhill. Bris	34	B2
Oakhill. W-S-M	105	D1
Oakhurst Rd. Bris	48	C3
Oakland Dr. Lock	105	F2
Oakland Rd. Bris	49	D1
Oakland Rd. Bris	64	C4
Oaklands Cl. Mang	52	A3
Oaklands Dr. Alm	24	A2
Oaklands Dr. Bris	51	D4
Oaklands Dr. Kingsw	66	B1
Oaklands Rd. Mang	52	A3
Oaklands. Clut	114	C3
Oaklands. Paul	131	F2
Oakleaze Rd. Thorn	8	B1
Oakleaze. Fr Cot	38	B4
Oakleigh Ave. Bris	64	B4
Oakleigh Cl. Back	76	A3
Oakleigh Gdns. Kingsw	66	B1
Oakley Rd. Bris	49	F4
Oakley. Bath	102	C3
Oakley. Cleve	73	D4
Oakmead Pk. Bris	64	A1
Oakridge Cl. Kingsw	66	A4
Oakridge Cl. Wins	125	D4
Oakridge La. Wins	125	D4
Oaks The. Win	94	C4
Oaksey Gr. Nail	60	A1
Oaktree Cres. St Gif	24	B1
Oaktree Ct. Bris	47	F4
Oaktree Gdns. Bris	78	C3
Oakwood Ave. Bris	49	D3
Oakwood Rd. Bris	49	D3
Oatlands Ave. Bris	80	A3
Oberon Ave. Bris	50	C1
Oclite Rd. Bath	101	E1
Odins Rd. Bath	101	E1
Okebourne Cl. Bris	35	D2
Okebourne Rd. Bris	35	D2
Old Ashley Hill. Bris	49	F1
Old Aust Rd. Alm	24	B3
Old Banwell Rd. Lock	106	A2
Old Barn La. But	94	A3
Old Barrow Hill. Bris	47	E4
Old Bond St. Bath	101	F3
Old Bread St. Bris	63	F3
Old Bristol Rd. Priddy	128	A2
Old Bristol Rd. W-S-M	89	D1
Old Chelsea La. Wrax	61	E2
Old Church Rd. Axb	125	E1
Old Church Rd. Cleve	57	E1
Old Church Rd. Nail	75	D4
Old Church Rd. W-S-M	104	B1
Old Coach Rd. Co Bi	124	C2
Old Down Rd. Ch Sod	42	B4
Old Down Rd. Gr Bad	30	C1
Old England Way. P St J	133	F4
Old Farm La. Bris	65	D3
Old Ferry Rd. Bath	101	E3
Old Fosse Rd. Bath	101	E1
Old Fosse Way. Mid No	132	C3
Old Frome Rd. Bath	118	C4
Old Gloucester Rd. Alve	15	D3
Old Gloucester Rd. Bris	25	E2
Old Gloucester Rd. Bris	37	D1
Old Gloucester Rd. Fr Cot	25	E2
Old Gloucester Rd. St Gif	37	D2
Old Gloucester Rd. St Gif	37	D4
Old Gloucester Rd. Thorn	9	D1
Old Gloucester Rd. Wint	37	D4
Old Hill. Win	94	B3
Old Hill. Wring	92	C2
Old King St Ct. Bris	63	F4
Old King St. Bath	101	F4
Old La. Farm	116	A3
Old La. Nail	59	E3
Old Manor Cl. Char	11	D3
Old Market St. Bris	63	F4
Old Midford Rd. Sosto	119	D4
Old Mill Rd. Portis	45	E3
Old Millard's Hill. Mid No	132	A2
Old Mills Ind Est. Paul	131	F1
Old Mills La. Paul	131	E2
Old Newbridge Hill. Bath	101	D4
Old Orchard St. Bath	102	A3
Old Orchard. Bath	102	A4
Old Park Hill. Bris	63	E4
Old Park Rd. Bris	47	E4
Old Park Rd. Cleve	57	F2
Old Park. Bris	63	E4
Old Pit Terr. Mid No	132	C2
Old Post Office La. W-S-M	104	B4
Old Priory Rd. E in G	47	D1
Old Quarry Rd. Bris	47	F4
Old Quarry Rise. Bris	47	F4
Old Quarry. Bath	101	E1
Old Rd. Rad	133	E1
Old Rectory Rd. Kings	11	F2
Old School La. Blea	122	B3
Old Sneed Ave. Bris	48	B2
Old Sneed Park. Bris	48	B2
Old Sneed Rd. Bris	48	B2
Old St. Cleve	57	F2
Old Station Cl. Wring	92	B1
Old Tarnwell. Pens	97	D1
Old Track. Li St	119	F4
Old Vicarage Green. Keyn	81	F3
Old Wall. Blea	121	E3
Old Water Gdns The. Blag	110	C1
Old Wells Rd. Bath	101	F1
Old Weston Rd. Back	77	D4
Old Weston Rd. Cong	91	D3
Oldacre Rd. Bris	80	A2
Oldbridge Rd. Whit	80	B2
Oldbury Chase. Kingsw	66	A1
Oldbury Court Dr. Bris	51	D3
Oldbury Court Rd. Bris	51	D3
Oldbury La. Thorn	8	A2
Oldbury La. Wick	67	E3
Oldfield La. Bath	101	F2
Oldfield Pl. Bris	62	C3
Oldfield Rd. Bath	101	F3
Oldfield Rd. Bris	63	D3
Oldfield. Cleve	57	F1
Oldfields La. Alve	25	E4
Oldlands Ave. Fr Cot	38	B4
Oldmead Wlk. Bris	78	C4
Oldmixon Cres. W-S-M	105	D2
Oldmixon Rd. W-S-M	105	D1
Oldmixon Rd. W-S-M	105	D1
Oldown Hill. Olve	14	B1
Oldville Ave. Cleve	57	E1
Olive Gdns. Alve	14	C2
Olveston Rd. Bris	49	F3
Olympus Cl. St Gif	36	B3
Olympus Rd. Bris	35	E4
Oolite Gr. Bath	118	B4
Oram Ct. Kingsw	65	F2
Orange Gr. Bath	102	A3
Orange St. Bris	63	F4
Orchard Ave. Bris	63	E3
Orchard Ave. Mid No	131	F1
Orchard Ave. Nail	58	C2
Orchard Ave. Thorn	8	B1
Orchard Bvd. Kingsw	66	A2
Orchard Cl. Back	77	D4
Orchard Cl. Ban	107	D2
Orchard Cl. Bi Sut	113	E2
Orchard Cl. Bris	48	C3
Orchard Cl. Char	11	D3
Orchard Cl. Keyn	81	E3
Orchard Cl. Kingsw	65	E4
Orchard Cl. Portis	45	E3
Orchard Cl. W-S-M	88	A2
Orchard Cl. W-S-M	88	C1
Orchard Cl. Westw	120	C2
Orchard Cl. Win	94	B4
Orchard Cl. Wring	92	C1
Orchard Cl. Yate	27	F1
Orchard Cres. Bris	47	E4
Orchard Dr. Aust	13	D4
Orchard Dr. Bris	79	D3
Orchard Dr. Wins	108	A2
Orchard End. E Harp	128	C2
Orchard Gdns. Kingsw	65	F4
Orchard Grange. Thorn	8	A1
Orchard La. Bris	63	E3
Orchard Lea. Alve	15	D3
Orchard Lea. E in G	47	E2
Orchard Pl. W-S-M	104	C4
Orchard Rd. Axb	125	E1
Orchard Rd. Back	76	A3
Orchard Rd. Bris	49	F2
Orchard Rd. Bris	64	C4
Orchard Rd. Cleve	57	E1
Orchard Rd. Fr Cot	38	B4
Orchard Rd. Kingsw	65	F4
Orchard Rd. Lo Ash	61	F1
Orchard Rd. Lock	105	E1
Orchard Rd. Nail	59	E1
Orchard Rd. Paul	131	F3
Orchard Rd. Puck	53	D3
Orchard Rise. Olve	14	A2
Orchard St. Bris	63	E3
Orchard St. W-S-M	104	C4
Orchard Terr. Bath	101	D3
Orchard The. Ban	107	D2
Orchard The. E in G	47	E2
Orchard The. Fr Cot	38	B4
Orchard The. Hi Cha	120	B3
Orchard The. Lock	106	A3
Orchard The. Pens	97	D1
Orchard The. Pens	97	F2
Orchard The. St Gif	36	C3
Orchard The. Tyth	16	A3
Orchard Vale. Kingsw	65	F4
Orchard Vale. Mid No	131	F1
Orchard Wlk. Chur	108	C2
Orchard Wlk. Kings	11	F2
Orchards The. Kingsw	65	F4
Oriel Gdns. Bath	85	E1
Oriel Gr. Bath	101	D2
Orion Dr. St Gif	36	B3
Orland Way. Kingsw	66	A2
Orlebar Gdns. Bris	34	A1
Orme Dr. Cleve	57	E3
Ormerod Rd. Bris	48	C3
Ormonds Cl. St Gif	24	C1
Ormsley Cl. St Gif	36	B4
Orpen Gdns. Bris	50	A3
Orpen Park. St Gif	24	B2
Orpheus Ave. St Gif	36	B3
Orwell Dr. Keyn	81	F2
Orwell St. Bris	63	F2
Osborne Ave. Bris	49	F2
Osborne Ave. W-S-M	104	C4
Osborne Cl. St Gif	36	B2
Osborne Rd. Bath	101	D4
Osborne Rd. Bris	49	D1
Osborne Rd. Bris	63	E2
Osborne Rd. Piln	22	A4
Osborne Terr. Bris	63	D1
Osborne Villas. Bris	63	E4
Oslings La. Bathf	86	A1
Osprey Ct. Bris	79	E3
Osprey Gdns. W-S-M	88	C1
Osprey Pk. Thorn	8	B2
Osprey Rd. Bris	64	B4
Ottawa Rd. W-S-M	104	C2
Otter Rd. Cleve	57	F1
Otterford Cl. Bris	80	A3
Ottery Cl. Bris	34	A1
Ottrells Mead. St Gif	24	B2
Oval The. Bath	101	E2
Over La. Alm	23	F1
Overdale. Mid No	132	C3
Overdale. Tims	116	C2
Overhill. E in G	47	E2
Overdale Rd. Mang	51	E3
Overhill Ct. Mang	51	E3
Overhill Rd. Mang	51	E3
Overnhill Ct. Mang	51	E3
Overnhurst Ct. Mang	51	E3
Overton Rd. Bris	49	F1
Owen Dr. Wrax	61	D2
Owen Gr. Bris	49	D3
Owen St. Bris	64	A4
Owls Head Rd. Kingsw	65	F3
Oxbarton. St Gif	36	C3
Oxen Leaze. St Gif	24	C1
Oxford Pl	102	B1
Oxford Pl. Bris	50	A1
Oxford Pl. Bris	62	C3
Oxford Pl. W-S-M	104	B4
Oxford St. Bris	63	E4
Oxford St. Bris	63	F2
Oxford St. Bris	63	A3
Oxford St. Bris	63	D3
Oxford St. Bris	64	B4
Oxford St. W-S-M	104	B4
Oxhouse La. Win	94	B3
Oxhouse La. Wrax	61	D3
Oxlease. Bris	79	E2
Oxleaze La. Bris	78	C2
Ozleworth. Kingsw	66	A4
Pack Horse La. Sosto	119	D4
Paddock Cl. St Gif	24	B1
Paddock Gdn. Bris	79	F2
Paddock Gdns. Alve	15	D3
Paddock The. Ban	107	D2
Paddock The. Cleve	57	E1
Paddock The. Portis	45	C2
Paddock Woods. Bath	102	B1
Paddocks The. Bath	102	A1
Paddocks The. Chur	108	B2
Paddocks The. Thorn	8	B1
Paddocks The. W-S-M	104	B1
Padfield Cl. Bath	101	D3
Padleigh Hill. Bath	101	D1
Padmore Ct. Bris	64	B4
Padstow Rd. Bris	79	F4
Pagans Hill. Ch Mag	95	E1
Pagans Hill. Ch St	95	E1
Page Rd. Kingsw	51	E2
Page's Ct. Yatt	91	E4
Pages Mead. Avon	47	E4
Painswick Ave. St Gif	36	A4
Painswick Dr. Yate	27	F1
Palace Yd Mews. Bath	101	F3
Palmdale Cl. Kingsw	66	A2
Palmer Row. W-S-M	104	C4
Palmer St. W-S-M	104	C4
Palmers Cl. Kingsw	66	A3
Palmers Leaze. St Gif	37	D3
Palmers Way. Lock	105	E1
Palmerston Rd. Bris	49	E2
Palmerston St. Bris	63	E2
Palmyra Rd. Bris	63	D1
Par The. Bath	101	D3
Parade The. Bris	23	F1
Parade The. Bris	47	F3
Parade The. Ch Sod	28	A1
Paradise Row. Pens	98	A3
Paragon Rd. W-S-M	87	E1
Paragon The. Bris	62	C3
Park Ave. Bath	101	F3
Park Ave. Bris	50	B2
Park Ave. Bris	63	F2
Park Ave. Bris	64	C4
Park Ave. Fr Cot	38	A4
Park Ave. St Gif	24	A1
Park Ave. Wint	37	F4
Park Ave. Yatt	74	A1
Park Batch. Blag	110	C2
Park Cl. Keyn	81	E3
Park Cl. Kingsw	65	F4
Park Cl. Kingsw	66	A3
Park Cres. Bris	37	E1
Park Cres. Bris	64	B4
Park Cres. Kingsw	66	A3
Park Farm Ct. Kingsw	65	F2
Park Gdns. Bath	101	E4
Park Gr. Bris	49	E3
Park Hill. Bris	47	F3
Park La. Bath	101	E4
Park La. Blag	110	C2
Park La. Bris	63	E4
Park La. Faulk	134	A1
Park La. Fr Cot	38	A3
Park La. N Nib	5	F4
Park Pl. Bath	101	F4
Park Pl. Bris	50	C2
Park Pl. Bris	63	D4
Park Pl. W-S-M	104	B4
Park Rd. Bath	101	D4
Park Rd. Bris	36	A1
Park Rd. Bris	47	F3
Park Rd. Bris	50	B3
Park Rd. Bris	63	D3
Park Rd. Cleve	57	E2
Park Rd. Cong	91	F2
Park Rd. Crom	10	A2
Park Rd. Keyn	81	F2
Park Rd. Kingsw	65	E4
Park Rd. Kingsw	66	A3
Park Rd. Mang	51	F3

Park Rd. Paul 131 E3
Park Rd. Thorn 8 A1
Park Row. Bris 63 E4
Park Row. Fr Cot 38 A4
Park St Ave. Bris 63 E4
Park St Mews. Bath 101 F4
Park St. Bath 101 F4
Park St. Bris 63 E4
Park St. Bris 64 A2
Park St. Bris 64 C4
Park St. H Up 20 A1
Park St. Ir Act 26 B2
Park The. Bitt 66 A1
Park The. Bris 37 D1
Park The. Keyn 81 F3
Park The. Kingsw 65 F4
Park The. St Gif 24 B2
Park The. Yatt 74 A1
Park View Ave. Thorn 8 B1
Park View Terr. Bris 64 C4
Park View. Kingsw 65 F4
Park View. Paul 131 E3
Park Way. Kingsw 66 A3
Park Way. Mid No 138 A4
Park Wood Cl. Bris 79 F2
Parker St. Bris 63 D2
Parkers Ave. Wick 67 E4
Parkers Barton. Bris 64 A3
Parkers Cl. Bris 35 E2
Parkfield Ave. Bris 64 B4
Parkfield Gdns. Bi Sut 113 E2
Parkfield Rd. Puck 53 D3
Parkhouse La. Keyn 81 E1
Parkhurst Ave. Bris 51 D2
Parkhurst Rd. W-S-M 105 D4
Parkland Way. Thorn 8 B2
Parklands Ave. W-S-M 88 C2
Parklands Rd. Bris 62 C2
Parklands. Kingsw 65 F4
Parklands. Paul 115 E1
Parkside Ave. Wint 37 F3
Parkside Gdns. Bris 50 A2
Parkstone Ave. Bris 49 F3
Parkwall Cres. Kingsw 66 A2
Parkwall Rd. Kingsw 66 A3
Parkway La. Tims 116 B2
Parkway. Tims 116 C1
Parliament St. Bris 64 A2
Parnall Cres. Yate 27 E2
Parnall Rd. Bris 51 D2
Parry Cl. Bath 101 D2
Parry's Cl. Bris 48 C3
Parry's La. Bris 48 C3
Parslow Barton. Bris 65 D4
Parson St. Bris 63 E1
Parsonage La. Win 94 C3
Parsonage La. Bath 101 F3
Parsonage La. Ched 125 F1
Parsonage La. Chil 137 E2
Parsonage La. Pens 97 E3
Parsonage La. Win 94 C3
Parsonage Rd. Lo Ash 62 B1
Parsons Ave. St Gif 36 C3
Parsons Gn. Cleve 73 E4
Parsons Green. W-S-M 89 D2
Parsons Mead. Back 76 C4
Parsons Paddock. Bris 80 A4
Parsons Way. Wins 124 B3
Partis College. Bath 101 D4
Partis Way. Bath 101 D4
Partition St. Bris 63 E3
Partridge. W-S-M 88 C1
Partridge Cl. Yate 27 F3
Partridge Rd. Puck 53 E2
Passage Leaze. Bris 47 E3
Passage Rd. Bris 35 D1
Passage Rd. Bris 35 D2
Passage Rd. Bris 35 D3
Passage St. Bris 63 F3
Pastures The. Westw 120 C2
Patch Croft. Cleve 73 E4
Patch Elm La. Wickw 26 C4
Patch La. Wickw 27 D4
Patchway Trading Est. Bris . 35 F4
Paul St. Bris 63 E4
Paul's Cswy. Cong 91 E2
Paulman Gdns. Lo Ash 77 F4
Paulmont Rise. Clut 114 C1
Paulto' Hill. Paul 132 A4
Paulton Dr. Bris 49 E2
Paulton La. Tims 132 B4
Paulton Rd. Mid No 131 F1
Paulton Rd. Paul 131 D4
Paulton Rd. Paul 131 E3
Paultow Ave. Bris 63 F2
Paultow Rd. Bris 63 F2
Paulwood Rd. Clut 114 C1
Pavey Cl. Bris 79 E2
Pavey Rd. Bris 79 E2
Pawlett Rd. Bris 79 E2
Pawlett Wlk. Bris 79 E2
Pawlett. W-S-M 105 D1
Paybridge Rd. Bris 78 C2
Payne Dr. Bris 64 A4
Payne Rd. Lock 105 E1
Peach Rd. Mang 51 F3
Peacock La. Kingsw 65 E4

Pear Tree Hey. Yate 27 F3
Pear Tree Rd. St Gif 24 B2
Pearces Hill. Bris 51 D4
Pearl St. Bris 63 D2
Pearsall Rd. Kingsw 65 F1
Pearse Cl. W-S-M 89 D3
Peart Cl. Bris 78 C3
Peart Dr. Bris 78 C2
Peartree La. Bris 65 D3
Peartree La. Kingsw 51 F1
Pedder Rd. Cleve 57 E1
Peel St. Bris 63 F4
Pegasus Rd. Bris 35 E4
Pelican Cl. W-S-M 105 F4
Pemberton Ct. Bris 51 E3
Pembery Rd. Bris 63 D2
Pembroke Ave. Bris 47 F3
Pembroke Gr. Bris 63 D4
Pembroke Pl. Bris 63 D3
Pembroke Rd. Bris 47 F3
Pembroke Rd. Bris 63 D2
Pembroke Rd. Bris 63 D4
Pembroke Rd. Kingsw 51 F1
Pembroke Rd. Portis 44 C2
Pembroke Rd. W-S-M 104 C2
Pembroke St. Bris 63 F4
Pembroke Vale. Bris 63 D4
Pen Park Rd. Bris 35 E1
Penard Way. Kingsw 65 F4
Penarth Dr. W-S-M 105 D4
Pendennis Ave. Mang 51 E2
Pendennis Pk. Bris 64 B1
Pendennis Rd. Mang 51 E2
Pendlesham Gdns. W-S-M . 88 A1
Pendock Cl. Kingsw 66 B1
Pendock Rd. Bris 51 E3
Pendock Rd. Wint 37 F3
Penfield Rd. Bris 50 A1
Penlea Ct. Bris 47 E4
Penn Gdns. Bath 101 D4
Penn Hill Rd. Bath 84 A1
Penn Lea Rd. Bath 84 A1
Penn Lea Rd. Bath 101 D4
Penn St. Bris 63 F4
Penn Way. Axb 125 E1
Pennard Ct. Bris 80 A3
Pennard Green. Bath 101 D3
Pennard. W-S-M 105 D1
Penngrove. Kingsw 66 A2
Pennine Gdns. W-S-M 88 A1
Pennine Rd. Kingsw 66 B2
Pennlea. Bris 79 E4
Penns The. Cleve 57 F1
Pennycress. W-S-M 105 E4
Pennyquick View. Bath 100 C3
Pennyquick. Cor 100 B3
Pennyroyal Gr. Bris 50 C2
Pennywell Rd. Bris 64 A4
Penpole Ave. Bris 47 F3
Penpole Cl. Bris 47 E4
Penpole La. Bris 47 F4
Penpole Pl. Bris 47 F3
Penrice Cl. W-S-M 88 B1
Penrith Gdns. Bris 49 E4
Penrose. Bris 79 F4
Pensfield Park. Bris 35 E2
Pensford Ct. Bris 80 B3
Pensford Hill. Pens 97 E3
Pensford La. Pens 97 D1
Pensford Old Rd. Pens 97 F2
Pentagon The. Bris 48 A3
Pentire Ave. Bris 79 D4
Pentland Ave. Thorn 15 F4
Peppershells La. Co Dan ... 98 B3
Pepys Cl. Keyn 82 B1
Pera Pl. Bath 102 A4
Percival Rd. Bris 62 C4
Percy St. Bris 63 E2
Peregrine Cl. W-S-M 88 C1
Perrin Cl. Clut 130 C4
Perrings The. Nail 75 F4
Perrinpit Rd. Fr Cot 25 F1
Perrott Rd. Kingsw 52 A1
Perry Cl. Wint 37 E3
Perry Rd. Bris 63 E3
Perry St. Bris 64 A4
Perrycroft Ave. Bris 79 D3
Perrycroft Rd. Bris 79 D3
Perrymans Cl. Bris 51 D3
Perrymead. Bath 102 A2
Perrymead. W-S-M 89 D3
Perrys Lea. St Gif 24 B1
Pesley Cl. Bris 79 D2
Peter's Terr. Bris 64 A4
Petercole Dr. Bris 79 D3
Peterside. Clut 130 C4
Peterson Sq. Bris 79 E2
Petersway Gdns. Bris 65 D3
Petherton Cl. Kingsw 65 F4
Petherton Gdns. Bris 80 A4
Petherton Rd. Bris 80 A4
Peto Gr. Westw 120 C2
Pettigrove Gdns. Kingsw ... 65 F4
Pettigrove Rd. Kingsw 65 F3
Pevensey Wlk. Bris 79 E4
Peverell Cl. Bris 34 C2
Peverell Dr. Bris 34 C2

Philadelphia Ct. Bris 63 F4
Philip St. Bris 63 E2
Philip St. Bris 64 A3
Philippa Cl. Bris 80 A4
Phillips Rd. W-S-M 105 D3
Phillis Hill. Paul 131 F2
Phippen St. Bris 63 F3
Phipps St. Bris 63 D2
Phoenix Gr. Bris 49 E3
Piccadilly Pl. Bath 102 A4
Pickedmoor La. O-on-S 7 E3
Pickwick Rd. Bath 85 D1
Picton La. Bris 49 F1
Picton St. Bris 49 F1
Pier Rd. Portis 45 F4
Pierrepont Pl. Bath 102 A3
Pierrepont St. Bath 102 A3
Pigeon La. Wring 93 F1
Pigott Ave. Bris 79 D2
Pilgrims Way. Avon 47 E4
Pilgrims Way. Ch St 112 B4
Pilgrims Way. Mang 51 E4
Pilgrims Way. W-S-M 88 C2
Pilgrims Wharf. Bris 64 C4
Pilkington Cl. Bris 36 B1
Pill Rd. Ab Lei 47 F1
Pill St. E in G 47 E2
Pill Way. Cleve 57 D1
Pillingers Rd. Kingsw 65 E4
Pilning St. Piln 23 D4
Pimm's La. W-S-M 88 A1
Pinchay La. Win 95 D2
Pinckney Green. Mon Far . 103 F3
Pincots La. Wickw 18 A2
Pine Cl. Thorn 8 B1
Pine Cl. W-S-M 88 B1
Pine Ct. Ch Mag 96 A2
Pine Ct. Keyn 81 E2
Pine Ct. Rad 133 D1
Pine Gr. Bris 36 A1
Pine Grove Pl. Bris 49 E2
Pine Hill. W-S-M 88 B1
Pine Lea. Blea 122 A4
Pine Rd. Bris 35 D2
Pine Ridge Cl. Bris 48 B2
Pine Wlk. Rad 132 C1
Pinecroft. Bris 79 F4
Pinecroft. Portis 44 C3
Pines Cl. Chil 137 D3
Pines La. Olve 14 B2
Pines Rd. Kingsw 66 B1
Pines Way. Bath 101 F3
Pines Way. Rad 133 D1
Pinewood Ave. Mid No 131 F1
Pinewood Cl. Bris 49 D4
Pinewood Gr. Mid No 131 F1
Pinewood Rd. Mid No 131 F1
Pinewood Way. Col 70 C4
Pinewood. Kingsw 51 F1
Pinhay Rd. Bris 79 D3
Pinkhams Twist. Bris 80 A3
Pioneer Ave. Bath 101 F1
Pipe La. Bris 63 E3
Pipe La. Bris 63 F3
Pipehouse La. Hi Cha 120 A2
Pipehouse La. Hin Cha 119 F2
Piper Rd. Yate 27 F2
Pippin Cl. P St J 133 E4
Pippin Ct. Kingsw 65 F2
Pit La. Back 76 A2
Pit La. Win 111 F3
Pit Rd. Mid No 132 A1
Pitch And Pay La. Bris 48 C2
Pitch And Pay Park. Bris ... 48 C2
Pitch La. Bris 49 E1
Pitchcombe Gdns. Bris 48 B4
Pitchcombe. Yate 39 E4
Pitcot La. Hol 138 A1
Pithay Ct. Bris 63 E4
Pithay The. Bris 63 E4
Pithay The. Paul 131 F3
Pitman Ct. Bath 85 E1
Pitman Rd. W-S-M 104 C3
Pitt Rd. Bris 49 F3
Pittville Cl. Thorn 8 B2
Pitway Cl. Paul 130 C2
Pitway La. Paul 130 B2
Pixash Bsns Centre. Keyn . 82 A3
Pixash La. Keyn 82 A3
Pizey Ave. Cleve 57 D1
Pizey Cl. Cleve 57 D1
Plain The. N St P 135 F2
Plain The. Thorn 8 A1
Players Cl. St Gif 37 D2
Playford Gdns. Bris 47 F4
Pleasant Pl. Bathf 86 B1
Pleasant Rd. Mang 51 E3
Pleshey Cl. W-S-M 88 A1
Ploughed Paddock. Nail ... 59 E1
Plover Cl. W-S-M 88 C1
Plover Cl. Yate 27 E1
Plovers Rise. Mid No 133 D2
Plumbers Hill. Bris 65 F4
Plumpton Cl. Cleve 57 F1
Plumpton Ct. Mang 51 F1
Plumptre Cl. Paul 131 F3
Plumptre Rd. Paul 131 F3

Plumtree Cl. Wins 108 A1
Plunder St. Brock 92 A4
Podium The. Bath 102 A3
Poets Cnr. Rad 132 B1
Poets' Cl. Bris 64 B4
Polden Cl. Nail 59 F1
Polden Rd. Portis 45 D3
Polden Rd. W-S-M 104 C4
Police Station Hill. Puck ... 53 D2
Polly Barnes Cl. Kingsw ... 65 D3
Polly Barnes Hill. Kingsw . 65 D3
Polygon Rd. Bris 63 D3
Polygon The. Bris 62 C3
Pomfret House. Bris 79 E2
Pomfrett Gdns. Bris 80 C3
Pomphrey Hill. Mang 52 A2
Ponsford Rd. Bris 80 A4
Ponting Cl. Bris 51 D1
Pool Cl. Win 95 D1
Pool Rd. Kingsw 51 F2
Poole St. Avon 47 D4
Poolemead Rd. Bath 100 C3
Poor Hill. Farm 115 F3
Pope's Wlk. Bath 102 A2
Poplar Ave. Bris 48 B3
Poplar Cl. Bath 101 E2
Poplar Cl. Kingsw 66 B3
Poplar Dr. Puck 53 D3
Poplar La. Wickw 18 A2
Poplar Pl. Bris 51 D2
Poplar Pl. W-S-M 104 C4
Poplar Rd. Bris 50 C1
Poplar Rd. Bris 65 D3
Poplar Rd. Bris 78 C4
Poplar Rd. Kingsw 66 B3
Poplar Way. Col 70 C4
Poplar Wlk. Lock 105 F3
Poplars The. E in G 47 D2
Poplars The. W-S-M 89 D1
Popular Terr. Kingsw 65 F4
Porlock Cl. Cleve 57 F1
Porlock Rd. W-S-M 104 C1
Porlock Gdns. Nail 59 F1
Porlock Rd. Bath 102 A1
Porlock Rd. Bris 63 E2
Port Elizabeth House. Bris . 35 D1
Port View. E in G 47 E3
Portbury Comm. Portis 45 F2
Portbury Gr. Bris 47 E3
Portbury Hundred The.
    Portb 46 B2
Portbury La. Wrax 60 C3
Portbury Way. Portb 46 C3
Portbury Wlk. Bris 47 E3
Portishead Rd. W-S-M 89 D2
Portishead Way. Bris 62 C2
Portland Cl. Nail 59 E1
Portland Ct. Bris 63 D3
Portland Dr. Portis 45 F2
Portland Pl. Bath 101 F4
Portland Pl. Kingsw 51 E2
Portland Sq. Bris 63 F4
Portland St. Bris 62 C4
Portland St. Bris 63 E4
Portland St. Kingsw 51 E2
Portmeade Dro. Axb 125 E1
Portmeirion Cl. Bris 80 A3
Portview Rd. Avon 47 D4
Portwall La E. Bris 63 F3
Portwall La. Bris 63 F3
Portway La. Ch Sod 29 D1
Portway. Bris 48 B2
Post Office La. Back 76 C4
Post Office La. Blag' 110 B2
Poston Way. Winsl 120 C4
Pottery Cl. W-S-M 105 D3
Potts Cl. Bathe 85 F2
Pound Dr. Bris 50 C3
Pound La. Bris 50 C3
Pound La. Nail 59 E2
Pound Mead. Win 94 B4
Pound Rd. Kingsw 51 F1
Pound The. Alm 24 A3
Pound The. O-on-S 7 D1
Pound The. Wring 93 E2
Pountney Dr. Bris 64 A4
Pow's Hill. Paul 132 B3
Pow's Orch. Mid No 132 A1
Pow's Rd. Kingsw 65 E4
Powis Cl. W-S-M 88 B1
Powlett Rd. Bath 102 A4
Poyntz Ct. Kingsw 65 F2
Poyntz Rd. Bris 79 F4
Pratten's La. Mang 51 E2
Preanes Green. W-S-M 89 D1
Preddy's La. Bris 65 D3
Prescot Cl. W-S-M 88 A1
Prescott. Yate 39 E4
Press Moor Dr. Kingsw 65 F2
Prestbury. Yate 39 E4
Preston Wlk. Bris 64 A1
Prestwick Cl. Bris 64 B1
Pretoria Rd. Bris 35 F4
Prewett St. Bris 63 F3
Priddy Cl. Bath 101 D3
Priddy Ct. Bris 80 A3

Priddy Dr Bris 80 A3
Priests Way. W-S-M 88 B1
Priestwood Cl. Bris 35 D2
Primrose Cl. Bris 65 E4
Primrose Cl. St Gif 24 B1
Primrose Dr. Thorn 8 B1
Primrose Hill. Bath 84 B1
Primrose La. Bris 51 E1
Primrose La. Mid No 132 A1
Primrose Terr. Bris 51 E1
Prince St. Bris 63 E3
Prince's Pl. Bris 49 F2
Prince's St. Bris 63 F4
Prince's St. Cleve 57 E2
Prince's St. Mid No 132 C3
Princes Ct. Kingsw 65 F2
Princes St. Bath 101 F3
Princes' La. Bris 62 C3
Princess Cl. Keyn 81 F2
Princess Gdns. Bris 50 B3
Princess Row. Bris 63 E4
Princess St. Bris 63 F2
Princess St. Bris 64 A4
Princess Victoria St. Bris .. 62 C3
Priors Hill. Tims 116 A1
Priors Lea. Yate 27 F1
Priory Ave. Bris 49 D4
Priory Cl. Bath 102 A1
Priory Cl. Mid No 132 A1
Priory Court Rd. Bris 49 D4
Priory Ct. Kingsw 65 E2
Priory Dene. Bris 49 D4
Priory Gdns. Bris 47 E4
Priory Gdns. Bris 49 F4
Priory Gdns. E in G 47 D2
Priory Park Rd. Bath 102 A1
Priory Rd. Bris 47 E3
Priory Rd. Bris 64 A1
Priory Rd. E in G 47 D2
Priory Rd. Keyn 81 F4
Priory Rd. Portb 46 B2
Priory Rd. W-S-M 105 D4
Priory Wlk. Portb 46 B2
Priston Cl. W-S-M 89 D3
Priston La. Pris 117 D3
Priston Rd. Engl 117 E3
Priston Rd. Pris 117 E3
Pritchard St. Bris 63 F4
Probyn Cl. Bris 51 D4
Proctor Cl. Bris 64 B1
Prospect Ave. Bris 51 D1
Prospect Cl. Alm 22 C1
Prospect Cl. Alm 23 D1
Prospect Cl. Fr Cot 37 F4
Prospect Cl. Wint 37 F2
Prospect Cres. Kingsw 51 F1
Prospect Gdns. Bathe 85 F3
Prospect La. Fr Cot 37 F4
Prospect Pl. Bath 84 B1
Prospect Pl. Bathf 86 B1
Prospect Pl. Bris 63 E2
Prospect Pl. Bris 64 B4
Prospect Pl. W-S-M 104 C4
Prospect Rd. Bath 102 B2
Prospect Rd. Piln 22 A3
Providence La. Lo Ash 61 F1
Providence Pl. Bris 63 F3
Providence St. Bris 63 E2
Prowse's La. Axb 125 D1
Prudham St. Bris 50 B1
Publow La. Pens 97 F3
Pucklechurch Trading Est.
    Puck 53 D3
Pudding Pie Cl. Chur 109 D3
Pudding Pie La. Chur 109 D3
Puffin Cl. W-S-M 105 F4
Pullen's Green. Thorn 8 A1
Pullin Ct. Kingsw 66 B3
Pulteney Ave. Bath 102 A3
Pulteney Bridge. Bath 102 A3
Pulteney Gdns. Bath 102 A3
Pulteney Gr. Bath 102 A3
Pulteney Mews. Bath 102 A4
Pulteney Rd. Bath 102 A3
Pump La. Bathf 86 A1
Pump La. Bris 63 F3
Pump La. Olve 14 B2
Pump La. Wring 93 E1
Pump Sq. E in G 47 E3
Purcell Wlk. Bris 79 E4
Purdey Rd. Bris 50 C2
Purdue Cl. W-S-M 89 D2
Purn La. W-S-M 122 A4
Purn Rd. W-S-M 121 F4
Purn Way. Blea 122 A4
Purplewent Dr. Bath 84 B1
Pursey Dr. St Gif 36 C3
Purton Cl. Kingsw 65 F3
Purton Rd. Bris 49 E1
Purving Row La. Lymp 122 B1
Purving Row. Lymp 122 B1
Puttingthorpe Dr. W-S-M . 105 E4
Puxley Cl. Bris 80 C3
Puxton La. Ban 90 B2
Puxton La. Pux 90 B2
Puxton Rd. Ban 90 B1
Puxton Rd. Pux 90 B1

Pye Cnr. Chur 108 B2
Pye Croft. St Gif 24 C2
Pyecroft Ave. Bris 49 E4
Pylewell La. Ship 108 B1
Pylle Hill Cres. Bris 63 F2
Pyne Point. Cleve 57 E2
Pynne Cl. Bris 80 C3
Pynne Rd. Bris 80 C3
Pyracantha Wlk. Bris 80 A3

Quadrangle The. West 39 E2
Quadrant E. Bris 51 E2
Quadrant The. Bris 49 D2
Quadrant The. St Gif 24 A2
Quadrant W. Bris 51 E2
Quadrant. St Gif 24 A2
Quaker La. Thorn 8 A1
Quaker's Cl. Mang 51 E4
Quaker's Rd. Mang 51 F4
Quantock Cl. Kingsw 66 B3
Quantock Rd. Bris 63 E2
Quantock Rd. Portis 45 D3
Quantock Rd. W-S-M 104 C3
Quantocks. Bath 102 A1
Quarries The. Alm 24 B3
Quarrington Rd. Bris 49 F3
Quarry Barton. Wint 37 E2
Quarry Cl. Bath 101 F1
Quarry Hay. Ch St 112 B4
Quarry Head. Alve 14 C3
Quarry Rd. Alve 14 C3
Quarry Rd. Wint 37 F2
Quarry Rd. Bath 102 B3
Quarry Rd. Bris 51 E2
Quarry Rd. Ch Sod 28 A1
Quarry Rd. Kingsw 65 E3
Quarry Rd. Wins 108 A1
Quarry Stps. Bris 49 D1
Quarry Way. Bris 50 C3
Quarry Way. Nail 59 E1
Quay St. Bris 63 E4
Quayside. Bris 64 C3
Quedgeley. Yate 39 E4
Queen Ann Rd. Bris 64 A3
Queen Charlotte St. Bris ... 63 E3
Queen Charlton La. Co Dan 80 C1
Queen Charlton La. Whit ... 80 C1
Queen Sq Ave. Bris 63 E3
Queen Sq Pl. Bath 101 F4
Queen Sq. Bath 101 F4
Queen Sq. Bris 63 E3
Queen Sq. Keyn 82 C2
Queen St. Avon 33 D1
Queen St. Bath 101 F3
Queen St. Bris 50 B2
Queen St. Bris 63 F4
Queen St. Bris 65 D4
Queen Victoria Rd. Bris 49 D2
Queen Victoria St. Bris 64 A3
Queen's Ave. Bris 63 D4
Queen's Ave. Portis 45 E3
Queen's Dr. Bath 102 A1
Queen's Dr. Bris 49 E3
Queen's Par Pl. Bath 101 F4
Queen's Par. Bris 63 E3
Queen's Rd. Bris 49 F3
Queen's Rd. Bris 63 D4
Queen's Rd. Bris 64 C4
Queen's Rd. Cleve 78 C2
Queen's Rd. Cleve 57 E2
Queen's Rd. Kingsw 66 A2
Queen's Rd. Nail 59 E1
Queen's Rd. Portis 44 C2
Queen's Rd. Puck 53 D3
Queen's Rd. Rad 133 D1
Queen's Rd. W-S-M 87 E1
Queen's Way. Portis 44 C2
Queen's Way. W-S-M 89 D2
Queens Down Gdns. Bris ... 64 A1
Queens Dr. Kingsw 65 D2
Queens Par. Bath 101 F4
Queens Rd. Ban 107 D2
Queens Rd. Bris 64 B1
Queens Rd. Keyn 81 E2
Queens Wlk. Thorn 8 A2
Queensdale Cres. Bris 64 A1
Queenshill Rd. Bris 64 A1
Queensholm Ave. Mang 37 F1
Queensholm Cl. Mang 37 F1
Queensholm Dr. Mang 37 F1
Queensway. St Gif 36 B3
Queenwood Ave. Bath 85 D1
Quickthorn Cl. Bris 80 A3
Quiet St. Bath 101 F3
Quilter Gr. Bris 79 E4

Raby Mews. Bath 102 A4
Rackfield Pl. Bath 101 D3
Rackham Cl. Bris 50 A3
Rackhay. Bris 63 E3
Rackley La. Co Bi 124 A1
Rackvernal Rd. Mid No ... 132 A1
Radford Hill. Paul 132 B4
Radford Hill. Tims 116 B1
Radley Rd. Bris 51 D2
Radnor Rd. Bris 49 D3
Radnor Rd. Bris 49 F3

Radstock Rd. Mid No 132 B1
Raeburn Rd. Bris 65 D3
Rag Hill. P St J 133 E3
Rag La. Wickw 17 E3
Raglan Cl. Chil 137 E2
Raglan La. Bris 65 D4
Raglan La. Win 94 C4
Raglan Pl. Bris 49 E2
Raglan Pl. Thorn 15 D4
Raglan Pl. W-S-M 87 E1
Raglan Rd. Bris 49 E2
Raglan Wlk. Keyn 81 E2
Ragland La. Bath 85 D1
Ragland St. Bath 85 D1
Railton Jones Cl. St Gif 36 C2
Railway Pl. Bath 102 A3
Railway St. Bath 102 A3
Railway Terr. Bris 51 E2
Railway View Pl. Mid No .. 132 A1
Rainham Ct. W-S-M 87 E1
Rains Batch. Priddy 126 C3
Raleigh Cl. Keyn 82 B1
Raleigh Rd. Bris 63 D2
Raleigh Rise. Portis 45 D3
Ralph Allen Dr. Bath 102 B2
Ralph Rd. Bris 49 F2
Ram Hill. West 38 C3
Ramscombe La. Bathe 85 F3
Ramsey Cl. W-S-M 88 C2
Ramsey Rd. Bris 49 F4
Ranchways. Portis 44 C2
Randall Cl. Kingsw 51 F1
Randall Rd. Bris 63 D3
Randolph Ave. Bris 79 D3
Randolph Ave. Yate 27 E3
Randolph Cl. Bris 79 D3
Rangers Wlk. Kingsw 65 E2
Rankers La. Co Dan 98 B3
Rannoch Rd. Bris 35 F1
Ranscombe Ave. W-S-M ... 88 B1
Ransford. Cleve 57 D1
Raphael Ct. Bris 63 F3
Ratcliffe Cl. St Gif 36 C3
Rathbone Cl. Fr Cot 38 B3
Raven Cl. W-S-M 88 C1
Ravendale Dr. Kingsw 66 A1
Ravenglass Cres. Bris 35 E1
Ravenhead Dr. Bris 80 A4
Ravenhill Ave. Bris 63 F1
Ravenhill Rd. Bris 63 F2
Ravens Wood. Kingsw 66 A2
Ravenscourt Rd. Bris 36 A4
Ravenscourt Rd. Bris 49 E1
Rawlins Ave. W-S-M 89 D3
Rayens Cl. Lo Ash 61 F1
Rayens Cross Rd. Lo Ash .. 61 F1
Rayleigh Rd. Bris 48 C4
Raymend Rd. Bris 63 F2
Raymend Wlk. Bris 63 F1
Raymill. Bris 65 D1
Raymore Rise. Lo Ash 61 F1
Raynes Rd. Bris 63 D2
Reach Hill La. Ch St 112 B3
Rector's Way. W-S-M 104 C3
Rectory Cl. Farm 116 A3
Rectory Cl. Yate 27 F2
Rectory Dr. Yatt 91 E4
Rectory La. Bris 36 A2
Rectory La. Co Mar 128 A3
Rectory La. Crom 17 D4
Rectory La. Tims 116 B1
Rectory Rd. E in G 47 D2
Rectory Rd. Fr Cot 38 A4
Rectory Way. Lymp 121 F1
Rectory Way. Yatt 91 E4
Red Hill. Tims 116 C1
Red Hill. Wring 93 E1
Red House La. Alm 24 A2
Red House La. Bris 48 C3
Red Rd. Berr 121 D1
Redacre. Wring 93 E2
Redcatch Rd. Bris 63 F1
Redcliff Backs. Bris 63 F3
Redcliff Hill. Bris 63 F3
Redcliff Mead La. Bris 63 F3
Redcliff St. Bris 63 F3
Redcliffe Cl. Portis 44 C2
Redcliffe Par E. Bris 63 F3
Redcliffe Par W. Bris 63 E3
Redcliffe Way. Bris 63 F3
Redcroft. Wring 93 E2
Redcross La. Bris 63 F4
Redcross St. Bris 63 F4
Redding Pit La. Win 94 C2
Reddings The. Co Mar 128 A4
Reddings The. Kingsw 51 F1
Redfield Gr. Mid No 138 A4
Redfield Hill. Bitt 66 C2
Redfield Rd. Bris 36 A4
Redfield Rd. Mid No 132 A1
Redford Cres. Bris 78 C2
Redford Wlk. Bris 78 C2
Redham La. Piln 23 D4
Redhill Cl. Bris 50 C2
Redhill Dr. Bris 50 C2
Redhill La. Aust 13 F3
Redland Ave. E in G 46 C3

Redland Court Rd. Bris 49 E1
Redland Gr. Bris 49 E1
Redland Green Rd. Bris 49 E2
Redland Hill. Bris 49 D1
Redland Park. Bath 100 C3
Redland Park. Bris 49 D1
Redland Rd. Bris 49 D1
Redland Terr. Bris 49 D1
Redlands Terr. Mid No ... 137 F4
Redlynch La. Co Dan 81 E1
Redshard La. Chur 109 D4
Redshelf Wlk. Bris 35 E2
Redwick Cl. Bris 34 B1
Redwick Gdns. Piln 22 B4
Redwick Rd. Piln 22 B4
Redwing Dr. W-S-M 88 C1
Redwood Cl. Kingsw 66 A2
Redwood Cl. Nail 60 A1
Redwood Cl. Rod 138 C4
Redwood La. Lo Ash 77 E4
Redwoods The. Keyn 81 E3
Reed Ct. Kingsw 65 F2
Reed's Row. Hill 19 E4
Reedley Rd. Bris 48 C3
Reedling Cl. Bris 50 C3
Regency Dr. Bris 65 D1
Regent Rd. Bris 63 E2
Regent St. Kingsw 65 E4
Regent St. W-S-M 104 B4
Regents Cl. Thorn 8 A1
Regents St. Bris 63 D4
Regil La. Win 94 C2
Regil La. Win 95 D3
Remenham Dr. Bris 49 D3
Remenham Park. Bris 49 D3
Rendcomb Cl. W-S-M 88 A1
Rene Rd. Bris 50 A1
Repton Rd. Bris 64 B2
Retort Rd. Avon 33 E2
Retreat The. Faulk 133 F2
Reubens Ct. W-S-M 88 C2
Reynold's Wlk. Bris 50 A4
Reynolds Cl. Keyn 82 A3
Rhode Cl. Keyn 82 A2
Rhodyate Hill. Brock 92 A4
Rhodyate Hill. Cong 91 F3
Rhodyate La. Brock 92 A4
Rhodyate The. Ban 107 E1
Rhodyate. Blag 110 B1
Rhyne Terr. W-S-M 104 B1
Ribblesdale. Thorn 15 E4
Richards Cl. W-S-M 89 D2
Richeson Cl. Bris 34 C1
Richeson Wlk. Bris 34 C1
Richmond Ave. Bris 49 F1
Richmond Ave. St Gif 36 C3
Richmond Cl. Bath 84 C1
Richmond Cl. Keyn 81 E2
Richmond Cl. Portis 45 F3
Richmond Dale. Bris 49 D1
Richmond Green. Nail 59 F1
Richmond Hill Ave. Bris ... 63 D4
Richmond Hill. Bath 84 C1
Richmond Hill. Bris 63 D4
Richmond Hts. Bath 84 C1
Richmond La. Bath 84 C1
Richmond La. Bris 63 D4
Richmond Park Rd. Bris ... 63 D4
Richmond Pl. Bath 84 C1
Richmond Rd. Bath 84 C1
Richmond Rd. Bris 49 F1
Richmond Rd. Bris 64 C4
Richmond Rd. Mang 52 A3
Richmond St. Bris 63 F2
Richmond St. W-S-M 104 B4
Richmond Terr. Avon 33 D1
Richmond Terr. Bris 63 D4
Ricketts La. W-S-M 89 D1
Rickford La. Blag 110 A2
Rickford Rd. Nail 59 F1
Rickford Rise. Blag 110 A2
Rickyard Rd. Wring 92 C1
Ride The. Kingsw 52 A1
Ridge Cl. Portis 45 D2
Ridge Cres. E Harp 128 C3
Ridge La. E Harp 128 B3
Ridge The. Bris 47 F4
Ridge The. Fr Cot 38 B4
Ridge The. Yatt 91 D4
Ridge View. Lo Ash 62 A1
Ridgehill. Bris 49 E3
Ridgemeade. Bris 80 A2
Ridgeway Ave. W-S-M ... 104 C3
Ridgeway Cl. E Harp 128 C3
Ridgeway Ct. Bris 35 D1
Ridgeway Gdns. Bris 80 B3
Ridgeway La. Bris 80 B3
Ridgeway Par. Bris 50 C2
Ridgeway Rd. Bris 50 C2
Ridgeway Rd. Lo Ash 62 A1
Ridgeway The. Bris 35 D1
Ridgeway The. W-S-M 88 A1
Ridgeway. Fr Cot 38 B4
Ridgeway. Nail 59 E1
Ridgeway. Yate 27 F1
Riding Barn Hill. Wick 67 D3
Ridingleaze. Bris 34 A1
Ridings Cl. Ch Sod 28 A1

Ridings Rd. Fr Cot 38 B3
Ridings The. Bris 78 C2
Ridings The. Fr Cot 38 B3
Ringspit La. Pens 97 F4
Ringswell Gdns. Bath 85 E1
Ringwell La. N St P 135 F2
Ringwell. N St P 135 F2
Ringwood Cres. Bris 35 E1
Ringwood Rd. Bath 101 E3
Ripley Rd. Bris 51 D1
Ripon Ct. Mang 37 F1
Ripon Rd. Bris 64 C3
Ripple The. Nail 59 E2
Rippleside Rd. Cleve 57 F3
Rippleside. Portis 45 E3
Risdale Rd. Bris 62 C1
Risedale Rd. Wins 125 D4
Rivendell. W-S-M 89 D2
River Rd. Ch Sod 28 A1
River Rd. E in G 46 C4
River St. Bris 63 F4
River Terr. Keyn 81 F3
River View. Bris 50 C3
Riverland Dr. Bris 78 C3
Riverleaze. Bris 48 A3
Riverleaze. Portis 44 C3
Rivers Rd. Bath 85 D1
Rivers St Mews. Bath 101 F4
Rivers St. Bath 101 F4
Riverside Bsns Park. Bris .. 64 B3
Riverside Cl. Bris 47 F3
Riverside Cl. Cleve 57 D1
Riverside Cl. Mid No 137 F4
Riverside Cotts. Kingsw ... 65 D1
Riverside Cotts. Rad 133 D1
Riverside Ct. Bath 101 F3
Riverside Ct. Bris 64 C3
Riverside Gdns. Mid No .. 137 F4
Riverside Mews. Bris 64 C3
Riverside Rd. Bath 101 F3
Riverside Rd. Mid No 137 F4
Riverside Way. Kingsw 65 E2
Riverside Wlk. Mid No ... 137 F4
Riverside. Ban 107 D3
Riverway. Nail 59 F2
Riverwood Rd. Bris 37 E1
Riviera Cres. Kingsw 51 F2
Roach's La. Gr Bad 30 B1
Road Hill. Col 70 B1
Road Two. Avon 22 A2
Roath Rd. Portis 45 E3
Robbins Cl. Marsh 69 F4
Robbins Cl. St Gif 36 C3
Robel Ave. Fr Cot 37 F4
Robert St. Bris 50 A1
Robert St. Bris 64 A4
Robertson Rd. Bris 50 B1
Robin Cl. Rod 138 A4
Robin Cl. W-S-M 105 F4
Robin Dr. Lock 105 F1
Robin Way. Ch Sod 40 A4
Robina Wlk. Bris 80 A4
Robinson Cl. Back 76 A3
Robinson Way. Back 76 A3
Rochester Cl. W-S-M 105 D1
Rochester Rd. Bris 64 C3
Rock Ave. Nail 59 E1
Rock Cl. Bris 64 C1
Rock Hall La. Bath 102 A1
Rock La. Bath 102 A1
Rock La. St Gif 36 C3
Rock Rd. Chil 137 E1
Rock Rd. Mid No 132 A1
Rock Rd. Wick 67 E4
Rock Rd. Yatt 91 E4
Rock St. Thorn 15 D4
Rock The. Bris 64 C2
Rockhill Est. Keyn 81 F2
Rockingham Gr. W-S-M ... 88 A1
Rockland Dr. Bris 50 B3
Rockland Rd. Mang 51 E4
Rockleaze Ave. Bris 48 C2
Rockleaze Rd. Bris 48 C2
Rockliffe Ave. Bath 102 A4
Rockliffe Rd. Bath 102 A4
Rocks La. Ba Gu 77 F1
Rocks La. Win 77 F1
Rockside Ave. Mang 51 F4
Rockside Dr. Bris 49 E3
Rockside Gdns. Fr Cot 38 B4
Rockside Gdns. Mang 51 F4
Rockstowes Way. Bris 35 E2
Rockwell Ave. Bris 34 A1
Rodborough Way. Kingsw . 66 A4
Rodborough. Yate 39 E4
Rodbourne Rd. Bris 49 F3
Rode Hill. Rode 136 C1
Rodford Way. Yate 39 E4
Rodfords Mead. Bris 80 A4
Rodmead Wlk. Bris 79 D2
Rodmoor Rd. Portis 45 E3
Rodney Ave. Bris 65 D4
Rodney Cres. Bris 36 A2
Rodney Pl. Bris 63 D4
Rodney Rd. Back 76 A3
Rodney Rd. Bris 65 D4

Rodney Rd. Keyn 82 C1
Rodney Wlk. Bris 51 D1
Rodney. W-S-M 105 D1
Rodway Hill Rd. Kingsw ... 52 A2
Rodway Hill. Sist 52 A2
Rodway Rd. Bris 36 A4
Rodway Rd. Mang 52 A3
Rodway View. Kingsw 51 F2
Roebuck Cl. W-S-M 89 D2
Roegate Dr. Bris 64 C3
Rogers Cl. Clut 114 C2
Rogers Cl. Kingsw 66 A3
Rokeby Ave. Bris 49 E1
Roman Rd. Bris 50 A1
Roman Rd. Winsc 107 F2
Roman Way. Bris 48 B2
Roman Way. Paul 131 E3
Roman Wlk. Bris 64 B2
Roman Wlk. St Gif 36 C3
Romney Ave. Bris 50 A3
Ronald Rd. Bris 50 C3
Ronayne Wlk. Bris 51 E3
Rook Rd. Keyn 81 F3
Rookery Cl. W-S-M 88 C2
Rookery La. Doyn 53 F2
Rookery La. Piln 23 D3
Rookery Rd. Bris 64 A2
Rookery Way. Bris 79 F2
Rooksbridge Wlk. Bath .. 101 D3
Roper's La. Wring 92 C2
Rose Acre. Bris 35 D2
Rose Gdns. W-S-M 89 D2
Rose Green Cl. Bris 50 C1
Rose Green Rd. Bris 50 C1
Rose Hill. Bath 85 E2
Rose La. Fr Cot 38 B3
Rose Mead. Bris 50 A4
Rose Meare Gdns. Bris 78 C4
Rose Oak La. Fr Cot 38 B4
Rose Rd. Bris 64 C4
Rose St. Bris 63 F3
Rose Wlk. Bris 51 E2
Rosebay Mead. Bris 50 C2
Roseberry Pk. Bris 64 B4
Roseberry Rd. Bath 101 E3
Roseberry Rd. Bris 64 B4
Rosebery Ave. Bris 50 A1
Rosedale Ave. W-S-M ... 105 D4
Rosedale Rd. Bris 51 E2
Roselarge Gdns. Bris 35 D1
Rosemary La. Bris 50 B1
Rosemary La. Hi Cha 120 A2
Rosemont Terr. Bris 63 D3
Rosemount La. Bath 102 A2
Rosery Cl. Bris 49 D4
Rosery The. Bris 51 E2
Rosevear. Bris 64 A4
Roseville Ave. Kingsw 66 A1
Rosewarn Cl. Bath 101 D2
Rosewell Ct. Bath 101 F3
Rosewood Gdns. Alve 14 C3
Rosling Rd. Bris 49 F3
Roslyn Ave. W-S-M 88 B1
Roslyn Rd. Bris 49 E1
Rossall Ave. St Gif 36 B3
Rossall Rd. Bris 64 B2
Rossendale Cl. W-S-M 88 C2
Rossiter Rd. Bath 102 A3
Rossiter's La. Bris 65 D3
Rosslyn Rd. Bath 101 D4
Rosslyn Way. Thorn 8 B2
Rotcombe La. Paul 115 E1
Rotcombe Vale. Paul 115 E1
Rounceval St. Ch Sod 28 A1
Roundhill Gr. Bath 101 D2
Roundhill Park. Bath 101 D2
Roundmoor Cl. Keyn 82 B2
Roundmoor Gdns. Bris ... 80 B4
Roundways. Fr Cot 38 B3
Rousham Rd. Bris 50 A2
Row La. Faulk 135 E1
Row Of Ashes La. But 94 A2
Row Of Ashes La. Wring .. 93 F2
Row The. Aust 13 D4
Rowacres. Bath 101 D2
Rowacres. Bris 79 F3
Rowan Cl. Bris 51 D1
Rowan Cl. Nail 60 A1
Rowan Ct. Rad 132 C1
Rowan Way. Chur 109 D3
Rowan Way. Kingsw 65 D2
Rowan Wlk. Keyn 81 E2
Rowans The. Bris 37 D1
Rowans The. Portis 45 E2
Rowberrow La. Ship 108 C1
Rowberrow La. Ship 125 F4
Rowberrow Way. Nail 59 F1
Rowberrow. Bris 35 D2
Rowland Ave. Bris 50 B2
Rowlands Cl. Bathf 86 A1
Rowlandson Gdns. Bris ... 50 A3
Rowley St. Bris 63 E2
Rownham Cl. Bris 62 C2
Rownham Ct. Bris 63 D3
Rownham Hill. Lo Ash 62 C3
Rownham Mead. Bris 63 D3
Rows The. W-S-M 88 C1

Roy King Gdns. Kingsw

Roy King Gdns. Kingsw 66 B3
Royal Albert Rd. Bris 49 D2
Royal Ave. Bath 101 F4
Royal Cl. Bris 34 B2
Royal Cres. Bath 101 F4
Royal Cres. W-S-M 104 B4
Royal Fort Rd. Bris 63 E4
Royal Park. Bris 63 D4
Royal Portbury Dock Rd.
  E in G 46 C3
Royal Prom. Bris 63 D4
Royal York Cres. Bris 62 C3
Royal York Cres. Bris 63 D3
Royate Hill. Bris 50 B1
Roycroft Rd. Bris 36 A1
Royston Wlk. Bris 35 E1
Rozel Rd. Bris 49 F3
Rubens Cl. Keyn 82 A3
Ruby St. Bris 63 D2
Ruddymead. Cleve 57 E1
Rudford Cl. St Gif 24 A1
Rudgeway Park. Alve 14 C1
Rudgeway Rd. Paul 131 F2
Rudgewood Cl. Bris 79 E2
Rudgleigh Ave. E in G 47 E2
Rudgleigh Rd. E in G 47 E2
Rudhall Gr. Bris 49 F4
Rudhall Green. W-S-M 89 D2
Rudmore Park. Bath 101 D4
Rudthorpe Rd. Bris 49 F3
Ruffet Rd. West 38 B2
Rugby Rd. Bris 64 B2
Runnymead Ave. Bris 64 B1
Runnymede. Kingsw 51 F1
Runswick Rd. Bris 64 B2
Rupert St. Bris 63 E4
Rupert St. Bris 64 B4
Rurdown Rd. Bris 49 F3
Rush Cl. St Gif 24 B1
Rush Hill. Bath 101 D1
Rush Hill. Paul 130 C2
Rush Hill. Ston E 130 C2
Rushgrove Gdns. Bi Sut .. 113 E2
Rushmoor Gr. Back 76 A3
Rushmoor La. Back 76 A3
Rushmoor. Cleve 57 D1
Rushton Dr. Fr Cot 38 B4
Rushway. Blag 110 A2
Rushy. Kingsw 66 A2
Ruskin Gr. Bris 50 A4
Ruskin Rd. Rad 132 B1
Russ St. Bris 63 F3
Russell Ave. Kingsw 65 F4
Russell Cl. Win 95 D3
Russell Gr. Bris 49 E3
Russell Rd. Bris 49 D2
Russell Rd. Bris 51 D1
Russell Rd. Cleve 57 E2
Russell St. Bath 101 F4
Russell Town Ave. Bris 64 A4
Russet Cl. Olve 14 A2
Russet Cl. Kings 11 F2
Russet Way. P St J 133 E4
Russett Cl. Back 76 A3
Russett Gr. Nail 75 E4
Rutherford Cl. Kingsw 66 A2
Ruthven Rd. Bris 79 F4
Rutland Ave. Kingsw 66 A1
Rutland Cl. W-S-M 105 E4
Rutland Rd. Bris 49 F2
Rydal Ave. Lock 106 A2
Rydal Rd. W-S-M 104 C2
Ryde Rd. Bris 64 A1
Rye Cl. Bris 78 C3
Ryecroft Ave. W-S-M 88 C1
Ryecroft Rd. Fr Cot 38 B4
Ryecroft Rise. Lo Ash 62 A1
Ryedown La. Bitt 66 B1
Ryland Pl. Bris 50 A1
Rylestone Cl. Fr Cot 37 F4
Rylestone Gr. Bris 48 C3
Rysdale Rd. Bris 48 C3

Sabrina Way. Bris 48 B2
Sadbury Cl. W-S-M 89 D2
Sadlier Cl. Bris 48 A4
Saffron Ct. Bath 102 A4
Saffrons The. W-S-M 89 D2
Sage Cl. Portis 44 C2
Sailsbort St. Bris 64 C4
Sailsbury Rd. Bris 64 B3
St John's Rd. Back 76 A3
St Agnes Ave. Bris 63 F1
St Agnes Cl. Nail 60 A1
St Agnes Wlk. Bris 63 F1
St Aidan's Cl. Bris 65 D3
St Aidan's Rd. Bris 65 D3
St Alban's Rd. Bris 49 D2
St Aldams Dr. Puck 53 D3
St Aldwyn's Cl. Bris 49 F4
St Andrew's Cl. Cong 91 E2
St Andrew's Dr. Cleve 57 D1
St Andrew's Par. W-S-M .. 104 C2
St Andrew's Rd. Avon 33 D2
St Andrew's Rd. Bris 49 F1
St Andrew's Terr. Bath 101 F4
St Andrews Cl. Nail 60 A1

St Andrews Cl. W-S-M 88 C2
St Andrews Rd. Back 76 A3
St Andrews Trading Est.
  Avon 33 E1
St Andrews. Kingsw 66 A3
St Andrews. Yate 27 F1
St Ann's Way. Bath 102 A3
St Anne's Ave. Keyn 81 E3
St Anne's Cl. Kingsw 66 A2
St Anne's Ct. Keyn 81 E3
St Anne's Dr. Fr Cot 38 B3
St Anne's Dr. Wick 67 D4
St Anne's Park Rd. Bris 64 C3
St Anne's Rd. Bris 64 B3
St Anne's Rd. Bris 65 D3
St Anne's Terr. Bris 64 C3
St Annes Dr. Kingsw 66 B2
St Anthony's Dr. Wick 67 D4
St Anthonys Cl. Mid No ... 132 A1
St Anway. Kingsw 66 B1
St Aubin's Ave. Bris 64 C2
St Aubyn's Ave. W-S-M 104 B1
St Augustine's Cl. Portis ... 44 C2
St Augustine's Par. Bris 63 E3
St Augustine's Pl. Bris 63 E3
St Austell Cl. Nail 76 A4
St Austell Rd. W-S-M 105 D4
St Barnabas Cl. Bris 63 F1
St Barnabas Cl. Mid No ... 132 A2
St Barnabas Cl. Sist 66 B4
St Bartholomew's Rd. Bris . 49 F2
St Bede's Rd. Bris 51 E1
St Bernard's Rd. Bris 47 F3
St Brelades Gr. Bris 64 C3
St Brendan's Way. Avon ... 33 D1
St Briavels Dr. Yate 39 E4
St Bridges Cl. W St L 88 A3
St Catherine's Ind Est. Bris . 63 E2
St Catherine's Mead.
  E in G 47 E2
St Catherine's Pl. Bris 63 E2
St Chad's Ave. Mid No 132 A1
St Chad's Green. Mid No .. 132 A1
St Charles Cl. Mid No 132 A1
St Christophers Cl. Bath .. 102 B4
St Clements Ct. Keyn 81 F2
St Clements Rd. Keyn 81 F2
St David's Ave. Kingsw 66 A3
St David's Cl. W-S-M 88 A1
St David's Cres. Bris 64 C3
St Dunstan's Rd. Bris 63 E1
St Edward's Rd. Bris 63 D3
St Edyth's Rd. Bris 48 B3
St Fagans Ct. Kingsw 66 A1
St Francis Dr. Wick 67 D4
St Francis Dr. Wint 37 F3
St Francis Rd. Bris 63 D2
St Francis Rd. Keyn 81 E3
St Gabriel's Rd. Bris 64 A4
St George's Hill. Bath 102 B4
St George's Hill. E in G 47 D2
St George's Rd. Bris 63 E3
St George's Rd. E in G 46 C4
St George's Rd. Keyn 81 E3
St Giles Barton. Hill 19 E4
St Gregory's Rd. Bris 49 F4
St Gregory's Wlk. Bris 49 F4
St Helen's Wlk. Bris 51 D1
St Helena Rd. Bris 49 D2
St Helens Dr. Kingsw 66 B1
St Helens Dr. Wick 67 E4
St Helier Ave. Bris 64 C2
St Hilary Cl. Bris 48 B3
St Ivel Way. Kingsw 66 B3
St Ives Cl. Nail 60 A1
St Ives Rd. W-S-M 105 D4
St James Cl. Thorn 8 B2
St James Cl. St Gif 24 B1
St James St. W-S-M 104 B4
St James' Barton. Bris 63 F4
St James's Par. Bath 101 F4
St James's Park. Bath 101 F4
St James's Pl. Mang 52 A3
St James's Sq. Bath 101 F4
St James's St. Bath 101 F4
St James's St. Mang 52 A3
St John St. H Up 20 A2
St John St. Thorn 8 A1
St John's Ave. Cleve 57 E2
St John's Bridge. Bris 63 E4
St John's Cl. P St J 133 D4
St John's Cl. W-S-M 87 E1
St John's Cres. Bris 63 F1
St John's Cres. Mid No 132 A1
St John's La. Bris 63 F1
St John's Pl. Bath 101 F1
St John's Rd. Bath 101 E4
St John's Rd. Bath 102 A4
St John's Rd. Bris 63 D2
St John's Rd. Cleve 57 E2
St John's Rd. Bris 63 E4
St John's Steep. Bris 63 E4
St Johns Ct. Keyn 81 F3
St Johns Way. Ch Sod 28 A1
St Jonhs' Rd. Bris 49 D1
St Jonhs Rd. Tims 116 A1
St Joseph's Rd. Bris 35 D2

St Joseph's Rd. W-S-M 87 F1
St Jude's Terr. W-S-M 88 B1
St Julian's Rd. Well 133 F3
St Kenya Cl. Keyn 81 F3
St Keyna Rd. Keyn 81 F3
St Kilda's Rd. Bath 101 E3
St Ladoc Rd. Keyn 81 E3
St Laud Cl. Bris 48 B3
St Leonard's Rd. Bris 49 F3
St Leonard's Rd. Bris 50 B1
St Lucia Cl. Bris 49 F4
St Lucia Cres. Bris 49 F4
St Luke St. Bris 64 A4
St Luke's Cres. Bris 63 F2
St Luke's Gdns. Bris 64 C1
St Luke's Rd. Bath 101 F2
St Luke's Rd. Bris 63 F2
St Luke's Rd. Mid No 131 F1
St Margaret's Cl. Back 76 A3
St Margaret's Cl. Keyn 81 E3
St Margaret's Dr. Bris 49 E3
St Margaret's La. Back 76 A3
St Margaret's Terr. W-S-M 104 B4
St Mark's Gr. Bris 50 A1
St Mark's Rd. Bath 102 A3
St Mark's Rd. Bris 50 A1
St Mark's Rd. Mid No 132 A1
St Mark's Terr. Bris 50 A1
St Marks Cl. Keyn 81 F3
St Marks Rd. W-S-M 89 D2
St Martin's Cl. Bris 64 A1
St Martin's Ct. Bath 101 F1
St Martin's Gdns. Bris 64 A1
St Martin's La. Marsh 69 F4
St Martin's Park. Marsh 69 F4
St Martin's Rd. Bris 64 A1
St Martin's Wlk. Bris 64 A1
St Martins W-S-M 88 C2
St Mary St. Thorn 15 D4
St Mary's Bldgs. Bath 101 F3
St Mary's Cl. Bath 102 A3
St Mary's Cl. Tims 116 A1
St Mary's Cl. W-S-M 105 D1
St Mary's Gdns. Chur 109 D3
St Mary's Gr. Nail 75 E4
St Mary's Park Rd. Portis .. 45 E2
St Mary's Park. Nail 75 E4
St Mary's Rd. Bris 47 E4
St Mary's Rd. Lo Ash 62 B3
St Mary's Rd. Lock 105 E1
St Mary's Rd. Portis 45 E2
St Mary's Rise. Rad 133 E1
St Mary's St. Axb 125 E1
St Mary's Way. Yate 27 F1
St Mary's Wlk. Bris 47 E3
St Marys Cl. Lock 105 E1
St Marys Way. Thorn 8 A1
St Matthew's Cl. W-S-M ... 87 E1
St Matthew's Rd. Bris 63 E4
St Matthias Park. Bris 63 F4
St Michael's Ave. Cleve 57 E1
St Michael's Cl. Wint 37 F4
St Michael's Hill. Bris 63 E4
St Michael's Park. Bris 63 E4
St Michael's Rd. Bath 101 E4
St Michaels Ct. Bris 65 D4
St Michaels Rd. Bath 101 D3
St Michael's Ave. W-S-M .. 89 D2
St Nicholas Cl. Winsl 120 B4
St Nicholas Cl. Bath 85 F1
St Nicholas Park. Bris 50 A1
St Nicholas Rd. W-S-M ... 104 B1
St Nicholas Rd. Whit 80 B2
St Nicholas St. Bris 63 E3
St Nicholas' Rd. Bris 49 F1
St Oswald's Ct. Bris 49 D2
St Oswald's Rd. Bris 49 D2
St Patrick's Ct. Bath 102 A3
St Patricks Ct. Keyn 81 F3
St Paul St. Bris 63 F4
St Paul's Rd. Bris 63 D4
St Paul's Rd. Bris 63 E2
St Paul's Rd. W-S-M 104 C3
St Pauls Pl. Bath 101 F3
St Pauls Pl. Mid No 132 A1
St Peter's Ave. W-S-M 87 E1
St Peter's Cres. Fr Cot 38 A4
St Peter's Rd. Rod 138 B4
St Peter's Rise. Bris 79 D4
St Peter's Wlk. Bris 49 D3
St Peters Rd. Portis 45 E2
St Phillips Causeway. Bris .. 64 A3
St Phillips Rd. Bris 64 A4
St Pierre Dr. Kingsw 66 A3
St Ronan's Ave. Bris 49 E1
St Saviour's Rd. Bath 85 E1
St Saviours Way. Bath 85 E1
St Silas St. Bris 64 A3
St Stephen's Ave. Bris 63 E3
St Stephen's Cl. Bath 101 F4
St Stephen's Ct. Bath 101 F4
St Stephen's Rd. Kingsw ... 51 F1
St Stephens Bsns Centre.
  Kingsw 66 B3
St Stephens Cl. Kingsw 51 F2
St Stephens Rd. Bath 101 F4
St Swithin's Pl. Bath 102 A4

St Thomas Rd. Mid No 132 A1
St Thomas St E. Bris 63 F3
St Thomas St. Bris 63 F3
St Vincent's Hill. Bris 49 D1
St Vincent's Rd. Bris 63 D3
St Werburgh's Park. Bris ... 50 A1
St Werburgh's Rd. Bris 49 F1
St Whytes Rd. Bris 79 E4
St Winifreds Dr. Bath 102 B1
Salcombe Gdns. W-S-M 89 D1
Salcombe Rd. Bris 64 A1
Salem Rd. Wint 37 F4
Salisbury Ave. Bris 65 D4
Salisbury Gdns. Mang 51 F3
Salisbury Rd. Bath 85 D1
Salisbury Rd. Bris 49 E1
Salisbury Rd. Mang 51 F3
Salisbury Rd. W-S-M 105 E4
Salisbury Terr. W-S-M 104 B4
Salisbury St. Bris 64 A3
Sally In The Wood Rd.
  Bathf 103 E3
Sallybarn Cl. Kingsw 65 F1
Sallys Way. Wint 37 F4
Sallysmead Cl. Bris 79 D2
Saltford Ct. Keyn 82 C2
Salthouse Ct. Cleve 57 D1
Salthouse Rd. Cleve 57 D1
Salthrop Rd. Bris 49 F2
Saltings Cl. Cleve 57 D1
Saltmarsh Dr. Bris 34 A1
Saltwell Ave. Whit 80 B3
Sambourne La. E in G 47 E2
Samian Way. St Gif 36 C3
Sampsons Rd. Bris 79 E2
Samuel St. Bris 64 B4
Samuel White Rd. Kingsw .. 65 E2
Samuel Wright Cl. Kingsw .. 66 B3
Sanctuary Gdns. Bris 48 B2
Sand Farm La. W St L 88 A3
Sand Hill. Bris 64 B2
Sand Rd. W St L 88 A1
Sandbach Rd. Bris 64 B2
Sandbed Rd. Bris 50 A1
Sandburrows Rd. Bris 78 C3
Sandburrows Wlk. Bris 78 C3
Sandcroft Ave. W-S-M 104 B1
Sandcroft. Bris 79 F3
Sandford Cl. Cleve 57 D1
Sandford Rd. Bris 63 D3
Sandford Rd. W-S-M 105 D4
Sandgate Rd. Bris 64 B2
Sandholm Rd. Bris 64 B1
Sandholme Cl. Mang 51 F4
Sandhurst Cl. St Gif 24 A1
Sandhurst Rd. Bris 64 B2
Sandhurst. Yate 39 E4
Sandling Ave. Bris 50 A4
Sandmead Rd. Wins 108 A2
Sandown Cl. Mang 37 F1
Sandown Rd. Bris 36 B2
Sandown Rd. Bris 64 B2
Sandpiper Dr. W-S-M 88 C1
Sandpits La. H Up 19 F1
Sandringham Ave. Mang ... 51 F4
Sandringham Park. Mang ... 51 F4
Sandringham Rd. Bris 64 B2
Sandringham Rd. Kingsw ... 65 F1
Sandringham Rd. St Gif 36 B2
Sandringham Rd. W-S-M . 104 C3
Sands Hill. Dyrh 54 C2
Sands La. Fr Cot 25 F1
Sandwich Rd. Bris 64 B2
Sandy Cl. St Gif 36 C3
Sandy La. Ab Lei 61 E4
Sandy La. Aust 13 D4
Sandy La. Bris 50 B2
Sandy La. Pens 96 C2
Sandy La. Wrax 47 D1
Sandy La. Wrax 61 E4
Sandy Lodge. Yate 39 F4
Sandy Park Rd. Bris 64 B2
Sandyleaze. Bris 48 C4
Sarabeth Dr. Pris 117 D2
Saracen St. Bath 102 A4
Sarah St. Bris 64 A4
Sargent St. Bris 63 F2
Sarum Cres. Bris 35 E1
Sassoon Ct. Kingsw 65 F3
Satchfield Cl. Bris 34 C1
Satchfield Cres. Bris 34 C1
Sates Way. Bris 49 E3
Saunders Rd. Kingsw 51 F2
Saunton Wlk. Bris 79 F4
Savages Wood Rd. St Gif .. 36 B4
Savages Wood Rd. St Gif .. 36 C4
Savernake Rd. W-S-M 88 C2
Saville Cres. W-S-M 105 E4
Saville Gate Cl. Bris 48 C2
Saville Pl. Bris 63 D3
Saville Rd. Bris 48 C2
Saville Rd. W-S-M 105 E4
Saville Row. Bath 101 F4
Savoy Rd. Bris 64 B2
Saw Cl. Bath 101 F3
Saw Mill La. Thorn 8 A1

Sawyers Ct. Cleve 57 F2
Saxby Cl. Cleve 57 D1
Saxby Cl. W-S-M 89 D2
Saxon Rd. Bris 50 A1
Saxon Rd. W-S-M 105 E4
Saxon Way. St Gif 24 B1
Saxon Way. Winsl 120 C4
Says La. Chur 109 D1
Sbi Centre. Kingsw 65 D3
Scandrett Cl. Bris 34 C1
Scaurs The. W-S-M 88 C1
School Cl. Bris 79 F2
School Cl. Hill 19 F4
School Cl. St Gif 36 B4
School La. Ba Gu 77 E3
School La. Bathe 85 F2
School La. Ch St 112 B4
School La. Paul 131 D2
School La. Ship 109 D1
School La. Wring 94 A4
School Rd. Bris 64 A2
School Rd. Bris 64 C2
School Rd. Fr Cot 38 A4
School Rd. Kingsw 65 E4
School Rd. Kingsw 66 B2
School Rd. Wring 92 C1
School Way. Piln 22 A3
School Wlk. Bris 50 B1
School Wlk. Yate 27 F1
Scobell Rise. Paul 115 E1
Scop The. Alm 24 A3
Score La. Blag 110 C1
Score The. Blag 110 C1
Scot La. Ch St 95 E1
Scotch Horn Cl. Nail 59 F1
Scotch Horn Way. Nail 59 F1
Scots Pine Ave. Nail 60 A1
Scott Cl. Kingsw 65 F3
Scott Lawrence Cl. Bris 51 D4
Scott Rd. W-S-M 105 D2
Scott Way. Ch Sod 39 F4
Scumbrum La. Farm 115 E1
Scumbrum La. Paul 115 E1
Sea Bank Rd. E in G 32 C1
Sea Mills La. Bris 48 B3
Seabrook Rd. W-S-M 88 B1
Seagry Cl. Bris 35 F1
Searl Court Ave. Bris 64 C2
Searle Cres. W-S-M 105 D3
Seaton Rd. Bris 50 B1
Seavale Rd. Cleve 57 E2
Seaview Rd. Portis 44 C2
Seaview Rd. Portis 44 C3
Seawalls Rd. Bris 48 B1
Seawalls. Bris 48 B1
Second Ave. Bath 101 E3
Second Ave. Rod 138 B4
Second Way. Avon 33 E1
Seddon Rd. Bris 50 A1
Sedgefield Gdns. Mang 37 F1
Sedgemoor Cl. Nail 75 E4
Sedgemoor Rd. Bath 101 F1
Sedgemoor Rd. W-S-M 87 F1
Sefton Park Rd. Bris 49 F2
Selbourne Cl. Bath 101 D4
Selbourne Rd. Bris 49 F3
Selbourne Rd. W-S-M 104 C2
Selbrooke Cres. Bris 51 E3
Selby Rd. Bris 51 D1
Selden Rd. Bris 80 C3
Selkirk Rd. Bris 51 E1
Selley Wlk. Bris 79 D3
Selwood Cl. W-S-M 105 E4
Selworthy Cl. Keyn 81 E3
Selworthy Gdns. Nail 59 F1
Selworthy Rd. Bris 64 A1
Selworthy Rd. W-S-M 105 D2
Selworthy. Kingsw 65 F4
Seneca Pl. Bris 64 B4
Seneca St. Bris 64 B4
Sercombe Park. Cleve 57 F2
Serlo Ct. W-S-M 88 C2
Seven Acres La. Bathe 85 F3
Seventh Ave. Bris 36 A1
Severn Ave. W-S-M 104 C3
Severn Cl. Char 11 D2
Severn Dr. Thorn 8 A1
Severn Grange. Bris 34 B2
Severn Rd. Avon 33 D3
Severn Rd. Avon 33 F4
Severn Rd. Bris 47 E3
Severn Rd. E in G 47 E3
Severn Rd. Piln 22 A3
Severn Rd. Portis 45 E3
Severn View Rd. Thorn 8 B2
Severn Way. Bris 23 F1
Severn Way. Keyn 81 F2
Severnmeade. Portis 44 C4
Severnwood Gdns. Piln 22 A3
Sevier Rd. Blea 123 E2
Sevier St. Bris 50 A1
Seville Rd. Portis 45 F4
Seward Terr. Rad 133 E1
Seymour Ave. Bris 49 F2
Seymour Cl. Cleve 57 F2
Seymour Cl. W-S-M 88 C2
Seymour Rd. Bath 102 A4

Seymour Rd. Bris 49 F2
Seymour Rd. Bris 50 A1
Seymour Rd. Kingsw 51 E1
Seymour Rd. Kingsw 51 F2
Seyton Wlk. St Gif 36 C3
Shackleton Ave. Yate 39 F4
Shadwell Rd. Bris 49 E2
Shaft Rd. Bath 102 B1
Shaft Rd. Piln 22 A4
Shaftesbury Ave. Bris 49 F1
Shaftesbury Rd. Bath 101 E3
Shaftesbury Rd. W-S-M 105 D4
Shaftesbury Terr. Bris 64 B4
Shaftesbury Terr. Mid No .. 133 D2
Shaftsbury Ave. Bath 101 E4
Shaftsbury Cl. Nail 75 E4
Shakespeare Ave. Bath 101 F2
Shakespeare Ave. Bris 50 A4
Shakespeare Rd. Rad 132 B3
Shaldon Rd. Bris 50 A2
Shallows The. Keyn 82 C2
Sham Castle La. Bath 102 B4
Shamrock Rd. Bris 50 B2
Shanklin Dr. Bris 36 A2
Shannon Ct. Thorn 15 E4
Shapcott Cl. Bris 64 A1
Shaplands. Bris 48 C3
Sharland Cl. Bris 48 C2
Shaw Cl. Bris 64 A4
Shaws Way. Bath 101 D3
Shaymoor La. Alm 23 D2
Sheene La. Bris 63 E2
Sheep Fair La. Marsh 69 F4
Sheeps Croft. Bris 79 D3
Sheepway. Portb 46 B3
Sheepwood Cl. Bris 35 D1
Sheepwood Rd. Bris 35 D1
Sheldare Barton. Bris 65 D4
Sheldon Cl. Cleve 57 F1
Sheldrake Dr. Bris 50 C3
Shellard Rd. Bris 36 A1
Shellards La. Alve 15 E2
Shellards Rd. Kingsw 65 F2
Shelley Ave. Cleve 57 E1
Shelley Cl. Bris 64 C4
Shelley Rd. Bath 101 F2
Shelley Rd. Rad 132 B3
Shelley Rd. W-S-M 105 D2
Shellmoor Ave. St Gif 24 A1
Shellmor Cl. St Gif 24 B1
Shelly Way. Bris 50 A4
Shepherds Cl. Mang 51 F3
Sheppard Rd. Bris 51 E3
Sheppards Gdns. Bath 84 A1
Shepperdine Rd. O-0n-S 1 B1
Sheppy's Mill. Cong 91 E3
Shepton Wlk. Bris 63 E1
Shepton. W-S-M 105 D1
Sherbourne Ave. St Gif 36 C4
Sherbourne Cl. Kingsw 51 F1
Sherbourne St. Bris 64 B4
Sherbourne's Brake. St Gif . 36 C3
Sheridan Rd. Bath 100 C3
Sheridan Rd. Bris 50 A4
Sheridan Way. Kingsw 66 A1
Sherrin Way. Bris 78 C2
Sherrings The. St Gif 36 A4
Sherston Cl. Bris 51 D3
Sherston Cl. Nail 60 A1
Sherston Rd. Bris 49 F4
Sherston Rd. Luck 31 F3
Sherwell Rd. Bris 64 B2
Sherwood Cl. Keyn 81 F3
Sherwood Cres. W-S-M 88 C2
Sherwood Rd. Bris 51 D1
Sherwood Rd. Keyn 81 F3
Shetland Rd. Bris 35 E1
Shetland Way. Nail 60 A1
Shickle Gr. Bath 101 E1
Shields Ave. Bris 36 A1
Shiels Dr. St Gif 36 B4
Shilton Cl. Kingsw 65 F4
Shimsey Cl. Bris 51 E3
Shiners Elms. Yatt 91 D4
Ship La. Bris 63 F3
Shipham Cl. Bris 80 A3
Shipham Cl. Nail 75 F4
Shipham La. Ship 108 A1
Shipham La. Wins 108 A1
Shipham Rd. Ched 125 F3
Shiplate Rd. Blea 122 C3
Shipley Rd. Bris 49 D4
Shire Gdns. Bris 47 E4
Shire Hill. Tor 56 A3
Shire Way. Yate 39 E3
Shirehampton Rd. Bris 48 B3
Shockerwick La. Bathf 86 B3
Shop La. Gr Bad 30 C1
Shophouse Rd. Bath 101 D3
Shoreditch. Ch St 112 B4
Short La. Litt 129 F1
Short La. Lo Ash 62 A1
Short St. Bris 64 A3
Short Way. Thorn 15 D4
Short Way. Wrax 61 D2
Shorthill Rd. West 39 E2
Shortlands Rd. Bris 34 A1
Shortwood Hill. Puck 52 C2

Shortwood Rd. Bris 79 F2
Shortwood Rd. Puck 53 D3
Shortwood View. Kingsw 65 F4
Shortwood Wlk. Bris 79 F2
Showering Rd. Bris 80 B3
Shrubbery Ave. W-S-M 87 E1
Shrubbery Cotts. Bris 49 D1
Shrubbery Rd. Mang 51 E3
Shrubbery Rd. W-S-M 87 E1
Shrubbery Terr. W-S-M 87 E1
Shrubbery Wlk W-S-M 87 E1
Shrubbery Wlk. W-S-M 87 E1
Shuter Rd. Bris 78 C3
Sibland Cl. Thorn 15 E4
Sibland Rd. Thorn 15 E4
Sibland Way. Thorn 15 E4
Sibland. Thorn 15 E4
Sidcot La. Wins 125 D4
Sidcot. Bris 65 D1
Sideland Cl. Bris 80 C3
Sidelands Rd. Bris 51 E3
Sidlence The. Char 11 D3
Sidings The. Co Mar 127 E4
Sidmouth Gdns. Bris 63 E1
Sidmouth Rd. Bris 63 F1
Sidney Hill Cottage Homes.
  Chur 108 C2
Signal Rd. Kingsw 51 F2
Silbury Rd. Bris 62 C1
Silbury Rise. Keyn 82 A1
Silcox Rd. Bris 79 E2
Silklands Gr. Bris 48 B4
Silver Birch Cl. St Gif 36 B4
Silver Ct. Nail 59 E1
Silver Mead. Cong 91 E1
Silver Moor La. Ban 106 C4
Silver St. Bris 63 E4
Silver St. Ch Mag 96 A2
Silver St. Cong 91 E1
Silver St. Hol 138 B1
Silver St. Kilm 139 D3
Silver St. Mid No 138 A4
Silver St. Nail 59 E1
Silver St. Rod 138 A4
Silver St. W in G 44 C1
Silver St. Wring 92 C1
Silverberry Rd. W-S-M 89 D1
Silverhill Rd. Bris 34 C2
Silverlow Rd. Nail 59 E1
Silverstone Way. Cong 91 E2
Silverthorne La. Bris 64 A3
Silverthorne Wharf. Bris 64 A3
Silverton Ct. Bris 63 F1
Simon's Cl. Paul 131 F3
Simons Cl. W-S-M 89 D1
Simplex Ind Est The.
  Kingsw 66 B2
Singapore Rd. W-S-M 104 C2
Single Hill. Well 134 A3
Sion Hill Pl. Bath 84 C1
Sion Hill. Bath 84 C1
Sion Hill. Bath 101 E4
Sion Hill. Bris 62 C4
Sion La. Bris 62 C4
Sion Pl. Bris 62 C4
Sion Rd. Bath 84 C1
Sion Rd. Bris 63 E2
Sir John's La. Bris 50 A3
Siskin Wlk. W-S-M 105 F4
Siston Centre The. Kingsw .. 52 A1
Siston Cl. Sist 52 A1
Siston Comm. Sist 52 A1
Siston La. Puck 52 C1
Siston Park. Sist 52 A1
Six Ways. Cleve 57 E2
Sixpence. Paul 115 E1
Sixth Ave. Bris 36 A1
Sixty Acres Cl. Wrax 61 D2
Skinner's Hill. Tims 132 C4
Skinners La. Chur 108 C2
Skippon Ct. Kingsw 65 F3
Sladacre La. Blag 110 C1
Slade La. Lymp 122 A1
Slade Rd. Portis 45 E3
Sladebrook Ave. Bath 101 E2
Sladebrook Rd. Bath 101 D2
Slate La. Co Dan 98 A4
Sleep La. Whit 80 B2
Slimbridge Cl. Ch Sod 39 F4
Sloan St. Bris 64 B4
Slough La. Co Ash 68 C3
Slymbridge Ave. Bris 35 D2
Small Down End. Winsc 107 F1
Small La. Bris 50 C3
Small St. Bris 63 E4
Small St. Bris 64 A3
Smallbrook La. Co Dan 98 A3
Smallcombe Cl. Mid No 132 C3
Smallcombe Rd. Mid No 132 C2
Smallway. Cong 91 E3
Smarts Green. Ch Sod 40 B4
Smeaton Rd. Bris 62 C3
Smithcourt Dr. St Gif 36 B3
Smithmead. Bris 79 D3
Smoke La. Avon 33 E4
Smyth Rd. Bris 63 D2
Smythe Croft. Bris 80 A2

Smyths Cl. Avon 33 D1
Snow Hill. Bath 85 D1
Snowberry Cl. W-S-M 89 D1
Snowberry Wlk. Bris 50 C1
Snowdon Cl. Bris 50 C2
Snowdon Rd. Bris 50 C2
Snowdon Vale. W-S-M 88 A1
Sodbury Rd. Wickw 18 A2
Solent Way. Thorn 15 E4
Solsbury Ct. Bathe 85 F2
Solsbury Way. Bath 85 D1
Somer Ave. Mid No 131 F1
Somer Lea. Chil 137 E3
Somer Rd. Mid No 131 F1
Somerby Cl. St Gif 36 B4
Somerdale Ave. Bath 101 E1
Somerdale Ave. Bris 64 A1
Somerdale Ave. W-S-M 105 E4
Somerdale Cl. W-S-M 105 E4
Somerdale Rd N. Keyn 81 F4
Somerdale Rd. Keyn 81 F4
Somerdale View. Bath 101 E1
Somermead. Bris 63 E1
Somerset Ave. Yate 27 F2
Somerset Cl. Kings 11 F2
Somerset Cres. St Gif 36 C3
Somerset Folly. Tims 116 A1
Somerset La. Bath 84 C1
Somerset Mews. W-S-M 104 C1
Somerset Pl. Bath 84 C1
Somerset Rd. Bris 64 A2
Somerset Rd. Cleve 57 F2
Somerset Rd. Portis 44 C3
Somerset Sq. Bris 63 F3
Somerset Sq. Nail 59 F1
Somerset St. Bris 63 E3
Somerset St. Bris 63 F3
Somerset Terr. Bris 63 E2
Somerset Way. Paul 131 F3
Somerton Cl. Kingsw 65 F4
Somerton Rd. Bris 49 F3
Somerton Rd. Cleve 57 F1
Somerton. W-S-M 105 D1
Somervale Rd. Rad 132 C1
Somerville Cl. Keyn 82 C1
Somerville Rd. Wins 108 A2
Sommerville Rd S. Bris 49 F1
Sommerville Rd. Bris 49 F2
Sophia Gdns. W-S-M 89 D2
Sorrel Cl. Thorn 8 B1
Soundwell Rd. Bris 65 E4
Soundwell Rd. Kingsw 51 E1
South Ave. Bath 101 E3
South Ave. Portis 45 E3
South Ave. Yate 27 D1
South Combe. Blea 122 A3
South Croft. Bris 49 E4
South Croft. Winsc 107 F1
South Dene. Bris 48 C3
South Gr. Bris 49 E3
South Gr. E in G 47 E2
South Green St. Bris 62 C3
South Hayes. Bris 50 A2
South Hill. Winsc 107 F1
South Lawn Cl. Lock 105 F2
South Lawn. Lock 105 F2
South Lea Rd. Bath 101 D4
South Liberty La. Bris 62 C1
South Meadows. Wring 92 C1
South Par. Bath 102 A3
South Par. Ch Mag 96 A2
South Par. W-S-M 104 B4
South Par. Yate 27 F1
South Rd. Alve 24 C3
South Rd. Bris 49 E1
South Rd. Bris 63 E2
South Rd. Kingsw 65 E4
South Rd. Lymp 122 A1
South Rd. Mid No 132 A1
South Rd. Portis 45 D4
South Rd. Tims 116 A1
South Rd. W-S-M 87 E1
South Rock Ind Est. Chil ... 137 E1
South Side. Cong 91 F3
South St. Bris 63 D2
South St. Chil 137 F1
South Terr. Bris 49 D1
South Terr. W-S-M 104 B4
South View Cres. Fr Cot 38 B3
South View Pl. Mid No 132 A1
South View Rd. Bath 101 E3
South View Rise. Fr Cot 38 B3
South View Terr. Yatt 74 A1
South View. Fr Cot 38 A4
South View. Kilm 139 D2
South View. Mang 51 F3
South View. Mid No 132 C3
South View. Portis 45 D4
South View. Tims 116 A1
South Wlk. Yate 27 F1
Southbourne Gdns. Bath ... 85 D1
Southcot Pl. Bath 102 A3
Southdown Ave. Bath 101 D2
Southdown Rd. Bath 101 D2
Southdown Rd. Bris 48 C4
Southdown. W-S-M 88 C2
Southend Rd. W-S-M 104 C2
Southern Way. Cleve 57 D1

Southernhay Ave. Bris 63 D3
Southernhay. Bris 63 D3
Southernhay. Kingsw 51 E2
Southey Ct. Kingsw 51 E1
Southey Rd. Cleve 57 E1
Southey St. Bris 49 F1
Southfield Ave. Kingsw 51 F1
Southfield Cl. Nail 59 F2
Southfield Cl. W-S-M 104 B1
Southfield Ct. Bris 49 D4
Southfield Pl. Bris 63 E2
Southfield Rd. Bris 49 D4
Southfield Rd. Bris 49 E1
Southfield Rd. Nail 59 F2
Southfield Road Trading Est.
  Nail 59 F2
Southfield. N St P 135 F2
Southfield. Rad 133 D1
Southgate. Bath 102 A3
Southlands Dr. Tims 116 A1
Southlands Way. Cong 91 F3
Southlands. Bath 84 A1
Southlands. Tyth 16 A2
Southleaze. Wins 125 D3
Southleigh Rd. Bris 63 D4
Southmead Rd. Bris 35 F1
Southmead Rd. W-S-M 105 D4
Southmead. Wins 125 D4
Southover Cl. Bris 49 D4
Southover Rd. Paul 115 C1
Southridge Hts. W-S-M 122 A4
Southsea Rd. Bris 36 A4
Southside Cl. Bris 48 A4
Southside Cres. W St L 88 A2
Southside. W-S-M 104 C4
Southstoke La. Sosto 118 C4
Southstoke Rd. Bath 101 F1
Southview Cl. Lock 105 F1
Southville Rd. Bris 63 E2
Southville Rd. W-S-M 104 C2
Southway Dr. Kingsw 66 B3
Southwell St. Bris 63 E4
Southwood Ave. Bris 48 B4
Southwood Dr E. Bris 48 A4
Southwood Dr. Bris 48 A4
Sovereign Gdns. Bris 48 C2
Spa La. Bath 85 E1
Spalding Cl. Bris 50 A2
Spaniorum View. Alm 22 C1
Spar Rd. Avon 33 E2
Spar Rd. Yate 27 E1
Spartley Dr. Bris 78 C3
Spartley Wlk. Bris 78 C3
Specklemead. Paul 131 E3
Speedwell Ave. Bris 64 B4
Speedwell Cl. Thorn 8 B1
Speedwell Rd. Bris 51 D1
Spencer Dr. W-S-M 89 D2
Spey Cl. Thorn 15 E4
Spider La. W-S-M 104 B4
Spindleberry Gr. Nail 60 A1
Spinners End. W-S-M 89 D2
Spinney Croft. Bris 78 C3
Spinney The. Fr Cot 38 A4
Spinney The. W-S-M 104 C1
Spires View. Bris 50 C3
Spratts Bridge. Ch Mag 96 A2
Spring Cres. Bath 102 A3
Spring Gardens Rd. Bath .. 102 A3
Spring Gardens Rd. Bath .. 102 A3
Spring Gdns. Bris 64 A1
Spring Ground Rd. Paul 131 F3
Spring Hill Dr. W-S-M 88 C1
Spring Hill. Bris 63 D4
Spring Hill. Kingsw 51 F1
Spring Hill. W-S-M 88 B1
Spring La. Bath 85 D1
Spring Rise. Portis 45 E2
Spring St Pl. Bris 63 F2
Spring St. Bris 63 F2
Spring Terr. W-S-M 88 B1
Spring Valley. W-S-M 88 B1
Springfield Ave. Bris 47 E3
Springfield Ave. Bris 49 F3
Springfield Ave. Mang 52 A4
Springfield Ave. W-S-M 88 B1
Springfield Bldgs. Mid No .. 133 D2
Springfield Bldgs. Paul 131 E1
Springfield Cl. Bath 101 D3
Springfield Cl. Mang 52 A4
Springfield Cres. Mid No ... 133 D2
Springfield Gdns. Ban 107 D2
Springfield Gr. Bris 49 E3
Springfield Hts. Mid No 132 C2
Springfield Lawns. Bris 47 E3
Springfield Pl. Mid No 132 C2
Springfield Rd. Bris 49 E1
Springfield Rd. E in G 47 E2
Springfield Rd. Mang 52 A4
Springfield Rd. Portis 45 E3
Springfield. P St J 133 E4
Springfield. Thorn 15 E4
Springfields. Bris 36 A1
Springhill Cl. Paul 131 E3
Springleaze. Bris 79 E3
Springleaze. Mang 52 A4
Springville Cl. Kingsw 66 A2

Springwater Park Ind Est.
  Bris 64 C4
Springwell. N St P 135 F2
Springwood Dr. Bris 34 B2
Spruce Way. Bris 35 F4
Square The. Alve 15 D2
Square The. Axb 125 E1
Square The. Ban 107 D2
Square The. Blag 109 F2
Square The. Bris 64 A1
Square The. Clut 114 C1
Square The. Mang 51 F2
Square The. Ship 125 F4
Square The. Tims 116 A1
Square The. Well 118 B1
Square The. Wins 124 C3
Squire La. Co Mar 111 E1
Squires Ct. Kingsw 65 F2
Squires Leaze. Thorn 8 B1
Stabbins Cl. W-S-M 89 D3
Stable Yd. Bath 101 E3
Stackpool Rd. Bris 63 E2
Staddlestones. Mid No 137 F4
Stadium Rd. Bris 49 E3
Stafford Cres. Thorn 8 A1
Stafford Pl. W-S-M 104 C4
Stafford Rd. Bris 50 A1
Stafford Rd. Portis 45 E2
Stafford Rd. W-S-M 104 C4
Stafford St. Bris 63 E2
Staffords Ct. Kingsw 66 A3
Stainer Cl. Bris 79 E4
Stalcombe La. Co Dan 99 D2
Stall St. Bath 102 A3
Stambrook Park. Bathe 85 F3
Stanbridge Rd. Mang 51 F3
Stanbury Ave. Bris 51 E3
Stanbury Rd. Bris 63 F2
Stancombe La. Back 76 C4
Standfast Rd. Bris 34 C2
Standish Ave. St Gif 24 B1
Standish Cl. Bris 34 C1
Standon Way. Bris 35 E1
Stane Way. Avon 47 E4
Stanfield Cl. Bris 50 B3
Stanford Cl. Fr Cot 37 F4
Stanford Pl. Bris 79 E4
Stanhope Pl. Bath 101 F3
Stanhope Rd. Kingsw 65 F1
Stanhope Rd. W-S-M 104 C2
Stanhope St. Bris 64 A3
Stanier Rd. Bath 101 F3
Stanle Hill. Bris 64 A2
Stanley Ave. Bris 36 A1
Stanley Ave. Bris 49 F2
Stanley Chase. Bris 50 C1
Stanley Cres. Bris 36 A1
Stanley Ct. Mid No 132 A1
Stanley Gdns. Kingsw 66 A2
Stanley Gr. W-S-M 104 C4
Stanley Mead. St Gif 24 C1
Stanley Park Rd. Kingsw ... 51 F2
Stanley Park. Bris 50 B1
Stanley Rd W. Bath 101 E3
Stanley Rd. Bris 49 E1
Stanley Rd. Kingsw 66 A4
Stanley St N. Bris 63 E2
Stanley St S. Bris 63 E1
Stanley St. Bris 63 E1
Stanley Terr. Bris 63 E1
Stanley Terr. Mid No 133 D2
Stanshalls Cl. Win 94 B4
Stanshalls Dr. Win 94 B4
Stanshalls Dr. Win 94 B4
Stanshaw Cl. Bris 51 D4
Stanshaw Rd. Bris 51 D4
Stanshawe Cres. Yate 27 F1
Stanshawes Dr. Yate 27 E1
Stanshawes Cl. St Gif 24 B1
Stanton Cl. Kingsw 51 F1
Stanton La. Pens 97 E2
Stanton Rd. Bris 35 F1
Stanton Wick La. Pens 97 D1
Stanway Cl. Bath 101 E1
Staple Gr. Keyn 81 E3
Staple Grove Cres. Bris 65 D4
Staplehill Rd. Bris 51 E2
Staples Cl. Cleve 57 F1
Staples Green. W-S-M 89 D2
Staples Hill. Hi Cha 120 B2
Staples Rd. Yate 27 E1
Stapleton Cl. Bris 50 B3
Stapleton Rd. Bris 50 A1
Stapleton Rd. Bris 50 B2
Star Barn Rd. Wint 37 F4
Star La. Bris 50 C2
Starcross Rd. W-S-M 89 D1
Starling Cl. W-S-M 105 F4
Starrs Cl. Axb 125 D1
Station App. Pens 97 E3
Station App. W-S-M 104 C4
Station Ave. Bris 51 D2
Station Cl. Ch Sod 40 B4
Station Cl. Kingsw 66 B4
Station La. Bris 50 A2
Station Rd. Alm 22 C2
Station Rd. Axb 125 E1

Station Rd. Back 76 A3
Station Rd. Back 77 D4
Station Rd. Bath 101 E4
Station Rd. Blag 110 C2
Station Rd. Bris 34 C2
Station Rd. Bris 36 A1
Station Rd. Bris 36 A2
Station Rd. Bris 47 E3
Station Rd. Bris 49 F1
Station Rd. Bris 49 F2
Station Rd. Bris 51 D2
Station Rd. Bris 64 B1
Station Rd. Char 11 D3
Station Rd. Cleve 57 E2
Station Rd. Clut 114 C2
Station Rd. Cong 91 E2
Station Rd. E in G 47 E2
Station Rd. Fr Cot 38 B3
Station Rd. Gr Bad 30 C1
Station Rd. Hi Cha 120 B3
Station Rd. Ir Act 26 B2
Station Rd. Keyn 81 F3
Station Rd. Kingsw 51 F2
Station Rd. Kingsw 66 B2
Station Rd. Lock 89 E1
Station Rd. Mid No 132 A1
Station Rd. Nail 59 F1
Station Rd. Piln 22 C2
Station Rd. Portb 46 B2
Station Rd. Portis 45 E3
Station Rd. St Gif 36 B4
Station Rd. W-S-M 88 C1
Station Rd. W-S-M 104 C4
Station Rd. Winsc 107 F2
Station Rd. Wint 37 F2
Station Rd. Wring 92 B1
Station Rd. Yate 27 E1
Station R d. Yatt 74 A1
Station R d. Wickw 18 A4
Staunton Fields. Whit 80 B2
Staunton La. Whit 80 B2
Staunton Rd. Ch Mag 96 A2
Staunton Way. Whit 80 B2
Staveley Cres. Bris 35 E1
Staverton Cl. St Gif 24 B1
Staverton Way. Kingsw 66 A4
Stavordale Gr. Bris 80 A3
Steam Mills. Mid No 137 F4
Stean Bridge Rd. St Gif 36 C3
Steel Ct. Kingsw 65 F2
Steel Mills. Keyn 81 F2
Stella Gr. Bris 63 D1
Stephen St. Bris 64 B4
Stephens Dr. Kingsw 65 F3
Stepney Rd. Bris 50 B1
Stepney Wlk. Bris 50 B1
Stepping Stones The. Bris .. 64 C3
Sterncourt Rd. Bris 51 D4
Stevens Cres. Bris 63 F2
Stevens La. Lymp 122 B2
Steway La. Bathe 86 A3
Stibbs Ct. Kingsw 65 F2
Stibbs Hill. Bris 65 D4
Stickland. Cleve 57 E1
Stidcot La. Tyth 16 B3
Stidcote La. Wickw 16 C3
Stile Acres. Bris 34 A1
Stilemead La. Co Mar 111 E1
Stillhouse La. Bris 63 E2
Stillingfleet Rd. Bris 79 E3
Stillman Cl. Bris 78 C2
Stinchcombe. Yate 27 F1
Stirling Cl. Yate 27 E2
Stirling Rd. Bris 64 B2
Stirling Way. Keyn 81 F2
Stirtingale Ave. Bath 101 E2
Stirtingale Rd. Bath 101 E2
Stitchings La. Engl 117 E4
Stitchings Shord La. Bi Sut 113 E2
Stock Hill. Thorn 7 E1
Stock La. Chur 109 D4
Stock La. Cong 91 F1
Stock Way N. Nail 59 F1
Stock Way S. Nail 59 F1
Stockhill Cl. Chil 137 E2
Stockhill Rd. Chil 137 E1
Stockmead. Chur 109 D3
Stockton Cl. Bris 79 F2
Stockton Cl. Kingsw 66 A2
Stockwell Ave. Mang 52 A3
Stockwell Cl. Mang 51 F4
Stockwell Dr. Mang 52 A3
Stockwell Glen. Mang 52 A4
Stockwood Cres. Bris 63 F1
Stockwood Hill. Keyn 81 E4
Stockwood La. Bris 80 C3
Stockwood La. Whit 80 C3
Stockwood Rd. Bris 81 D4
Stodelegh Cl. W-S-M 89 D2
Stoke Bridge Ave. St Gif 36 B3
Stoke Hamlet. Bris 48 C3
Stoke Hill. Bris 48 C2
Stoke Hill. Ch St 112 B4
Stoke La. Bris 48 C3
Stoke La. Bris 50 C4
Stoke La. St Gif 36 B4
Stoke Mead. Li St 119 F4
Stoke Meadows. St Gif 24 B1

Stoke Paddock Rd. Bris 48 B3
Stoke Park Rd S. Bris 48 C2
Stoke Park Rd. Bris 48 C2
Stoke Rd. Bris 49 D1
Stoke Rd. Portis 45 E3
Stoke View Rd. Bris 50 C2
Stoke View. Bris 36 A2
Stokefield Cl. Thorn 8 A1
Stokeleigh Wlk. Bris 48 B3
Stokemead. St Gif 36 B4
Stokes Croft. Bris 63 F4
Stokes Ct. Kingsw 66 A2
Stone La. Wint 37 F2
Stone's Cross. Bath 132 A1
Stoneable Rd. Mid No 133 D2
Stoneage La. P St J 117 D1
Stoneberry Rd. Bris 80 A2
Stonebridge Park. Bris 50 C1
Stonebridge Rd. W-S-M 104 C2
Stonebridge. Cleve 57 E1
Stonechat Gdns. Bris 50 C3
Stonehenge La. Nail 59 F2
Stonehill. Kingsw 65 F2
Stonehouse Cl. Bath 102 A1
Stonehouse La. Bath 102 A1
Stoneleigh Cres. Bris 64 A1
Stoneleigh Rd. Bris 64 A1
Stoneleigh Wlk. Bris 64 A1
Stoneleigh. Ch Mag 96 A2
Stonewell Dr. Cong 91 E2
Stonewell Gr. Cong 91 E2
Stonewell La. Cong 91 E2
Stonewell Park Rd. Cong 91 E2
Stoney Steep. Wrax 60 A2
Stoney Stile Rd. Alve 15 D3
Stoneyard La. Litt 129 E1
Stoneyfield Cl. E in G 47 D3
Stoneyfields. E in G 47 D2
Stores Rd. Avon 33 E2
Stormont Cl. W-S-M 104 C2
Stothard Rd. Bris 50 A4
Stottbury Rd. Bris 50 A2
Stoulton Gr. Bris 35 D2
Stourden Cl. Bris 51 D4
Stourton Dr. Kingsw 65 F2
Stover Rd. Yate 27 D1
Stover Trading Est. Yate 27 D1
Stowell Hill Rd. Tyth 16 A3
Stowey Bottom. Bi Sut 113 F3
Stowey Park. Yatt 91 E4
Stowey Rd. Yatt 91 E4
Stowick Cres. Bris 34 B1
Stradbrook Ave. Bris 65 D4
Stradling Ave. W-S-M 104 C3
Stradling Rd. Bris 34 B1
Straight St. Bris 63 F3
Straits Par. Bris 51 D3
Stratford Cl. Bris 79 F2
Stratford La. Co Mar 112 C1
Strathmore Rd. Bris 49 F3
Stratton Cl. St Gif 36 B4
Stratton Rd. Keyn 82 C2
Stratton St. Bris 63 F4
Strawberry Cl. Nail 59 E1
Strawberry Gdns. Nail 75 E4
Strawberry Hill. Cleve 57 F2
Strawberry La. Dun 78 C2
Strawbridge Rd. Bris 64 A4
Stream Cl. Bris 35 E2
Stream Side. Mang 51 F3
Stream The. Bris 37 D1
Streamcross. Yatt 74 C1
Streamleaze Ct. Thorn 15 D4
Streamleaze. Ch Mag 96 A2
Streamleaze. Thorn 15 D4
Streamside Rd. Ch Sod 28 A1
Streamside. Ch Mag 96 A2
Streamside. Cleve 57 F2
Street End La. Blag 110 B1
Street End. Blag 110 B1
Street The. Alve 15 D3
Street The. Bi Sut 113 F2
Street The. Ch St 112 B4
Street The. Chil 137 E3
Street The. Co Mar 111 E1
Street The. Co Mar 128 A4
Street The. Farm 115 F3
Street The. Luck 31 F2
Street The. N Nib 5 E1
Street The. Olve 14 A2
Street The. Rad 132 B1
Street The. Win 94 C1
Stretford Ave. Bris 64 B4
Stretford Rd. Bris 64 B4
Stride Cl. Piln 22 A3
Strode Comm. Alve 14 C3
Strode Gdns. Alve 14 C3
Strode Rd. Cleve 57 E1
Stroud Rd. Bris 35 F4
Stroud Rd. Bris 47 F3
Stuart Pl. Bath 101 E3
Stuart Rd. W-S-M 105 D3
Stuart St. Bris 64 B4
Stumpwell La. N Nib 5 F1
Sturden La. Bris 37 E2
Sturdon Rd. Bris 63 D2
Sturmer Cl. Yate 27 F2
Sturminster Cl. Bris 80 B3

Sturminster Rd. Bris 80 B4
Sullivan Cl. Bris 79 E3
Sumerlin Dr. Cleve 57 F2
Summer Hill. Bris 64 A2
Summer La N. W-S-M 89 D1
Summer La. Ban 106 C2
Summer La. Bath 102 B1
Summer La. Lock 89 D1
Summer St. Bris 63 E2
Summerfield Rd. Bath 85 D1
Summerfield. W-S-M 89 D2
Summerhayes. Kingsw 66 B3
Summerhill Rd. Bath 84 B1
Summerhill Rd. Bris 64 C4
Summerhill Terr. Bris 64 C4
Summerhouse. Nail 59 A2
Summerlands Rd. W-S-M . 105 D4
Summerlands. Back 76 A3
Summerlea. Pris 117 D3
Summerleaze. Bris 51 E2
Summerleaze. Keyn 81 F4
Summers Dr. Doyn 54 A1
Summers Mead. Yate 27 F2
Summers Rd. Bris 50 A1
Summers Terr. Bris 50 A1
Sundays Hill. Alm 24 A2
Sundayshill La. Falf 9 E4
Sundayshill La. Rock 9 E4
Sunderland Pl. Bris 63 D4
Sunderland St. Bath 102 A4
Sundridge Park. Yate 39 F4
Sunfield Rd. Lock 105 F2
Sunningdale Cl. Nail 60 A1
Sunningdale Dr. Kingsw 66 A3
Sunningdale Rd. W-S-M 88 C2
Sunningdale. Bris 63 D4
Sunningdale. Yate 39 F4
Sunny Bank. Bris 51 D1
Sunny Hill. Bris 48 B4
Sunny Wlk. Bris 51 D1
Sunnybank. Mang 51 F3
Sunnydene. Bris 64 B2
Sunnyhill Dr. Bris 47 F3
Sunnymead. Keyn 81 F2
Sunnymead. Mid No 131 F1
Sunnymeade Rd. Nail 59 F2
Sunnyside Cres. Cleve 57 E2
Sunnyside La. Yate 27 E1
Sunnyside Rd N. W-S-M ... 104 C3
Sunnyside Rd. Cleve 57 E2
Sunnyside Rd. W-S-M 104 C3
Sunnyside View. P St J 133 E4
Sunnyside. Bris 48 C3
Sunnyside. Clut 115 D2
Sunnyside. Fr Cot 38 A4
Sunnyvale Dr. Kingsw 66 A2
Sunnyvale. Cleve 57 D1
Sunnyvale. Tims 132 C4
Sunridge Cl. Mid No 137 F4
Sunridge Park. Mid No 137 F4
Sunridge. Mang 51 E3
Sunrise Gr. Bris 64 B2
Surrey Rd. Bris 49 F2
Surrey St. Bris 63 F4
Sussex Pl. Bris 49 F1
Sussex St. Bris 64 A3
Sutherland Ave. Bris 51 F4
Sutherland Ave. Yate 27 E2
Sutherland Dr. Lock 105 E1
Sutherland Pl. Bris 49 D1
Sutton Ave. Bris 64 B2
Sutton Hill Rd. Bi Sut 113 D2
Sutton La. Wring 93 F1
Sutton Park. Bi Sut 113 E2
Sutton St. Bath 102 A4
Swainswick Gdns. Bath 85 E1
Swainswick La. Bathe 85 E2
Swainswick. Bris 79 F3
Swaish Dr. Kingsw 66 A2
Swallow Cl. Rod 138 A4
Swallow Dr. Bris 35 F4
Swallow Gdns. W-S-M 105 F4
Swallow Park. Thorn 8 B2
Swallow St. Bath 102 A3
Swallows Ct. St Gif 36 C2
Swan Cl. W-S-M 105 F4
Swan La. Fr Cot 25 D1
Swan La. Wint 37 E4
Swancombe. Blag 110 C1
Swancombe. W in G 59 F4
Swane Rd. Bris 80 C3
Swangrove. Wint 37 F3
Swanley La. Newp 4 A3
Swanmoor Cres. Bris 35 D2
Sweets Cl. Kingsw 51 F1
Sweets Rd. Kingsw 51 F1
Swift Cl. W-S-M 88 C1
Swinhay La. N Nib 5 E1
Swiss Dr. Bris 62 C1
Swiss Rd. Bris 62 C1
Swiss Rd. W-S-M 104 C4
Sycamore Cl. Bris 50 C1
Sycamore Cl. Kingsw 65 D2
Sycamore Cl. Nail 59 F1
Sycamore Cl. Ship 125 F4
Sycamore Cl. W-S-M 105 D4
Sycamore Dr. Bris 35 F4

Sycamore Rd. Rad 133 D1
Sydenham Bldgs. Bath 101 F3
Sydenham Hill. Bris 49 E1
Sydenham La. Bris 49 F1
Sydenham Rd. Bath 101 F3
Sydenham Rd. Bris 49 E1
Sydenham Rd. Bris 64 A2
Sydenham Way. Kingsw 65 E2
Sydney Bldgs. Bath 102 A3
Sydney House. E in G 47 E2
Sydney Mews. Bath 102 A4
Sydney Pl. Bath 102 A4
Sydney Rd. Bath 102 A4
Sydney Row. Bris 63 D3
Sydney Wharf. Bath 102 A4
Sylvan Way. Bris 48 B4
Sylvia Ave. Bris 63 F2
Symes Ave. Bris 79 E2
Symington Rd. Bris 51 D3
Syston Way. Kingsw 51 E1

Tabernacle Rd. Kingsw 65 E3
Tackley Rd. Bris 50 A2
Tadwick La. Bathe 84 C4
Tailor's Ct. Bris 63 E4
Talbot Ave. Bris 51 E1
Talbot Rd. Bris 64 B1
Talgarth Rd. Bris 49 F2
Tallis Gr. Bris 79 E3
Tamar Cl. Thorn 15 E4
Tamar Dr. Keyn 82 A2
Tamar Rd. Bris 64 B3
Tamar Rd. W-S-M 89 D1
Tamblyn Cl. Mid No 133 D2
Tamsin Ct. Keyn 81 F3
Tamworth Rd. Keyn 81 F2
Tanhouse La. Ir Act 27 E4
Tanhouse La. Yate 27 E4
Tankard's Cl. Bris 63 E4
Tanner Cl. Kingsw 65 F3
Tanners Ct. Bris 37 D1
Tanners Ct. Thorn 15 D4
Tanners La. Marsh 69 F4
Tanorth Cl. Bris 80 A2
Tanorth Rd. Bris 79 F2
Tanyard The. Kingsw 66 A1
Tapsters. Kingsw 66 A2
Tarnock Ave. Bris 80 A4
Tarnwell. Pens 97 D1
Taunton Rd. W-S-M 89 D2
Taunton Wlk. Bris 50 A4
Taveners Ind Est. Nail 59 F2
Taverner Cl. Bris 79 E4
Tavistock Rd. Bris 63 F1
Tavistock Rd. W-S-M 89 D1
Tavistock Wlk. Bris 63 F1
Tawny Way. W-S-M 105 F4
Taylor Cl. Kingsw 65 F4
Taylor Ct. W-S-M 89 D2
Taylor Gdns. Bris 78 C2
Tayman Cl. Bris 49 F3
Tayman Ridge. Bitt 82 B4
Taynton Cl. Kingsw 66 B1
Teal Cl. St Gif 24 B1
Teal Cl. W-S-M 88 C1
Teddington Cl. Bath 101 E2
Teesdale Cl. W-S-M 105 E4
Teewell Ave. Kingsw 51 F2
Teewell Cl. Kingsw 51 F2
Teewell Hill. Kingsw 51 F2
Teignmouth Rd. Bris 63 F1
Teignmouth Rd. Cleve 57 F2
Telephone Ave. Bris 63 E3
Telford Wlk. Bris 51 D1
Tellisford La. N St P 135 F2
Templar Rd. Yate 27 F1
Temple Back. Bris 63 F3
Temple Gate. Bris 63 F3
Temple St. Bris 63 D1
Temple St. Bris 63 F3
Temple St. Keyn 81 F3
Temple Way Underpass.
    Bris 63 F4
Temple Way. Bris 63 F3
Templeland Rd. Bris 78 C3
Tenby Rd. Keyn 81 E2
Tenby St. Bris 64 A4
Tennessee Gr. Bris 49 E3
Tennis Court Ave. Paul 131 E3
Tennis Court Rd. Paul 131 E3
Tennis Rd. Bris 64 A1
Tenniscourt Rd. Kingsw 52 A1
Tennyson Ave. Cleve 57 D1
Tennyson Cl. Keyn 81 F3
Tennyson Rd. Bath 101 E4
Tennyson Rd. Bris 49 F3
Tennyson Rd. W-S-M 105 D2
Tenterk Cl. Blea 122 A3
Tenth Ave. Bris 36 A1
Tereslake Green. Bris 35 E2
Terrace Wlk. Bath 102 A3
Terrell Gdns. Bris 64 B4
Terrell St. Bris 63 E4
Terry Hill. Kilm 139 E4
Tetbury Cl. St Gif 36 B4
Tetbury Gdns. Nail 60 A1
Tetbury Rd. Bris 65 D4
Teviot Rd. Keyn 82 A2

Tewkesbury Rd. Bris 50 A1
Tewther Rd. Bris 79 E2
Teyfant Rd. Bris 79 F2
Teyfant Wlk. Bris 79 F2
Thackeray Ave. Cleve 57 F2
Thackeray Rd. Cleve 57 F2
Thackeray Wlk. Bris 50 A4
Thames Cl. Char 11 D2
Thanet Rd. Bris 63 D1
Thatcher Cl. Portis 45 E2
Thatchers Cl. Bris 65 D4
The Timbers. Rod 138 A4
The Triangle. Wring 92 B1
The Tyning. Hi Cha 120 A2
The Weal. Bath 84 B1
There-and-back-again La.
    Bris 63 E4
Theresa Ave. Bris 49 F2
Theynes Croft. Lo Ash 62 A1
Thicket Ave. Bris 51 E2
Thicket Rd. Bris 51 E2
Thicket Wlk. Thorn 8 B1
Thiery Rd. Bris 64 B1
Thingwall Park. Bris 50 C2
Third Ave. Bath 101 E3
Third Ave. Bris 36 A1
Third Ave. Rod 138 B4
Third Way. Avon 33 E1
Thirlmere Ct. Kingsw 66 B3
Thirlmere Rd. Bris 36 A4
Thirlmere Rd. W-S-M 105 D2
Thistle St. Bris 63 D2
Thomas Cl. Ban 107 D2
Thomas La. Bris 63 F3
Thomas Pring Wlk. Bris 51 D1
Thomas St N. Bris 49 E1
Thomas St. Bath 102 A4
Thomas St. Bris 49 F1
Thomas St. Bris 63 F4
Thomas St. Bris 64 A4
Thompson Rd. Bris 80 C3
Thomson Rd. Bris 64 A4
Thorn Cl. W-S-M 89 D1
Thorn Cl. Yate 27 E1
Thornbank Pl. Bath 101 F3
Thornbury Dr. W-S-M 104 B1
Thornbury Rd. Alve 15 D3
Thornbury Rd. W-S-M 104 B1
Thorndale Cl. W-S-M 105 E4
Thorndale. Bris 63 D4
Thornhayes Cl. Fr Cot 38 A4
Thornleigh Rd. Bris 49 F3
Thornmead Gr. Bris 35 D1
Thornycroft Cl. Bris 50 A4
Three Queens' La. Bris 63 F3
Three Wells Rd. Bris 78 C2
Thrissell St. Bris 64 A4
Throgmorton Rd. Bris 79 F4
Thrubwell La. But 94 A2
Thrush Cl. W-S-M 105 F4
Thurlestone. Bris 80 A3
Thurloe Rd. Bris 50 B1
Thurston's Barton. Bris 50 B1
Tibberton. Kingsw 66 A4
Tibbott Rd. Bris 80 B3
Tibbott Wlk. Bris 80 B3
Tichborne Rd. Bris 64 B4
Tichborne Rd. W-S-M 87 F1
Tickenham Hill. Nail 59 F3
Tickenham Rd. Cleve 58 A3
Tide Gr. Bris 48 A4
Tidenham Way. Bris 23 F1
Tiffany Ct. Bris 63 F3
Tiledown Cl. Clut 114 C1
Tiledown. Clut 114 C1
Tilley Cl. Farm 116 A3
Tilley Cl. Keyn 82 A1
Tilley La. Farm 115 F3
Tilling Rd. Bris 49 F4
Tilling Wlk. Bris 49 F4
Tilting Rd. Thorn 8 A1
Timber Dene. Bris 50 B2
Timbercombe Wlk. Bris 80 B3
Timsbury Rd. Bris 63 F1
Timsbury Rd. Farm 116 A3
Timsbury Rd. Paul 115 F1
Timsbury Wlk. Bris 63 F1
Tindell Ct. Kingsw 65 F2
Tinker's La. Co Mar 128 A4
Tinker's La. Hol 139 D1
Tintagel Cl. Keyn 81 E2
Tintern Ave. Bris 64 B4
Tintern Cl. Kingsw 65 F3
Tippetts Rd. Kingsw 65 E3
Tirley Way. W-S-M 88 A1
Titan Barrow. Bathf 86 B1
Tiverton Gdns. W-S-M 89 D1
Tiverton Rd. Cleve 57 F1
Tiverton Wlk. Bris 51 D1
Tockington La. Alm 24 A4
Tockington La. Olve 24 A4
Tockington La. Piln 24 A4
Tockington Park La. Alve .. 24 A4
Toddington Cl. Yate 39 E4
Toghill La. Doyn 68 A4
Toll Down Way. Burt 43 D2
Toll Rd. W-S-M 121 F4
Tolland. W-S-M 105 D1

Tollbridge Rd. Bath

Tollbridge Rd. Bath 85 F2
Tone Rd. Cleve 57 E1
Top Rd. Ship 125 F4
Tor Cl. W-S-M 89 D1
Tormarton Cres. Bris 34 C2
Tormarton Rd. A Tur 42 C3
Tormarton Rd. Marsh 56 A2
Tormarton Rd. Marsh 70 A4
Tormynton Rd. W-S-M 88 C2
Toronto Rd. Bris 50 A4
Torpoint Rd. Bris 63 E1
Torrance Cl. Kingsw 66 B3
Torridge Rd. Keyn 82 A2
Torrington Ave. Bris 79 F4
Torrington Cres. W-S-M 89 D2
Tortworth Rd. Bris 49 F3
Totnes Cl. W-S-M 89 D1
Totshill Dr. Bris 79 F2
Totshill Gr. Bris 79 F2
Totterdown La. W-S-M 105 D1
Totterdown Rd. W-S-M 104 C2
Touching End La. Marsh 69 F4
Touchstone Ave. St Gif 36 C3
Tovey Rd. W-S-M 88 C2
Tower Hill. Bris 63 F4
Tower House La. Wrax 60 A2
Tower La. Bris 63 E4
Tower La. Kingsw 66 A3
Tower Rd N. Kingsw 66 A4
Tower Rd S. Kingsw 66 A3
Tower Rd. Bris 51 E1
Tower Rd. Portis 45 D2
Tower St. Bris 63 F3
Tower Wlk. W-S-M 87 E1
Towerhead Rd. Ban 107 E2
Town Barton. N St P 135 F2
Town End. N St P 135 F2
Townsend Cl. Bris 80 C3
Townsend La. Alm 23 A3
Townsend Rd. Bris 80 C3
Townsend Rd. W-S-M 89 D3
Townsend. Alm 23 F2
Townsend. E Harp 129 D3
Townwell. Crom 10 A1
Tracy Wlk. Bris 79 F4
Trafalgar Rd. Bath 84 A1
Trafalgar Terr. Bris 63 D1
Tralee Wlk. Bris 63 E1
Tramway Rd. Bris 64 B2
Tranmere Ave. Bris 35 D2
Tranmere Gr. Bris 35 D2
Tranton La. Rock 2 B2
Tratman Wlk. Bris 34 C2
Travers Cl. Bris 79 E3
Travers Wlk. St Gif 36 C3
Trawden Cl. W-S-M 88 A1
Tredegar Rd. Bris 51 D2
Tree Leaze. Yate 27 F1
Treefield Pl. Bris 50 A1
Treefield Rd. Cleve 57 E1
Tregarth Rd. Bris 62 C1
Trelawn Cl. Lock 89 E1
Trelawney Ave. Bris 64 B4
Trelawney Park. Bris 64 B2
Trelawney Rd. Bris 49 E1
Tremlett Mews. W-S-M 89 D2
Trench La. St Gif 25 D1
Trenchard Rd. Keyn 82 B2
Trenchard St. Bris 63 E4
Trendlewood Park. Bris 50 C3
Trendlewood Way. Nail 60 A1
Trenleigh Dr. W-S-M 89 D1
Trent Dr. Thorn 15 E4
Trent Gr. Keyn 82 A2
Trentham Cl. Bris 50 A1
Tresham Cl. St Gif 24 B1
Trevanna Rd. Bris 62 C1
Trevelyan Rd. W-S-M 104 C4
Trevelyan Wlk. Bris 34 C2
Treverdowe Wlk. Bris 34 B2
Trevethin Cl. Kingsw 65 E4
Trevisa Gr. Bris 35 E2
Trewartha Cl. W-S-M 104 C4
Trewartha Park. W-S-M 104 C4
Trewint Gdns. Bris 79 F4
Triangle Centre The. Cleve . 57 E2
Triangle E. Bath 101 E3
Triangle N. Bath 101 E3
Triangle South. Bris 63 D4
Triangle The. Cleve 57 E2
Triangle W. Bath 101 E3
Triangle West. Bris 63 D4
Trident Cl. Mang 38 A1
Trim Bridge. Bath 101 F3
Trim St. Bath 101 F3
Trin Mills. Bris 63 E3
Trinder Rd. E in G 47 D2
Trinity Cl. Bath 101 F3
Trinity Ct. Nail 59 E1
Trinity Pl. W-S-M 87 E1
Trinity Rd. Bath 102 A1
Trinity Rd. Bris 64 A4
Trinity Rd. Nail 59 E1
Trinity Rd. W-S-M 87 E1
Trinity St. Bath 101 F3
Trinity St. Bris 63 E3
Trinity Wlk. Bris 64 A4
Tripps Cnr. Yatt 91 E4

Troon Dr. Kingsw 66 A3
Troon. Yate 39 F4
Troopers Hill Rd. Bris 65 D4
Trossachs Dr. Bath 102 B4
Trowbridge Rd. Bris 35 E1
Trowbridge Wlk. Bris 35 E1
Truro Rd. Bris 63 D2
Truro Rd. Nail 60 A1
Trym Cross Rd. Bris 48 B3
Trym Rd. Bris 49 D4
Trym Side. Bris 48 B3
Trymleaze. Bris 48 B3
Trymwood Cl. Bris 34 C1
Tucker St. Bris 63 F4
Tucker's La. Co Mar 127 F4
Tuckett La. Bris 51 E4
Tuckingmill La. Co Dan 98 C3
Tuckmill. Cleve 57 D1
Tudor Cl. Kingsw 66 B2
Tudor Mews. W-S-M 104 C4
Tudor Rd. Bris 49 F1
Tudor Rd. Bris 50 B1
Tudor Rd. Kingsw 65 E3
Tudor Rd. Portis 45 F2
Tudor Rd. W-S-M 89 D2
Tuffley Rd. Bris 49 E4
Tugela Rd. Bris 78 C4
Tuggy's La. Hin Cha 119 F1
Tunbridge Rd. Bris 35 E2
Tunbury Ave. Nail 60 A1
Tunbury Cl. W-S-M 88 C2
Tunbury. Yate 39 F4
Turner Cl. Keyn 82 A3
Turner Ct. W-S-M 88 C2
Turner Gdns. Bris 50 A3
Turner Way. Cleve 57 D1
Turner's Terr. Faulk 134 A1
Turners Ct. Kingsw 65 F2
Turnpike Gate. Wickw 18 A3
Turnpike Rd. Co Bi 124 C2
Turnpike Rd. Ship 125 F4
Turtlegate Ave. Bris 78 C2
Turtlegate Wlk. Bris 78 C2
Turville Dr. Bris 50 A3
Tutton Way. Cleve 57 F1
Tweed Cl. Thorn 15 E4
Tweed Rd. Cleve 57 E1
Tweeny La. Kingsw 66 B3
Twenty Acres Rd. Bris 35 D1
Twerton Farm Cl. Bath 101 D3
Twickenham Rd. Bris 49 E3
Twinhoe La. Well 118 C1
Two Acres Rd. Bris 80 A4
Two Mile Ct. Bris 65 E4
Two Stones La. Ch Sod 40 B4
Two Trees. Priddy 126 C4
Twomile Hill Rd. Bris 65 F4
Twynings The. Kingsw 51 F1
Tybalt Way. St Gif 36 C3
Tyler Cl. Kingsw 65 F3
Tyler Green. W-S-M 89 D2
Tyler St. Bris 64 A3
Tyndale Ave. Bris 51 D2
Tyndale Ave. Yate 27 E2
Tyndale Cl. N Nib 5 F2
Tyndale Rd. Kingsw 51 F1
Tyndale View. Thorn 15 D4
Tyndall Ave. Bris 63 E4
Tyndall Rd. Bris 64 A4
Tyndall's Park Mews. Bris ... 63 E4
Tyndall's Park Rd. Bris 63 E4
Tyne Rd. Bris 49 D4
Tyne St. Bris 50 A1
Tyning Cl. Bris 80 A4
Tyning Cl. Yate 27 F1
Tyning End. Bath 102 A3
Tyning Hill. Mid No 133 D2
Tyning La. Bath 85 D1
Tyning Rd. Bath 85 F1
Tyning Rd. Bath 102 B3
Tyning Rd. Bris 79 F2
Tyning Rd. Keyn 82 C1
Tyning Rd. P St J 133 E4
Tyning Rd. Winsl 120 C4
Tyning The. Bath 102 A3
Tynings The. Cleve 57 D1
Tynings Way. Clut 114 C2
Tynings Way. Westw 120 C2
Tynte Ave. Bris 79 E2
Tyntesfield Rd. Bris 79 D2
Tyrone Wlk. Bris 79 E4
Tyrrel Way. St Gif 36 C3
Tytherington Rd. Alve 16 A3

Ubley Dr. Priddy 127 D4
Ullswater Cl. Kingsw 66 B3
Ullswater Cl. Yate 27 F1
Ullswater Dr. Bath 85 D1

Ulswater Rd. Bris 35 E1
Uncombe Cl. Back 76 B4
Under La. Wring 93 E1
Underbanks. E in G 47 E2
Underhill Ave. Mid No 131 F1
Underhill Dr. W-S-M 104 B1
Underhill La. Mid No 131 F1
Underhill La. Ston E 131 F1
Underleaf Way. P St J 133 E4
Undertown La. Co Mar 128 A4
Undertown. Co Mar 128 A4
Underwood Ave. W-S-M 88 A1
Underwood Cl. Alve 15 D2
Underwood End. Wins 108 A2
Underwood Rd. Portis 45 E2
Union Pas. Bath 102 A3
Union Pl. W-S-M 104 B4
Union Rd. Bris 64 A3
Union St. Bath 102 A3
Union St. Bris 63 F4
Union St. Nail 59 E1
Union St. W-S-M 104 B4
Unity Cl. Keyn 82 A3
Unity Rd. Keyn 82 A3
Unity St. Bris 63 E3
Unity St. Bris 63 F4
Unity St. Bris 65 E4
University Cl. Bris 48 C2
University Rd. Bris 63 E4
University Wlk. Bris 63 E4
Uphill Dr. Bath 85 D1
Uphill Rd N. W-S-M 104 B2
Uphill Rd S. W-S-M 104 C1
Uphill Rd. Bris 49 F3
Uphill Way. W-S-M 104 B1
Upjohn Cres. Bris 79 E2
Uplands Cl. Li St 119 F4
Uplands Dr. Keyn 82 C1
Uplands Rd. Bris 51 E2
Uplands Rd. Keyn 82 C1
Uplands The. Nail 75 E4
Upper Bath Rd. Thorn 15 D4
Upper Belgrave Rd. Bris 49 D1
Upper Belmont Rd. Bris 49 F1
Upper Berkeley Pl. Bris 63 D4
Upper Bloomfield Rd.
   Bath 101 E1
Upper Borough Walls.
   Bath 101 F3
Upper Bristol Rd. Bath 101 E4
Upper Bristol Rd. Clut 114 B2
Upper Bristol Rd. W-S-M 88 A1
Upper Byron Pl. Bris 63 D4
Upper Chapel La. Fr Cot 38 B3
Upper Cheltenham Pl. Bris .. 49 F1
Upper Church La. Bris 63 E4
Upper Church La. Lock 105 E1
Upper Church Rd. W-S-M 87 E1
Upper Church St. Bath 101 F3
Upper Cranbrook Rd. Bris ... 49 D2
Upper East Hayes. Bath 85 D1
Upper Farm Cl. N St P 135 F2
Upper Hedgemead Rd.
   Bath 102 A4
Upper Lambridge St. Bath ... 85 E1
Upper Lansdown Mews.
   Bath 84 C1
Upper Maudlin St. Bris 63 E4
Upper Mount Pleasant.
   Hi Cha 120 A2
Upper Myrtle Hill. E in G 47 E2
Upper New Rd. Ched 115 E2
Upper Oldfield Park. Bath . 101 F3
Upper Perry Hill. Bris 63 E2
Upper Pitching. Chil 137 E3
Upper Rd. Hin Ble 129 F3
Upper Sandhurst Rd. Bris ... 64 B2
Upper St. Bris 64 A2
Upper St. Dyrh 54 C2
Upper Stanton. Pens 97 D1
Upper Station Rd. Kingsw ... 51 E2
Upper Stone Cl. Fr Cot 38 B4
Upper Strode. Win 111 F4
Upper Sydney St. Bris 63 D2
Upper Tockington Rd. Olve . 14 A1
Upper Town La. Bath 94 B4
Upper Wells St. Bris 63 E4
Upper York St. Bris 63 F4
Upton La. Ch Mag 95 F4
Upton La. Dun 95 F4
Upton Rd. Bris 63 D2
Upton. W-S-M 105 D1
Urchinwood La. Cong 91 F2
Urfords Dr. Bris 51 E3

Vain End. W-S-M 88 C2
Valda Rd. W-S-M 88 B1
Vale Cres. Lock 89 E1
Vale End. Nail 59 E1
Vale La. Bris 79 E4
Vale St. Bris 64 A2
Vale The. Puck 52 C3
Vale View Terr. Bathe 85 F2
Vale View. Rad 133 D1
Valentine Cl. Bris 80 A3
Valerian Cl. Bris 47 F3
Valetta Cl. W-S-M 104 C2

Valley Cl. Nail 59 F1
Valley Gdns. Mang 51 F4
Valley Gdns. Nail 59 F1
Valley Rd. Bris 79 D4
Valley Rd. Cleve 57 F3
Valley Rd. Kingsw 66 B3
Valley Rd. Lo Ash 62 B4
Valley Rd. Mang 52 A3
Valley Rd. Portis 44 C2
Valley Rd. W in G 45 D1
Valley View Cl. Bath 85 D2
Valley View Rd. Bath 85 E2
Valley View Rd. Paul 131 F3
Valley Way Rd. Nail 59 F2
Valley View. Clut 114 C2
Valley Wlk. Mid No 132 A1
Valls The. St Gif 36 C3
Valma Rocks. Bris 65 D3
Van Diemen's La. Bath 84 C1
Vandyke Ave. Keyn 81 F3
Vane St. Bath 102 A4
Vassall Ct. Bris 51 D3
Vassall Rd. Bris 51 D3
Vattingstone La. Alve 14 C3
Vaughan Cl. Bris 34 C2
Vayre Cl. Ch Sod 28 A1
Veale The. Blea 122 B3
Vee La. Win 94 B4
Vellore La. Bath 102 A4
Ventnor Ave. Bris 64 C4
Ventnor Rd. Bris 36 A2
Ventnor Rd. Bris 50 C1
Venus La. Clut 114 C2
Venus St. Cong 91 F1
Vera Rd. Bris 50 C1
Verbena Way. W-S-M 89 D1
Vereland Rd. Lock 105 F2
Verlands. Cong 91 F3
Vernals La. N Nib 11 E4
Vernham Gr. Bath 101 E1
Vernon Cl. Keyn 82 B2
Vernon La. Co Bi 124 A2
Vernon Park. Bath 101 E3
Vernon St. Bris 63 F2
Vernon Terr. Bath 101 E3
Vernslade. Bath 84 A1
Verrier Rd. Bris 64 B4
Verwood Dr. Kingsw 66 B1
Vicarage Cl. W-S-M 89 D2
Vicarage Ct. Kingsw 65 D3
Vicarage Gdns. P St J 133 D4
Vicarage La. Ba Gu 77 E3
Vicarage La. Co Bi 124 A2
Vicarage La. Co Dan 98 B3
Vicarage La. Hill 19 E4
Vicarage La. N St P 135 F2
Vicarage La. Olve 14 A2
Vicarage Rd. Bris 63 D2
Vicarage Rd. Bris 64 B4
Vicarage Rd. Bris 79 D3
Vicarage Rd. Fr Cot 38 B3
Vicarage Rd. Kingsw 65 D3
Vicarage Rd. Lo Ash 62 B3
Vicarage Rd. Piln 22 B4
Vicars Cl. Bris 51 D2
Victor Rd. Bris 63 E2
Victor St. Bris 64 A3
Victoria Ave. Bris 64 B4
Victoria Bldgs. Bath 101 E3
Victoria Bridge Rd. Bath ... 101 F3
Victoria Cl. Bath 101 E3
Victoria Cl. Portis 45 E3
Victoria Cl. Thorn 8 A2
Victoria Cotts. Sosto 118 C4
Victoria Cres. Piln 22 A3
Victoria Ct. Portis 45 E3
Victoria Gdns. Bathe 85 F2
Victoria Gdns. Bris 49 E1
Victoria Gr. Bris 63 F2
Victoria Parade. Bris 64 B4
Victoria Park. Bris 51 D3
Victoria Park. Bris 51 E1
Victoria Park. W-S-M 87 E1
Victoria Pl. Bris 63 E2
Victoria Pl. Paul 131 E3
Victoria Pl. W-S-M 104 B4
Victoria Quadrant. W-S-M . 104 B4
Victoria Rd. Avon 47 D4
Victoria Rd. Bath 101 E3
Victoria Rd. Bris 64 A3
Victoria Rd. Cleve 57 F2
Victoria Rd. Keyn 82 B2
Victoria Rd. Kingsw 65 E3
Victoria Rd. Kingsw 66 B3
Victoria Sq. Bris 63 D4
Victoria Sq. Portis 45 E3
Victoria Sq. W-S-M 104 B4
Victoria St. Bris 63 F3
Victoria St. Mang 51 E3
Victoria Terr. Bath 101 E3
Victoria Terr. Bris 62 C3
Victoria Terr. Bris 64 A3
Victoria Terr. Paul 131 F3
Victoria Wlk. Bris 49 E1
Vigor Rd. Bris 79 D3
Village Cl. Yate 27 E1
Villice La. Co Mar 128 A4
Villiers Rd. Bris 50 A1

Wardour Rd. Bris

Vilner La. Thorn 15 D4
Vimpany Cl. Bris 34 C2
Vimpennys La. Alm 22 C1
Vincent Cl. Bris 34 B1
Vine Gdns. W-S-M 89 D1
Viner's La. A Tur 43 D3
Vinery The. Wins 125 D4
Vineyard La. Kings 11 F3
Vining Wlk. Bris 64 A4
Vinney Ave. Mang 52 A4
Vinney La. Hort 28 C4
Vintery Leys. Bris 49 D4
Virginia Cl. Ch Sod 28 A1
Vivian St. Bris 63 E2
Vivien Ave. Mid No 132 A1
Vowell Cl. Bris 79 D2
Vynes Cl. Nail 60 A1
Vynes Way. Nail 60 A1
Vyvyan Rd. Bris 63 D4
Vyvyan Terr. Bris 63 D4

Wade Rd. Yate 27 D2
Wade St. Bris 63 F4
Wadehurst Ind Pk. Bris 64 A4
Wades Rd. Bris 36 A2
Wadham Dr. Bris 37 D1
Wadham St. W-S-M 104 B4
Wagtail Gdns. W-S-M 105 F4
Wainbridge Cres. Piln 22 B4
Wainbrook Dr. Bris 50 B1
Wainwright Cl. W-S-M 89 D2
Waits Cl. Ban 106 C2
Wakedean Gdns. Yatt 74 A1
Wakeford Rd. Mang 52 A4
Walcot Gate. Bath 102 A4
Walcot St. Bath 102 A4
Waldegrave House. Bris 79 E2
Waldegrave Rd. Bath 84 C1
Waldegrave Terr. Mid No .. 133 D2
Walden Rd. Keyn 82 A2
Walford Ave. Lock 89 D2
Walk Mill La. Kings 11 F2
Walk The. Kings 11 F3
Walker Cl. Bris 64 A4
Walker Cl. Mang 52 A4
Walker St. Bris 63 E4
Walker Way. Thorn 15 D4
Wall Green. Axb 125 E1
Wallace La. E Harp 128 C2
Wallace Rd. Bath 85 D1
Wallenge Cl. Paul 131 F3
Wallenge Dr. Paul 131 F3
Walley La. Ch Mag 113 D4
Wallingford Rd. Bris 79 E4
Walliscote Ave. Bris 49 E3
Walliscote Grove Rd.
   W-S-M 104 C4
Walliscote Rd S. W-S-M 104 B2
Walliscote Rd. Bris 49 E3
Walliscote Rd. W-S-M 104 B3
Wallscourt Rd S. Bris 36 A1
Wallscourt Rd. Bris 36 A1
Wallsend La. Tor 55 E3
Wallycourt Rd. Ch St 112 C4
Walnut Ave. Yate 28 A1
Walnut Bldgs. Mid No 133 D2
Walnut Cl. Axb 125 D1
Walnut Cl. E in G 47 D2
Walnut Cl. Keyn 81 E2
Walnut Cl. Kingsw 51 F1
Walnut Cl. Nail 75 F4
Walnut Cl. Thorn 8 B1
Walnut Cl. W-S-M 105 D1
Walnut Cres. Kingsw 65 F4
Walnut Dr. Bath 101 F2
Walnut Dr. Col 70 C3
Walnut La. Kingsw 66 A4
Walnut Tree Cl. Alm 24 A3
Walnut Wlk. Bris 79 D3
Walnut Wlk. Keyn 81 E2
Walsh Ave. Bris 80 A4
Walsh Cl. W-S-M 105 D1
Walshe Ave. Ch Sod 28 A1
Walsingham Rd. Bris 49 F1
Walter St. Bris 63 D2
Walton Ave. Bris 64 B3
Walton Cl. Keyn 81 E2
Walton Cl. Kingsw 66 B1
Walton Dro. W in G 58 B3
Walton Heath. Yate 27 F1
Walton Rd. Bris 47 E3
Walton Rd. Cleve 57 F2
Walton Rise. Bris 49 D4
Walton St. Bris 50 A1
Walton. W-S-M 105 D1
Walwyn Cl. Bath 101 D3
Walwyn Gdns. Bris 79 E2
Wansbeck Rd. Keyn 82 A2
Wansbrough Rd. W-S-M 89 D2
Wanscow Wlk. Bris 49 D3
Wansdyke Ct. Bris 80 A3
Wansdyke Rd. Bath 101 E1
Wapley Hill. West 39 F2
Wapley Rd. Dod 40 A2
Wapping Rd. Bris 63 E3
Warden Rd. Bris 63 E2
Wardour Rd. Bris 79 E4

Wareham Cl. Nail

Wareham Cl. Nail 59 E1
Warleigh Dr. Bathe 86 A2
Warleigh La. Bathf 103 E3
Warleigh La. Mon Far 103 E3
Warman Cl. Bris 80 C3
Warman Rd. Bris 80 C3
Warmington Rd. Bris 80 B4
Warminster Rd. Bath 103 D3
Warminster Rd. Bris 50 A1
Warminster Rd. Hin Cha ... 119 F3
Warminster Rd. Li St 120 A4
Warne Park. W-S-M 105 D3
Warne Rd. W-S-M 105 D3
Warner Cl. Brock 92 A4
Warner Cl. Kingsw 65 F3
Warns The. Kingsw 66 A2
Warren Cl. Lock 105 E1
Warren Cl. St Gif 24 B2
Warren Croft. N Nib 5 F2
Warren Gdns. Bris 80 C3
Warren La. Lo Ash 61 F1
Warren Rd. Bris 36 A2
Warren Way. Yate 27 F2
Warrilow Cl. W-S-M 89 D3
Warrington Rd. Bris 64 B1
Warth La. W ST L 89 D4
Warwick Ave. Bris 50 A1
Warwick Cl. Kingsw 66 A1
Warwick Cl. Thorn 8 A1
Warwick Cl. W-S-M 105 E4
Warwick Gdns. Clut 114 B2
Warwick Rd. Bath 101 D4
Warwick Rd. Bris 49 D1
Warwick Rd. Bris 50 A1
Warwick Rd. Keyn 81 E2
Washing Pound La. Nail 59 D2
Washing Pound La. Whit 80 A2
Washingpool Hill Rd. Olve .. 14 B3
Washingpool La. Avon 33 F4
Washington Ave. Bris 50 B1
Washpool La. Engl 100 C1
Watch Elm Cl. St Gif 36 C3
Watchhouse Rd. E in G 47 E2
Watchill Ave. Bris 78 E3
Watchill Cl. Bris 78 C3
Water La. Bris 63 F2
Water La. Bris 63 F3
Water La. Bris 64 B1
Water La. E in G 47 E2
Water La. Kingsw 65 D1
Water La. Mid No 132 A2
Water St. E Harp 128 C2
Water's La. Bris 49 D4
Waterbridge Rd. Bris 78 C3
Watercress Rd. Bris 49 F2
Waterdale Cl. Bris 49 E4
Waterdale Gdns. Bris 49 E4
Waterford Cl. Thorn 15 E4
Waterford Park. Rad 132 C1
Waterford Rd. Bris 49 D3
Waterloo Bldgs. Bath 101 D3
Waterloo Pl. Bris 64 A4
Waterloo Rd. Bris 63 F4
Waterloo Rd. Rad 133 D1
Waterloo St. Bris 62 C4
Waterloo St. Bris 63 F4
Waterloo St. W-S-M 104 B4
Watermore Cl. Fr Cot 38 B4
Waters Rd. Bris 65 E4
Waters Rd. Kingsw 65 E4
Waterside Cres. Rad 132 B1
Waterside Dr. St Gif 24 A1
Waterside La. Kilm 138 C3
Waterside Park. Portis 44 B2
Waterside Rd. Rad 132 B1
Waterside Way. Rod 138 B4
Watery La. Bath 101 D3
Watery La. Chil 138 A2
Watery La. Doyn 68 A4
Watery La. Nail 59 E1
Watery La. Win 95 D2
Wathen Rd. Bris 49 F2
Watkins Yd. Bris 49 D4
Watley's End Rd. Wint 37 F4
Watling Way. Bris 47 E4
Watson Ave. Bris 64 B2
Watson's Rd. Kingsw 65 F2
Watters Cl. Fr Cot 38 B3
Wavell Cl. Yate 27 E2
Waveney Rd. Keyn 82 A2
Waverley Rd. Back 76 A4
Waverley Rd. Bris 47 F3
Waverley Rd. Bris 49 E1
Waverley Rd. Ir Act 27 D1
Waverley Rd. W-S-M 104 C2
Waverley St. Bris 50 A1
Wayacre Dro. Blea 121 F3
Wayfield Gdns. Bathe 85 F2
Wayford Cl. Keyn 82 A2
Wayland Rd. W-S-M 88 C2
Wayleaze. Fr Cot 38 B4
Wayside Cl. Fr Cot 38 A4
Wayside Dr. Cleve 57 F3
Wayside. W-S-M 88 B1
Weare Ct. Bris 63 D3
Weatherley Ave. Bath 101 E1
Weavers Cl. Kings 11 F2
Webb St. Bris 64 A4

Webbington Rd. Co Bi 124 B2
Webbs Heath. Sist 66 C4
Webbs Wood Rd. St Gif 36 C3
Webbs Wood. St Gif 36 C4
Wedgewood Rd. Mang 37 E1
Wedgwood Cl. Bris 80 A3
Wedgwood Rd. Bath 101 D3
Wedmore Cl. Kingsw 65 F4
Wedmore Park. Bath 101 D2
Wedmore Rd. Cleve 57 D1
Wedmore Rd. Keyn 82 B2
Wedmore Rd. Nail 75 F4
Wedmore Vale. Bris 63 F1
Weedon Cl. Bris 50 A1
Weekesley La. Tims 116 B1
Weetwood Rd. Cong 91 F3
Weight Rd. Bris 64 B4
Weind The. W-S-M 88 B1
Weir La. Ab Lei 61 F3
Weir La. Marsh 69 F4
Weir Rd. Cong 91 F2
Well Cl. Lo Ash 62 A1
Well Cl. W-S-M 105 D1
Well Cl. Wins 125 D4
Well House Cl. Bris 48 C2
Well La. Yatt 91 E4
Well Park. Cong 91 F2
Welland Rd. Keyn 81 F2
Wellard Cl. W-S-M 89 D2
Wellgarth Rd. Bris 64 A1
Wellgarth Wlk. Bris 64 A1
Wellington Ave. Bris 49 F1
Wellington Bldgs. Bath 84 A1
Wellington Cres. Bris 49 F1
Wellington Dr. Bris 49 E3
Wellington Dr. Yate 27 D1
Wellington Hill W. Bris 49 F3
Wellington Hill. Bris 49 F3
Wellington La. Bris 49 F1
Wellington Mews. Bris 47 E3
Wellington Park. Bris 49 D1
Wellington Pl. Bris 37 D1
Wellington Pl. W-S-M 104 B4
Wellington Rd. Bris 63 F4
Wellington Rd. Kingsw 51 E1
Wellington Rd. Yate 27 F2
Wellington Terr. Cleve 57 E3
Wellington Wlk. Bris 49 E4
Wellow La. Hin Cha 119 E1
Wellow La. N St P 135 E3
Wellow La. P St J 133 E3
Wellow Mead. P St J 133 D4
Wellow Rd. Well 134 A4
Wellow Tyning. P St J 133 E3
Wells Cl. Bris 80 B3
Wells Cl. Nail 60 A1
Wells Rd. Bath 101 F3
Wells Rd. Bris 64 A1
Wells Rd. Bris 80 B4
Wells Rd. Ch Mag 95 F4
Wells Rd. Chil 137 F2
Wells Rd. Cleve 57 E1
Wells Rd. Dun 95 F4
Wells Rd. Mid No 132 B1
Wells Rd. N St P 135 E2
Wells Rd. Paul 131 D3
Wells Sq. Rad 132 B1
Wells St. Bris 63 D2
Wellsea Gr. W-S-M 105 D4
Wellstead Ave. Yate 27 E1
Wellsway. Bath 101 F1
Wellsway. Keyn 81 F2
Welsford Ave. Bris 50 B2
Welsford Rd. Bris 50 B2
Welsh Back. Bris 63 E3
Welton Gr. Mid No 132 A2
Welton Rd. Rad 132 C1
Welton Vale. Mid No 132 A1
Welton Wlk. Bris 50 A1
Wemberham Cres. Yatt 74 A1
Wemberham La. Yalt 90 C4
Wenmore Cl. Mang 37 E1
Wentforth Dr. Bris 51 E1
Wentwood Dr. W-S-M 105 D1
Wentworth Rd. Bris 49 E2
Wentworth. Kingsw 66 A3
Wentworth. Yate 27 F1
Wesley Ave. Kingsw 65 E2
Wesley Ave. Rad 132 B1
Wesley Cl. Kingsw 51 E2
Wesley Dr. W-S-M 89 D2
Wesley Hill. Kingsw 51 E1
Wesley La. Kingsw 51 E1
Wesley Pl. Bris 49 D1
Wesley Rd. Bris 49 D4
Wesley St. Bris 63 E2
Wessex Ave. Bris 49 F4
Wessex Rd. W-S-M 105 D1
West Ave. Bath 101 E3
West Broadway. Bris 49 E3
West Cl. Bath 101 D3
West Coombe. Bris 48 B3
West Croft. Bris 49 E4
West Croft. Cleve 57 D1
West Dene. Bris 48 B3
West Dundry La. Dun 78 C1
West End. Bris 63 E3

West End. Bris 63 E4
West Garston. Ban 107 D2
West Gr. Bris 49 F1
West Hay Rd. Wring 92 B2
West Hill Gdns. Portis 45 E3
West Hill Gdns. Rad 132 C1
West Hill Rd. Rad 132 B1
West Hill. Portis 45 E3
West Hill. Wrax 60 A3
West La. Win 94 A4
West Lea Rd. Bath 84 A1
West Leaze Pl. St Gif 36 C3
West Links Cl. W-S-M 88 A2
West Littleton Rd. Marsh 55 F1
West Mall. Bris 62 C4
West Par. Bris 48 B4
West Park Rd. Mang 51 F3
West Park. Bris 63 D4
West Point Row. St Gif 24 B2
West Priory Cl. Bris 49 D4
West Rd. Lymp 122 A1
West Rd. Mid No 132 A2
West Ridge. Fr Cot 38 B4
West Rocke Ave. Bris 48 B3
West Rolstone Rd. Ban 89 F1
West Shrubbery. Bris 49 D1
West St. Axb 125 D1
West St. Ban 107 D2
West St. Bris 63 E2
West St. Bris 63 F4
West St. Kingsw 65 E4
West St. Tyth 16 A3
West St. W-S-M 104 B4
West Town Ave. Bris 64 B1
West Town Gr. Bris 80 B4
West Town La. Bris 64 B1
West Town Park. Bris 80 B4
West Town Rd. Back 76 A3
West Town Rd. Bris 47 E4
West Tyning. Marks 99 F1
West View Rd. Bathe 86 A2
West View Rd. Bris 63 D2
West View Rd. Keyn 81 F3
West View. Alve 14 C2
West Way. Bris 35 F2
West Way. Cleve 57 F2
West Wick. Lock 89 E1
West Wlk. Yate 27 F1
West. St Gif 24 A1
Westacre Cl. Bris 35 D1
Westaway Cl. Yatt 91 E4
Westaway Park. Yatt 91 E4
Westbourn Rd. Bris 64 A4
Westbourne Ave. Cleve 57 D1
Westbourne Ave. Keyn 81 F3
Westbourne Cres. Cleve 57 D1
Westbourne Gr. Bris 63 E2
Westbourne Pl. Bris 63 D4
Westbourne Rd. Mang 51 F4
Westbourne Terr. Bris 51 F4
Westbrook Park. Charl 84 A1
Westbrook Rd. Bris 80 B4
Westbrook Rd. W-S-M 88 B1
Westbrooke Ct. Bris 63 D3
Westbury Court Rd. Bris 49 D4
Westbury Cres. W-S-M 104 C1
Westbury Ct. Bris 49 D4
Westbury Hill. Bris 49 D4
Westbury La. Bris 48 B4
Westbury Park. Bris 49 D2
Westbury Rd. Bris 49 D2
Westcourt Dr. Kingsw 66 A2
Westcroft. Blag 110 C1
Westend La. O-on-S 7 D3
Westend Rd. Wickw 17 F3
Westend Rd. Yate 17 F3
Westering Cl. Mang 52 A3
Westerleigh Cl. Mang 51 F4
Westerleigh Rd. Bath 102 A1
Westerleigh Rd. Cleve 57 D1
Westerleigh Rd. Mang 52 A4
Westerleigh Rd. Puck 53 E4
Westerleigh Rd. West 39 E2
Westerleigh Rd. Yate 39 E4
Western Ave. Fr Cot 26 A1
Western Ct. Cleve 57 E2
Western Dr. Bris 79 F3
Western La. E Harp 128 B2
Western La. Priddy 128 B2
Western Rd. Bris 49 F3
Westfield Cl. Back 76 A3
Westfield Cl. Bath 101 F2
Westfield Cl. Keyn 81 E3
Westfield Cl. Kingsw 65 E3
Westfield Cl. W-S-M 104 B1
Westfield Cres. Ban 107 D2
Westfield Dr. Back 76 A3
Westfield Ind and Trading Est.
   Rod 138 B4
Westfield La. St Gif 36 C2
Westfield Park S. Bath 101 D4
Westfield Park. Bath 101 D4
Westfield Park. Bris 49 D1
Westfield Pl. Bris 62 C4
Westfield Rd. Back 76 A3
Westfield Rd. Ban 107 D2

Westfield Rd. Bris 49 D4
Westfield Rd. W-S-M 104 B1
Westfield Terr. Rad 132 B1
Westfield Way. St Gif 24 B1
Westfield. Cleve 73 E4
Westgate Bldgs. Bath 101 F3
Westgate St. Bath 101 F3
Westhall Rd. Bath 101 E4
West Hill Gdns. Portis 45 E3
Westland Ave. Kingsw 66 B2
Westleigh Cl. Yate 27 E1
Westleigh Park. Bris 80 A4
Westleigh Rd. Bris 35 E1
Westmarch Way. W-S-M 89 D2
Westmarsh La. O-on-S 7 D3
Westmarsh. O-on-S 7 D3
Westmead Gdns. Charl 84 A1
Westmead Rd. Bris 65 D4
Westminster Cl. Bris 49 D4
Westminster Rd. Bris 64 B4
Westmoreland Dr. Bath 101 F3
Westmoreland Rd. Bath 101 F3
Westmoreland Rd. Bris 49 D2
Westmoreland St. Bath 101 F3
Westmoreland Station Rd.
   Bath 101 F3
Westmorland Terr. Ch Sod .. 41 E4
Weston Ave. Bris 64 B4
Weston Cl. Bris 48 B4
Weston Cres. Bris 49 F3
Weston Dro. W in G 58 C4
Weston Farm La. Bath 84 A1
Weston Ind Est. W-S-M 105 D2
Weston La. Bath 101 E4
Weston Park Court. Bath 84 B1
Weston Park E. Bath 84 B1
Weston Park W. Bath 84 B1
Weston Park. Bath 84 B1
Weston Rd. Bath 101 E4
Weston Rd. Berr 121 D3
Weston Rd. Cong 91 D3
Weston Rd. Lo Ash 77 E4
Weston Rd. Wrax 61 D2
Weston Way. Lock 105 F1
Weston Wood Rd. Portis 45 E2
Westons Way. Kingsw 65 F4
Westover Cl. Bris 34 C1
Westover Dr. Bris 35 D1
Westover Gdns. Bris 48 C4
Westover Rd. Bris 35 D1
Westover Rise. Bris 35 D1
Westview Orchard. Hi Cha . 120 A3
Westview. Paul 131 E3
Westward Cl. Wring 92 B1
Westward Dr. E in G 47 E2
Westward Gdns. Lo Ash 62 A1
Westward Rd. Bris 78 C4
Westway. Nail 59 F1
Westwood Ave. Paul 115 E1
Westwood Cl. W-S-M 88 C1
Westwood Cres. Bris 64 B3
Westwood Ct. Westw 120 C2
Westwood Rd. Bris 80 B4
Westwoods. Bathe 86 A2
Wetherby Ct. Mang 37 F1
Wetherell Pl. Bris 63 D4
Wetlands La. Portis 45 E2
Wexford Rd. Bris 79 E4
Weymouth Rd. Bris 63 F1
Weymouth St. Bath 102 A4
Wharf La. Portb 46 A3
Wharf Rd. Bris 50 C2
Wharfedale. Thorn 15 E4
Wharfside. Lymp 121 F2
Wharncliffe Cl. Bris 80 A3
Wharncliffe Gdns. Bris 80 A3
Whatley Rd. Bris 49 D1
Wheatfield Dr. St Gif 24 B1
Wheathill Cl. Keyn 81 E3
Wheelers Cl. Mid No 132 B1
Wheelers Dr. Mid No 132 B1
Wheelers Rd. Mid No 132 B1
Whinchat Gdns. Bris 50 C3
Whippington Ct. Bris 63 F4
Whistley La. E Harp 128 C3
Whitby Rd. Bris 64 B3
Whitchurch La. Bris 79 F3
Whitchurch La. Bris 80 A2
Whitchurch La. Dun 79 E1
Whitchurch Rd. Bris 79 D3
White Cross Gate. Paul 130 C3
White Hill. Well 133 F3
White Horse Rd. Winsl 120 C4
White House La. Badg 123 D2
White House Rd. Yatt 91 F4
White Lodge Park. Portis 45 E3
White Lodge Rd. Kingsw 51 F2
White Ox Mead La. Well ... 117 F1
White St. Bris 63 F4
White Tree Rd. Bris 49 D2
Whitebrook La. P St J 133 D4
Whitebrook La. Tims 132 C4
Whitecroft Way. Kingsw 66 A4
Whitecross Ave. Bris 80 B3
Whitecross La. Ban 107 D2
Whitecross Rd. E Harp 128 C2
Whitecross Rd. W-S-M 104 C3
Whitefield Ave. Bris 51 D1
Whitefield Ave. Kingsw 65 E3

Whitefield Cl. Bathe 86 A2
Whitefield Cl. Kingsw 51 E2
Whitefield Rd. Bris 51 D1
Whitefields. Ch Sod 28 A1
Whitegate Cl. Blea 122 A3
Whitehall Ave. Bris 50 C1
Whitehall Gdns. Bris 64 B4
Whitehall Rd. Bris 64 B4
Whitehall Trading Est. Bris .. 64 B4
Whitehouse La. Bris 63 E2
Whitehouse La. Litt 129 F1
Whitehouse La. Wrax 60 A3
Whitehouse Pl. Bris 63 E2
Whitehouse Rd. Piln 22 B4
Whitehouse St. Bris 63 F2
Whiteladies Rd. Bris 49 D1
Whitelands Hill. Mid No 133 D2
Whiteleaze. Bris 49 E4
Whiteoak Way. Nail 75 E4
Whites Hill. Bris 65 D3
Whitesfield Rd. Nail 59 E1
Whiteshill. Wint 37 E2
Whiteway Ave. Bath 101 D2
Whiteway Cl. Bris 64 C3
Whiteway Ct. Bris 65 D4
Whiteway Mews. Bris 65 D4
Whiteway Rd. Bath 101 D2
Whiteway Rd. Bris 51 D1
Whitewells Rd. Bath 85 D1
Whitewood Rd. Bris 50 C1
Whitfield Rd. Thorn 8 B1
Whiting Rd. Bris 79 D2
Whitland Ave. Bris 79 D3
Whitland Rd. Bris 79 D3
Whitley Cl. Yate 27 E2
Whitley Mead. St Gif 36 C2
Whitling St. Win 95 D1
Whitmead Gdns. Bris 79 E2
Whitmore Ave. Bris 65 D2
Whitson St. Bris 63 E4
Whitting Rd. W-S-M 104 C3
Whittington Dr. W-S-M 88 B1
Whittington Rd. Bris 51 E3
Whittock Rd. Bris 80 B3
Whittock Sq. Bris 80 B4
Whittucks Cl. Kingsw 65 E2
Whittucks Rd. Kingsw 65 E2
Whitwell Rd. Bris 80 A4
Whytes Cl. Bris 49 D4
Wick Cres. Bris 64 B2
Wick Ct. W-S-M 89 D1
Wick House Cl. Keyn 82 B2
Wick La. Bitt 67 D1
Wick La. Lymp 121 F1
Wick La. Pens 97 E2
Wick La. Tims 116 C1
Wick Rd. Berr 121 E1
Wick Rd. Bi Sut 113 E2
Wick Rd. Bris 64 B2
Wick Rd. Bris 64 C3
Wick Rd. Lymp 121 E1
Wick Rd. Piln 22 B4
Wickets The. Bris 35 F1
Wickets The. Kingsw 51 E1
Wickfield. Cleve 57 E1
Wickham Cl. Ch Sod 40 B4
Wickham Ct. Bris 50 B3
Wickham Glen. Bris 50 B3
Wickham Hill. Bris 50 B3
Wickham View. Bris 50 B3
Wicklow Rd. Bris 79 F4
Wickwar Rd. Ch Sod 28 A3
Wickwar Rd. Kings 11 F2
Wickwar Rd. Wickw 17 D1
Wickwar Rd. Yate 28 A3
Widcombe Cl. Bris 65 D2
Widcombe Cres. Bath 102 A3
Widcombe Hill. Bath 102 B2
Widcombe Rise. Bath 102 A3
Widcombe. Bris 80 A3
Wigmore Gdns. W-S-M 88 B1
Wigton Cres. Bris 35 E1
Wilbye Gr. Bris 79 E3
Wilcox Cl. Kingsw 65 E3
WildCountry La. Ba Gu 77 F3
Wildcountry La. Lo Ash 77 F3
Wildcroft Rd. Bris 49 D2
Wilder St. Bris 63 F4
Willada Cl. Bris 63 D1
William Daw Cl. Ban 106 C2
William Mason Cl. Bris 64 A4
William St. Bath 102 A4
William St. Bris 49 F1
William St. Bris 51 D2
William St. Bris 63 F2
William St. Bris 64 A3
William St. Bris 64 B4
Williams Cl. Kingsw 65 F2
Williamson Rd. Bris 49 F2
Williamstowe. Bath 102 B1
Willinton Rd. Bris 79 F4
Willis Rd. Kingsw 51 F1
Williton Cres. W-S-M 104 C2
Willmott Cl. Bris 79 F2
Willoughby Cl. Alve 15 D2
Willoughby Cl. Bris 79 D4

Willoughby Cl. Bris

Willoughby Rd. Bris ... 49 F3
Willow Cl. Bris ... 35 F4
Willow Cl. Char ... 11 D2
Willow Cl. Cleve ... 57 F2
Willow Cl. Kingsw ... 66 B3
Willow Cl. Lo Ash ... 61 F1
Willow Cl. Lock ... 89 E1
Willow Cl. Portis ... 45 E2
Willow Cl. Rad ... 132 C1
Willow Cl. W-S-M ... 104 C1
Willow Cl. Wick ... 67 D3
Willow Dr. Blea ... 122 B3
Willow Dr. Lock ... 105 F1
Willow Dr. Lock ... 105 F3
Willow Gdns. Lock ... 89 E1
Willow Gr. Bris ... 51 E1
Willow Green. Bath ... 101 F2
Willow Rd. Kingsw ... 65 E2
Willow Way. Fr Cot ... 38 B3
Willow Wlk. Bris ... 35 D2
Willow Wlk. Keyn ... 81 E2
Willowdown. W-S-M ... 88 C2
Willowfalls The. Bath ... 85 F2
Willows Shopping Centre The.
  Mang ... 51 F3
Willows The. Bris ... 37 D1
Willows The. Nail ... 59 F2
Willows The. St Gif ... 36 B4
Willows The. Yate ... 27 E1
Wills Dr. Bris ... 64 A4
Willsbridge Hill. Kingsw ... 66 A1
Willway St. Bris ... 63 E2
Willway St. Bris ... 63 F4
Wilmot Ct. Kingsw ... 66 A3
Wilmots Way. E in G ... 47 E2
Wilmott House. E in G ... 47 E2
Wilson Pl. Bris ... 63 F4
Wilson St. Bris ... 63 F4
Wilton Cl. Bris ... 35 E1
Wilton Gdns. W-S-M ... 104 B4
Wiltons. Wring ... 92 B1
Wiltshire Ave. Kingsw ... 65 E3
Wiltshire Ave. Yate ... 28 A2
Wiltshire Pl. Kingsw ... 51 F2
Wiltshire Way. Bath ... 85 D1
Wilverley Ind Est. Bris ... 64 C1
Wimbledon Rd. Bris ... 49 E3
Wimblestone Rd. Winsc ... 107 F1
Wimborne Rd. Bris ... 63 E1
Winash Cl. Bris ... 80 B4
Wincanton Cl. Nail ... 60 A1
Winchcombe Cl. Nail ... 76 A4
Winchcombe Gr. Bris ... 47 F3
Winchcombe Rd. Fr Cot ... 38 A4
Winchester Ave. Bris ... 64 B2
Winchester Rd. Bath ... 101 E3
Winchester Rd. Bris ... 64 B2
Wincroft. Kingsw ... 66 B2
Windcliff Cres. Bris ... 47 F4
Windermere Rd. Bris ... 36 A4
Windermere Way. Kingsw ... 66 B3
Windmill Cl. Bris ... 63 F2
Windmill Farm Bsns Cen.
  Bris ... 63 E2
Windmill Hill. Bris ... 63 E2
Windmill Hill. Lock ... 106 A1
Windmill La. Bris ... 34 B2
Windrush Cl. Bath ... 100 C2
Windrush Ct. Thorn ... 15 E4
Windrush Green. Keyn ... 82 A2
Windrush Rd. Keyn ... 82 A2
Windsor Ave. Bris ... 65 D3
Windsor Ave. Keyn ... 81 F2
Windsor Bridge Rd. Bath ... 101 E4
Windsor Cl. Cleve ... 57 E1
Windsor Cl. St Gif ... 36 C2
Windsor Cres. Bris ... 34 B2
Windsor Ct. Bath ... 101 E4
Windsor Ct. Bris ... 62 C3
Windsor Ct. Mang ... 51 F4
Windsor Ct. Wick ... 67 E4
Windsor Dr. Yate ... 27 E1
Windsor Gr. Bris ... 64 A4
Windsor Pl. Bris ... 62 C3
Windsor Pl. Mang ... 52 A3
Windsor Rd. Bris ... 49 F1
Windsor Rd. Kingsw ... 65 F1
Windsor Rd. W-S-M ... 88 B1
Windsor Terr. Bris ... 62 C3
Windsor Terr. Bris ... 63 F2
Windwhistle Circ. W-S-M ... 104 C2
Windwhistle La. W-S-M ... 104 C2
Windwhistle Rd. W-S-M ... 104 B2
Wine St. Bath ... 102 A3
Wine St. Bris ... 63 E4
Wineberry Cl. Bris ... 50 B1
Winfield Rd. Sist ... 66 B4
Winford Cl. Portis ... 45 F2
Winford Gr. Bris ... 79 D4
Winford La. Dun ... 78 B1
Winford Rd. Ch Mag ... 95 F2
Wingard Cl. W-S-M ... 104 B1
Wingfield Rd. Bris ... 63 F1
Winifred's La. Bath ... 84 C1
Winkworth Pl. Bris ... 49 F1
Winnowing End. Wins ... 108 A2
Winsbury Way. St Gif ... 24 B1
Winscombe Cl. Keyn ... 81 E3

Winscombe Dro. Ship ... 125 E3
Winscombe Dro. Wins ... 125 E3
Winscombe Hill. Wins ... 124 C3
Winscombe Rd. W-S-M ... 105 D4
Winsford St. Bris ... 64 A4
Winsham Cl. Bris ... 80 A3
Winsley Hill. Winsl ... 120 A3
Winsley Rd. Bris ... 49 E1
Wint Hill. Ban ... 107 D1
Winterbourne Hill. Wint ... 37 E3
Winterbourne Rd. St Gif ... 36 C3
Winterfield Park. Paul ... 131 F2
Winterfield Rd. Paul ... 131 F3
Winterstoke Cl. Bris ... 63 D1
Winterstoke Rd. Bris ... 62 C2
Winterstoke Rd. W-S-M ... 105 D2
Winterstoke Underpass. Bris 62 C2
Winton St. Bris ... 63 F2
Wistaria Ave. Ch Sod ... 28 A1
Wisteria Ave. Lock ... 105 E1
Witch Hazel Rd. Bris ... 79 F2
Witchell Rd. Bris ... 64 B4
Witcombe Cl. Kingsw ... 51 F1
Witcombe. Yate ... 39 E4
Witherlies Rd. Bris ... 50 C3
Withey Cl E. Bris ... 48 C3
Withey Cl W. Bris ... 48 C3
Witheys The. Whit ... 80 B2
Withies La. Mid No ... 138 A4
Withies Park. Mid No ... 137 F4
Withington Cl. Kingsw ... 66 B1
Withleigh Rd. Bris ... 64 A1
Withyditch La. Pris ... 117 E2
Withymead Rd. Marsh ... 70 A4
Withypool Gdns. Bris ... 80 A3
Withywood Gdns. Bris ... 78 C2
Withywood Rd. Bris ... 78 C2
Witney Cl. Keyn ... 82 B2
Woburn Cl. Kingsw ... 65 F3
Woburn Rd. Bris ... 50 A2
Wolferton Rd. Bris ... 49 F1
Wolfridge Gdns. Bris ... 35 D2
Wolfridge La. Alve ... 14 C2
Wolfridge Ride. Alve ... 14 C2
Wolseley Rd. Bris ... 49 E2
Wolvers Hill Rd. Ban ... 106 C3
Wolvers Hill Rd. Lock ... 106 C3
Wolvershill Park. Ban ... 107 D2
Wood End Wlk. Bris ... 48 B3
Wood Hill Park. Portis ... 45 D4
Wood Hill. Cong ... 91 F3
Wood Kilns The. Yatt ... 74 A1
Wood La. Axb ... 125 E1
Wood La. Hork ... 19 D1
Wood La. W in G ... 59 F4
Wood La. W-S-M ... 87 F1
Wood Rd. Kingsw ... 65 E4
Wood St. Bath ... 101 F3
Wood St. Bath ... 101 F3
Wood St. Bris ... 50 A1
Woodbine Rd. Bris ... 64 B4
Woodborough Cres. Wins . 125 D4
Woodborough Dr. Wins ... 125 D4
Woodborough La. Mid No ... 133 D2
Woodborough Rd. Mid No . 133 D2
Woodborough Rd. Wins ... 124 C4
Woodborough Rd. Wins ... 125 D4
Woodborough St. Bris ... 50 A1
Woodbridge Rd. Bris ... 64 A1
Woodbury La. Bris ... 49 D1
Woodchester Rd. Bris ... 49 E4
Woodchester. Kingsw ... 51 F2
Woodchester. Yate ... 39 F4
Woodcliff Ave. W-S-M ... 88 B1
Woodcliff Rd. W-S-M ... 88 B1
Woodcote Rd. Bris ... 51 D2
Woodcote Wlk. Bris ... 51 D1
Woodcote. Kingsw ... 65 E3
Woodcroft Ave. Bris ... 50 B1
Woodcroft Cl. Bris ... 64 C2
Woodcroft Rd. Bris ... 64 C2
Woodcroft. Bi Sut ... 113 E2
Woodend La. Rock ... 2 C1
Woodend Rd. Fr Cot ... 38 B4
Woodend. Kingsw ... 65 E3
Woodfield Rd. Bris ... 49 D1
Woodfinch Cres. Puck ... 53 E2
Woodford Cl. Nail ... 60 A1
Woodgrove Rd. Bris ... 34 B1
Woodhall Cl. Mang ... 51 F3
Woodhill Ave. Portis ... 45 E3
Woodhill Rd. Portis ... 45 D4
Woodhill Views. Nail ... 59 F2
Woodhouse Ave. Alve ... 24 B4
Woodhouse Cl. Alve ... 24 B3
Woodhouse Gr. Bris ... 49 F3
Woodhouse Rd. Bath ... 101 D3
Woodhurst Rd. W-S-M ... 105 D4
Woodington Ct. Kingsw ... 65 F2
Woodington Rd. Cleve ... 57 E1
Woodland Ave. Kingsw ... 51 E1
Woodland Cl. Wrax ... 61 D2
Woodland Cotts Winsl ... 120 B3
Woodland Glade. Cleve ... 57 F3
Woodland Gr. Bath ... 102 C3
Woodland Gr. Bris ... 48 B3
Woodland Rd. Bris ... 63 E4
Woodland Rd. Crom ... 10 A2

Woodland Rd. Nail ... 59 F2
Woodland Rd. W-S-M ... 104 B2
Woodland Terr. Bris ... 49 D1
Woodland Terr. Kingsw ... 65 F4
Woodland Way. Bris ... 51 E1
Woodland Way. Wrax ... 61 D2
Woodlands Ct. St Gif ... 24 A2
Woodlands Dr. Winsl ... 120 A3
Woodlands La. Alve ... 24 C3
Woodlands La. St Gif ... 24 B2
Woodlands Park. Bath ... 85 E1
Woodlands Park. St Gif ... 24 B2
Woodlands Rd. Char ... 11 D2
Woodlands Rd. Cleve ... 57 E2
Woodlands Rd. Portis ... 45 F4
Woodlands Rd. Tyth ... 16 A3
Woodlands Rise. Mang ... 51 E3
Woodlands The. Pris ... 116 C2
Woodlands. Mang ... 51 F3
Woodlands. St Gif ... 24 B2
Woodlands. Tyth ... 16 A3
Woodleaze. Bris ... 48 A3
Woodleigh Gdns. Bris ... 80 B3
Woodleigh. Thorn ... 8 B1
Woodmancote Rd. Bris ... 49 F1
Woodmancote. Yate ... 39 E4
Woodmans Cl. Ch Sod ... 40 A4
Woodmans Rd. Ch Sod ... 40 A4
Woodmans Vale. Ch Sod ... 40 B4
Woodmarsh Cl. Bris ... 80 A2
Woodmead Gdns. Bris ... 79 E2
Woodmead La. Doyn ... 54 A1
Woodmill. Nail ... 74 A1
Woodpecker Ave. Rod ... 138 A4
Woodpecker Dr. W-S-M ... 105 F4
Woods Hill. Li St ... 120 A4
Woodside Ave. W-S-M ... 105 D1
Woodside Gdns. Portis ... 44 C3
Woodside Gr. Bris ... 34 B2
Woodside Rd. Bris ... 64 C3
Woodside Rd. Cleve ... 57 F3
Woodside Rd. Fr Cot ... 38 B4
Woodside Rd. Kingsw ... 65 E4
Woodside Rd. Mang ... 51 E4
Woodside. Bris ... 48 B2
Woodside. Mid No ... 131 F1
Woodspring Ave. W-S-M ... 88 A2
Woodspring Cres. W-S-M ... 88 A2
Woodstock Ave. Bris ... 49 E1
Woodstock Cl. Kingsw ... 65 F4
Woodstock Rd. Bris ... 49 E1
Woodstock Rd. Kingsw ... 65 F4
Woodstock Rd. W-S-M ... 105 D4
Woodview Cl. Bris ... 47 F4
Woodview Dr. Brock ... 92 A4
Woodview Terr. Nail ... 59 F1
Woodview Terr. W-S-M ... 105 D3
Woodview. Chil ... 137 F3
Woodview. Cleve ... 57 F2
Woodview. Paul ... 131 E3
Woodward Dr. Kingsw ... 65 F2
Woodwell Rd. Bris ... 47 F3
Woodyleaze Dr. Kingsw ... 65 E3
Wookey Cl. Nail ... 75 F4
Woolcot St. Bris ... 49 D1
Wooler Rd. W-S-M ... 104 C4
Woollard La. Pens ... 80 B1
Woollard La. Whit ... 80 B1
Woolley La. Charl ... 85 D2
Woolley Rd. Bris ... 80 C3
Wootton Cres. Bris ... 64 C3
Wootton Pk. Bris ... 65 A1
Wootton Rd. Bris ... 64 C3
Worcester Bldgs. Bath ... 85 D1
Worcester Cl. Bris ... 51 D1
Worcester Cres. Bris ... 63 D4
Worcester Gdns. Nail ... 75 E4
Worcester Park. Bath ... 85 D1
Worcester Pl. Bath ... 85 D1
Worcester Rd. Bris ... 63 D4
Worcester Rd. Kingsw ... 51 E1
Worcester Terr. Bris ... 63 D4
Worcester Villas. Bath ... 85 D1
Wordsworth Rd. Bris ... 50 A4
Wordsworth Rd. Cleve ... 57 E1
Wordsworth Rd. W-S-M ... 105 D2
Workshop Rd. Avon ... 33 E2
World's End La. Keyn ... 82 B3
Worldsend La. Stone ... 2 C4
Worle Ct. W-S-M ... 88 C2
Worle Parkway. W-S-M ... 89 D1
Worlebury Cl. W-S-M ... 88 A2
Worlebury Hill Rd. W-S-M ... 88 B2
Worlebury Park Rd. W-S-M . 88 A1
Wormcliffe La. Box ... 86 C2
Worrall Rd. Bris ... 49 D1
Worrel's La. Wint ... 37 E2
Worsley St. Bris ... 64 B4
Worth Cl. Kingsw ... 65 F3
Worthies The. Lymp ... 122 A1
Worthing Rd. Bris ... 35 F4
Worthy Cres. Lymp ... 122 A1
Worthy La. W-S-M ... 104 C4
Worthy Pl. W-S-M ... 104 B4
Worthy Rd. Avon ... 33 F4
Worthys The. St Gif ... 37 D3
Wotton Rd. Char ... 11 D3
Wotton Rd. Ir Act ... 26 C3

Wotton Rd. W-u-E ... 11 F3
Wotton Rd. Wickw ... 27 D4
Wrangle Farm Green. Cleve 57 F1
Wraxall Gr. Bris ... 79 D4
Wraxall Hill. Wrax ... 60 B3
Wraxall Rd. Kingsw ... 66 A3
Wren Cl. W-S-M ... 105 E4
Wren Dr. Bris ... 51 D3
Wrenbert Rd. Mang ... 51 E3
Wrington Cl. St Gif ... 36 B4
Wrington Cres. Bris ... 79 D4
Wrington Hill. Cong ... 92 C3
Wrington Hill. Wring ... 92 C3
Wrington La. Cong ... 91 F3
Wrington Mead. Cong ... 91 F3
Wrington Rd. Cong ... 91 F3
Wroughton Dr. Bris ... 79 E2
Wroughton Gdns. Bris ... 79 E2
Wroxham Dr. St Gif ... 36 B4
Wyatt Ave. Bris ... 78 C3
Wyatt Cl. Bris ... 78 C3
Wyatt's Cl. Nail ... 59 E1
Wychwood. Kingsw ... 65 F3
Wyck Beck Rd. Bris ... 35 D2
Wycliffe Rd. Bris ... 49 D4
Wycombe Gr. Bris ... 64 B1
Wye Croft Cl. Bris ... 35 E2
Wye Ct. Thorn ... 15 E4
Wyedale Ave. Bris ... 48 A4
Wykis Ct. Kingsw ... 65 F3
Wyllie Ct. W-S-M ... 89 D3
Wymbush Cres. Bris ... 79 E3
Wymbush Gdns. Bris ... 79 E3
Wyndham Cres. Bris ... 65 D2
Wyndham Cres. E in G ... 47 D2
Wyndham Way. Portis ... 45 F3
Wynstones The. Kingsw ... 65 E4
Wynter Cl. W-S-M ... 89 D2
Wytham Rd. Keyn ... 82 A2

Yadley Cl. Wins ... 125 D4
Yadley La. Wins ... 125 D3
Yadley Way. Wins ... 125 D4
Yanleigh Cl. Dun ... 78 B3
Yanley La. Lo Ash ... 78 B4
Yarbury Way. W-S-M ... 89 D1
Yate Rd. Ir Act ... 26 C2
Yate Rocks. Yate ... 27 F4
Yelverton Rd. Bris ... 64 C1
Yeo Bank La. K Sey ... 72 C1
Yeo Cl. W-S-M ... 105 D3
Yeo Ct. Cong ... 91 E2
Yeo La. Lo Ash ... 61 F1
Yeo Moor. Cleve ... 57 F1
Yeo Way. Cleve ... 57 D1
Yeolands Dr. Cleve ... 57 D1
Yeoman's Cl. Bris ... 48 B3
Yeomans Orch. Wring ... 92 C2
Yeomanside Cl. Bris ... 80 B3
Yeomead. Nail ... 59 F2
Yeomeads. Lo Ash ... 61 F1
Yeoward Rd. Cleve ... 57 F1
Yew Tree Cl. Bi Sut ... 113 E2
Yew Tree Cl. Blag ... 109 F3
Yew Tree Cl. Nail ... 59 E1
Yew Tree Dr. Kingsw ... 51 F2
Yew Tree Gdns. E in G ... 47 E2
Yew Tree Gdns. Nail ... 59 E1
Yew Tree Gdns. Wins ... 108 A2
Yew Tree La. Co Mar ... 128 A4
Yew Tree La. K Sey ... 73 D1
Yew Tree Park. Cong ... 91 E2
Yewcroft Cl. Bris ... 80 A2
Yewtree Batch. But ... 94 A1
Yomede Park. Bath ... 101 D4
York Ave. Bris ... 49 F2
York Cl. Mang ... 37 F1
York Cl. St Gif ... 36 B2
York Cl. W-S-M ... 89 D2
York Cl. Yate ... 27 F2
York Gdns. Bris ... 62 C3
York Gdns. Bris ... 63 D3
York Gdns. Wint ... 37 F4
York Pl. Bris ... 63 D4
York Pl. Bris ... 63 E3
York Rd. Bris ... 49 F1
York Rd. Bris ... 50 B1
York Rd. Bris ... 63 F2
York Rd. Kingsw ... 51 F2
York St. Bath ... 102 A3
York St. Bris ... 49 D1
York St. Bris ... 50 A1
York St. Bris ... 63 F4
York St. Bris ... 64 B4
York St. W-S-M ... 104 B4

Zetland Rd. Bris ... 49 E1
Zig Zag. Cleve ... 57 E2
Zinc Rd. Avon ... 33 E2
Zion Hill. Ston E ... 137 D4

STREET ATLASES ORDER FORM

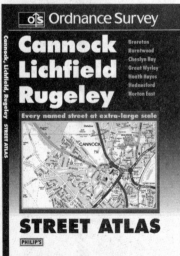

COLOUR LOCAL ATLASES

	PAPERBACK	
	Quantity @ £3.50 each	£ Total
CANNOCK, LICHFIELD, RUGELEY	☐ 0 540 07625 2	➤ ☐
DERBY AND BELPER	☐ 0 540 07608 2	➤ ☐
NORTHWICH, WINSFORD, MIDDLEWICH	☐ 0 540 07589 2	➤ ☐
PEAK DISTRICT TOWNS	☐ 0 540 07609 0	➤ ☐
STAFFORD, STONE, UTTOXETER	☐ 0 540 07626 0	➤ ☐
WARRINGTON, WIDNES, RUNCORN	☐ 0 540 07588 4	➤ ☐

COLOUR REGIONAL ATLASES

	HARDBACK	SPIRAL	POCKET	
	Quantity @ £10.99 each	Quantity @ £8.99 each	Quantity @ £5.99 each	£ Total
BERKSHIRE	☐ 0 540 06170 0	☐ 0 540 06172 7	☐ 0 540 06173 5	➤ ☐
	Quantity @ £10.99 each	Quantity @ £8.99 each	Quantity @ £4.99 each	£ Total
MERSEYSIDE	☐ 0 540 06480 7	☐ 0 540 06481 5	☐ 0 540 06482 3	➤ ☐
	Quantity @ £12.99 each	Quantity @ £9.99 each	Quantity @ £4.99 each	£ Total
DURHAM	☐ 0 540 06365 7	☐ 0 540 06366 5	☐ 0 540 06367 3	➤ ☐
EAST KENT	☐ 0 540 07483 7	☐ 0 540 07276 1	☐ 0 540 07287 7	➤ ☐
WEST KENT	☐ 0 540 07366 0	☐ 0 540 07367 9	☐ 0 540 07369 5	➤ ☐
	Quantity @ £12.99 each	Quantity @ £9.99 each	Quantity @ £5.50 each	£ Total
GREATER MANCHESTER	☐ 0 540 06485 8	☐ 0 540 06486 6	☐ 0 540 06487 4	➤ ☐
TYNE AND WEAR	☐ 0 540 06370 3	☐ 0 540 06371 1	☐ 0 540 06372 X	➤ ☐
	Quantity @ £12.99 each	Quantity @ £9.99 each	Quantity @ £5.99 each	£ Total
BIRMINGHAM & WEST MIDLANDS	☐ 0 540 07603 1	☐ 0 540 07604 X	☐ 0 540 07605 8	➤ ☐
BUCKINGHAMSHIRE	☐ 0 540 07466 7	☐ 0 540 07467 5	☐ 0 540 07468 3	➤ ☐
CHESHIRE	☐ 0 540 07507 8	☐ 0 540 07508 6	☐ 0 540 07509 4	➤ ☐
DERBYSHIRE	☐ 0 540 07531 0	☐ 0 540 07532 9	☐ 0 540 07533 7	➤ ☐
EDINBURGH & East Central Scotland	☐ 0 540 07653 8	☐ 0 540 07654 6	☐ 0 540 07656 2	➤ ☐
GLASGOW & West Central Scotland	☐ 0 540 07648 1	☐ 0 540 07649 X	☐ 0 540 07651 1	➤ ☐

PHILIP'S

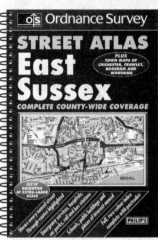
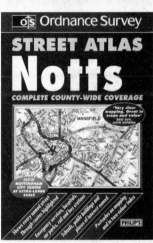
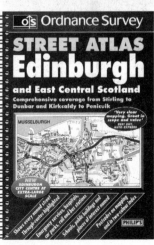

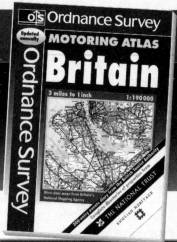